QFD

QFD

The Customer-Driven Approach to Quality Planning and Deployment

Edited by
Shigeru Mizuno
Yoji Akao

APO
Asian Productivity Organization

Published in 1994 by
Asian Productivity Organization
4-14, Akasaka 8-chome
Minato-ku, Tokyo 107 Japan

Distributed in North America, the United Kingdom, and Western Europe by
Quality Resources
A Division of The Kraus Organization Limited
One Water Street
White Plains, NY 10601

Originally published in Japanese under the title *Hinshitsu Kino Tenkai*, edited by Shigeru Mizuno and Yoji Akao. Copyright © 1978 by Shigeru Mizuno and Yoji Akao. English translation by the Asian Productivity Organization based on revisions made by Shigeru Mizuno and Yoji Akao under an agreement with JUSE Press, Ltd. through the Japan Foreign-Rights Centre.

ISBN: 92-833-1121-3 (cloth)
92-833-1122-1 (paper)

Cover design by Joseph DePinho

Printed in Hong Kong by Nordica International, Ltd.

First printing 1994

Preface to the Revised English Edition

Quality function deployment (QFD), which began in Japan, has quickly spread to the United States and many other countries, but not until 1990 did a translation of a Japanese book on the subject appear.* Because portions of the original version of the present volume and other works on QFD, when translated from the original Japanese, have been somewhat loosely interpreted and applied, the correct methods have not yet been fully communicated.

Although QFD was developed to facilitate quality assurance (QA), the basic concept of QA has been largely ignored, and QFD has sometimes been preempted for a pattern that elevates the mechanics of a product above customer satisfaction. Even when the position of the customer is captured in the demanded-quality deployment table, technical characteristics, methods, and procedures have often been intermingled. This misapplication or incomplete use of QFD is regrettable.

Fifteen years have passed since the Japanese edition of this book was published; it was the first of its kind anywhere. The editors long intended to publish an English translation, but its publication in its original scope is a project whose time has passed. The translated volume of case studies cited above, which I edited, was based on a book published in 1988 in Japan. Prof. Mizuno and I, however, felt that the present work, which preceded that volume by several years and which presents the original statement on QFD, should be brought out in English. As members of the editing and translation loop, we have rewritten parts of this book with a view toward accomplishing this goal.

The major revisions are in several areas. What is currently Part I is a revised and supplemented version of Chapter 1, and the section entitled "Development History of Quality Function Deployment" from that chapter has been made the Appendix. The original chapter on "A Total Quality Function Deployment System" has been rewritten, expanded, and added to what is now Part I in order to give readers a total picture of QFD at the outset. Part V, "Recent Approaches and Future Issues of Quality Function Deployment," is new to this edition yet draws in part upon Chapter 6 in the original edition. In recognition of the international reader, a few of the Japanese citations in the bibli-

---

*Yoji Akao, ed., *Quality Function Deployment: Integrating Customer Requirements into Product Design* (Cambridge, MA: Productivity Press, 1990).

ography have been omitted. Readers interested in the historical transitions may consult the earlier volume.

During the preparation of this revised manuscript, I worked with my coeditor, Dr. Shigeru Mizuno. To my great sorrow, at the midpoint of the project, Dr. Mizuno passed away. The revisions to Part I and to the Epilogue, and the last part of Chapter 12 are his final contributions to the field.

All of us in the field of quality have been greatly affected by the central role that Dr. Mizuno played in promoting Japanese company-wide total quality control. For him, QFD was one of the final areas he investigated in his search for the new. Thus, the Epilogue stresses Dr. Mizuno's intentions and has been included as is. The entire quality control community mourns the passing of this great teacher.

Currently, there is a growth in the number of books on QFD. This book, however, is intended to provide a definitive guide to understanding the nature of QFD. I trust that, with correct application, it will be helpful in every aspect of total quality management.

Finally, I express my deep gratitude to Katsuharu Arai of the Union of Japanese Scientists and Engineers (JUSE) Press for his efforts and patience in coordinating the development of the revised text. For the English translation, I express my gratitude to Glenn H. Mazur for his excellent efforts.

Yoji Akao
August 1993

Preface to the First Edition

Exercises that identify the actions required for quality planning and quality assurance to create a step-by-step system of objectives and means of implementation are called "deployment of quality functions." Systematically clarifying the precise relationships involved in quality itself, such as the relationship between the quality of completed products and that of each subsystem and of each part, or clarifying the relationship of assured qualities at each phase, is called "deployment of quality." In this book, the deployment of quality functions and deployment of quality are generally called "quality function deployment."

Without companywide quality control (CWQC) or total quality management (TQM), it is impossible to achieve adequate results. (Total quality control [TQC] was proposed by Feigenbaum, and when it was introduced in Japan, was called companywide quality control [CWQC] because it involved activities at all levels of an organization. Japan continues to use the term TQC, but activities equivalent to CWQC are now called total quality management [TQM] in the United States. For this reason, we have translated the Japanese expression TQC as TQM.) If efforts to assure quality are carried out at each phase or by each department independently, without collaboration or consideration of the relationship to each other, as was frequently done in the past, then obviously such quality control activities cannot be called companywide. Similarly, the demanded quality cannot be attained when standardization is performed without clarification of the relationship between the customer-demanded quality characteristics and the product quality characteristics or the relationship between the quality of a completed product and the quality of its component parts. Nor can a stabilized process be relied upon, no matter how many efforts have been made, if the control chart was prepared from inappropriate control characteristics. Furthermore, quality assurance activities must be implemented all the way through service activities, including product maintenance and repair, on these quality characteristics that are so closely related, causing actions or efforts to achieve consistent quality control to be implemented with complete certainty.

Quality function deployment has been recognized as an effective system for achieving the above goals. Particularly since 1975, it has been tried by many companies and has provided an approach to TQM with impressive results reported. Quality deployment was invented in Japan around 1966. The method of function deployment itself was not particularly new, but its application in quality control began quite recently. The analytic method, formerly the one most often used in quality control, was certainly an effective method of problem solving. The use of analysis alone, however, was limited when new activities needed to be executed comprehensively and systematically, and when quality control was to be implemented as a system. Hence, function deployment received recognition for its effectiveness in these areas.

Employing quality control activities to meet the dynamic requirements of a new era (a shifting to wide-variety, small-lot production methods to meet diversifying demanded quality in a low-growth period, and developing and providing high-quality products without allowing the slightest room for defects) means that companies can no longer employ conventional quality control with a focus on single-problem solving. Rather, companywide quality control must be implemented as a coherent system. Furthermore, it must be the kind of quality control that not only delivers agreed-upon quality and assures manufacturing quality but also assists in determining what quality a product should have, that is, assuring design quality. Actual examples clearly show that quality function deployment is essential for companywide quality control in this new era. This activity is only part of a continuum, however (as of 1978). Approaches and terminologies are still not uniform, and the basic research has not been fully completed. Despite this deficiency, however, a bold decision was made to complete this book for publication in order to demonstrate one direction quality control activities can take.

The editors have long been interested in these efforts and have been indirectly instrumental in QFD activities within companies. Our deep appreciation goes to those who provided a detailed presentation of the valuable application examples at each company. These were made possible not only by those who presented their company case studies and by the editors but also by cooperation from many corporate leaders and their staffs.

It is our hope that these methods will be implemented by many more companies with good results. Experience and comments from readers will be greatly appreciated.

May 1978
The Editors

Contents

The Structure of this Book

Part I is an overview. Chapter 1 is an introduction to the quality function deployment way of thinking. Chapter 2 gives the background and concept of the quality chart, which serves as the quarterback in QFD. Chapter 3 presents the steps of the quality deployment procedures and serves as a reference for actual application.

Parts II and III are divided among the phases of QFD from sales to manufacturing; each topic is written on by individuals from companies that offer unique solutions. Chapter 4 concerns the demanded quality deployment chart, a compilation of demanded items mentioned by users during the sales phase. It also details how the chart is used. The information gained is transmitted to the development and engineering departments, where the quality chart will be used to convert the items into quality characteristics. Chapter 5 presents a priority-based method of using the quality chart as a merchandising strategy during the planning and design phases. Actual cases are presented. The chapter also explains the meaning of the quality chart. Chapter 6 uses actual cases to illustrate how design quality based on user demands is established in the design phase and is tied to the engineering technology. The chapter also introduces *simultaneous multidimensional design*, which makes high-efficiency production possible by increasing the number of standardized parts for product lines consisting of a series of models and types.

Chapter 7 discusses process design and quality deployment in the production engineering phase, provides a method of connecting the quality chart and the QC process chart, and explains in detail the QA chart, which plays a central role.

Chapter 8 treats the selection of critical-to-safety parts that may be related to product liability and critical-to-function parts and special ways to control them, process capability improvement, and worker skill upgrading for this purpose.

Chapter 9 concerns manufacturing methods deployment, that is, deploying the means to achieve the quality, as opposed to quality deployment, which is deployment of the targets. It shows how to select the least costly process or operation method that still assures the quality level deployed from the production engineering point of view.

Chapter 10 explains how to prepare the QC process chart in the manufacturing phase. This is a method in which control items are established by determining the higher-level functions from the upper end of the process. By connecting this method with deployment from upstream activities, both design quality and manufacturing quality can be incorporated into the QC process chart.

Part IV (Chapter 11) will be helpful to understanding the overall picture of QFD because it contains a case study from Kubota that follows QFD through almost every phase.

Chapter 12 describes reliability deployment, cost deployment, and technology deployment; they are advanced deployments that appeared subsequent to the first edition of this book. Chapter 13 begins with the current status of QFD in the United States and then discusses its future progress, including activities taking place in Japan.

The Appendix presents the history of quality function deployment: its birth and evolution. This should serve as a reference for readers. The Epilogue, in the form of a dialogue between the late Dr. Shigeru Mizuno, one of the editors, and his son, Norikazu Mizuno – "Using QFD to Implement Companywide Quality Control" – replaces the Afterword.

PART I
Quality and Quality Function Deployment

1

Introduction

Shigeru Mizuno

QUALITY PROBLEMS TODAY

The New Era of Quality Arrives

The significance of quality has never been more critical to business managers. At a special presentation at the Quality Control Conference in 1972, I introduced the expression "the new era of quality." Later it was learned that the term had also been used abroad. That this view is shared by others is encouraging. These words herald an age in which quality has never been more important.

The new era of quality has eight characteristics.

1. A switch from quantity to quality
2. A switch from "buyer beware" (caveat emptor) to "seller beware" (caveat venditor)
3. A concern for product safety, public responsibility, and product liability
4. A shift from focus on the consumer to focus on society
5. Demands for conservation of energy and other natural resources
6. Diversification and globalization of quality
7. Passive product liability and active product liability
8. Management of quality (management makes quality a priority).

The meaning of point 2 is that formerly, when customers bought an inferior quality product, they were to blame. Now it is considered the responsibility of the seller. When buying fish, for example, it was the buyer's responsibility to determine whether the fish was fresh, perhaps by observing the eye color. If the buyer was not sufficiently attentive, the piece purchased might not be fresh. Currently, raw fish is typically prepackaged so that the shopper cannot smell it to determine freshness. Consequently, it is the seller who must assure the quality of the product.

The product liability portion of point 3 is the case of holding liable for compensation a manufacturer or supplier of a product that has caused injury or economic loss to the user. Such cases are rising in both numbers and extent in the United States, and also in Japan.

If a defective product results in injury, there is a responsibility not only to the user but also to affected third parties. If environmental damage occurs, responsibility may extend to society. This is the meaning of point 4, "a shift from focus on the consumer to focus on society."

Point 6, on the diversification of quality, is self-explanatory. Nevertheless, it is necessary to be alert to this diversification and also to radical changes in user-demanded quality caused by rapid changes in lifestyles and by the environment. Furthermore, in this age of global commerce, the demands for quality products and services in foreign markets are diverse and complex.

In point 7, "passive product liability" and "active product liability" are terms I created. A company fearful of product liability claims will continue to produce the same product; this is termed "passive." However, this does not allow industries to meet their obligation to society of producing and supplying new products that offer new functions and uses in response to changing market demands. This is called "active" product liability.

Considering the above issues, management in industry must make quality the priority and proceed to this new era of quality. This is point 8, the management of quality.

Thoughts on Quality Control

The increasingly high quality level of Japanese products has resulted from the quality control efforts made by each company. However, in coping with quality-related problems in the new era of quality, conventional quality control activities may be inadequate.

First, how products are made to conform to set standards is important, but what types of products should be made is becoming more important. Quality assurance activities are more than prevention of recurring defects during manufacturing; they are precautions against the occurrence of defects in the first place. In other words, quality planning and quality design as premanufacturing phases have become critical.

Second, in regard to product-liability issues, quality assurance activities for postmanufacturing phases make it necessary to consider ease of maintenance and service. Such activities are required to cover situations even when a product is misused with no injury to the user. Quality assurance in the strict sense is based on confirmation. If we accept the premise that it is essential to include premanufacturing as well as postmanufacturing phases, it is necessary to augment the QA function. QA activities in the postmanufacturing phases of maintenance and service are a strong promise to the user. Traditionally, quality planning and quality design were engineering activities and not included in quality control activities. They are, however, currently implemented as critical quality control activities. In this sense, quality assurance must now include the premanufacturing phases or all activities that assure quality. Instead of "quality assurance," perhaps QA should be called "*Q*uality *A*ctivities."

Third, conventional quality control identifies defects, poor conditions, and problems while seeking their causes. It indicates which activities are critical to prevent recurrence. To identify or to analyze the causes of the undesired results, powerful statistical methods exist, making quality control very effective compared with other control technologies. I feel, however, that quality control is simply diagnostics.

When it becomes necessary to fulfill the quality plan, it is no longer sufficient merely to analyze. For example, how do we undertake new product development where no defect record has been established? In this case, the analytic technique indicated is a *design approach*, a deployment of functions in which implementation methods are considered according to the purpose of the product or service. This contrasts with the *analytic approach*, which searches for the causes that lead to certain results.

Fourth, in new product development, the quality plan phase now relies only on technology. In the manufacturing phase, technology is certainly vital; however, it is viewed as opposing quality control. Some individuals involved in the quality control field describe technology and quality control as wheels on an automobile, parallel but never crossing paths. Use of quality control to plan improvements in technology and to plan engineering activities (which I call standardization of engineering technology) is a critical part of quality control. Generally, this is not adequately understood.

When quality control is promoted in a company, in most cases strong resistance comes from researchers and design engineers who feel they are capable in their engineering technology.

Fifth, corporate structures generally create many special tasks. They typically include marketing, design, production engineering, and manufacturing. In addition, staff departments exist for planning, market research, personnel, and general administration. The division of corporate tasks demonstrates the specialized duties of each department.

The quality function refers to activities for assuring quality; activities with this purpose are called cross-functional activities. The activities managing these cross-functional activities are quality assurance, cost, and production control, concerning Q (quality), C (cost), and D (delivery and production quantity). These cross-functional activities and their control are all interdepartmental. The division of tasks generally is not represented by typical tasks that cross departmental lines.

Sixth, sales, production volume, manufacturing cost, and other items critical to management each have quantified targets divided among all departments. The efforts expended to achieve these targets are sometimes called *management by objectives.* When the method to achieve these targets is unclear because of inadequate deployment or analysis, it is no surprise that the efforts to achieve the targets are not effective.

Identification of effective implementation measures is part of TQM promotion, particularly in the face of challenging goals that seem impossible to achieve. Thus, it is natural that these *hoshin** management activities take place in the company. Many companies, while promoting TQM, discover that *hoshin* management can be implemented effectively only with TQM. *Hoshin* management is implemented not merely to achieve quality targets but also to link TQM activities for fulfillment of all critical management objectives.

Solving the problems for which conventional quality control activities have not been adequate is a better way of meeting the requirements of the new era of quality. Quality function deployment as detailed in this book is the powerful tool needed.

QUALITY DEPLOYMENT AND QUALITY FUNCTION DEPLOYMENT

The Quality System

Promotion of quality control in a company requires management. The critical steps are to clarify the aims of quality control, or *P*lan; to

*Translator's note: The Japanese term *hoshin* is retained here. While it is commonly translated as "policy," the English word inadequately expresses the depth of the original. Essentially, *hoshin* management is a system of deploying corporate strategies and plans into yearly activities, promoted by specific targets and implementation means at all levels in the organization.

identify the tasks to be implemented, or *Do*; to monitor the tasks to see if they are carried out properly, or *Check*; and to take corrective actions based on the results of monitoring, or *Act*. These activities must be performed on a companywide basis, and a method for linking the various departments and organizational levels must be clearly established and quickly enacted. This system of links is a "quality system." A. V. Feigenbaum describes such a system: "The quality system is the network of administrative and technical procedures required to produce and deliver a product of specified quality standards."[1]

Traditionally, the raison d'être of quality control (QC) activities was to ensure product quality, and therefore was limited to the manufacturing phase. In this new era of quality, however, QC must encompass every step in the life of the product, from quality planning to scrap. For this purpose, the *Plan*, *Do*, *Check*, *Act* (PDCA) sequence must cover all quality control activities. Furthermore, each quality control step must include PDCA to establish objectives, the tasks to implement them, monitoring the tasks, and taking corrective actions. In addition, the activities at each step must be organized and coordinated, and they must be converted into a system in order to achieve the goals common to overall QC activities. The system is a complex one formed from structural components such as manpower and machines, in order to achieve these common goals.

As stated previously, conventional QC activities do not always specify the objective to be accomplished. The quality targets, the first step of a quality system, are not clear. Also, although the QC activities are often performed in each step, they are not coordinated to accomplish the quality objectives.

According to Feigenbaum's definition of a quality system, it includes not only the activities to produce, to supply, and to use quality but also the pursuit of quality itself. Feigenbaum's approach to TQM, however, involves only the former; the quest for quality itself is not evident. The types of quality control process charts (those that identify control characteristics in the manufacturing process) in Japanese factories are not found in the United States or Europe, perhaps because these quality characteristics are considered issues for the company's engineering technology rather than for its quality control. Study of these characteristics is critical to QC; thus Japanese QC is probably more advanced because QC process charts are used with a purpose.[2]

The pursuit of quality has not always been an adequately emphasized part of QC in Japan. Nor can we say that there was adequate study of activities to plan for and to assure quality. Both quality and the activities to assure it should define and establish relationships that are clear at each step. In the following chapters, this process will be explained.

Quality Elements

As J. M. Juran states, the main determinant of product quality is "fitness for use."[3] The word "use" implies a system that considers the context of product use. If we look at how an automobile is used, we must consider a system that includes the vehicle itself, the road, the driver, and cargo. The quality required for an automobile must include these in its system. While we employ words like "mechanical," "electrical," or "chemical" to describe products, if we do not look systematically, we have a one-sided view of quality. For example, one problem vehicles experience is the rusting out of the exhaust pipe. Although the automobile can be considered a mechanical product, it is at the same time a chemical one.

The definition of quality must not be confined to fitness for use or utility; it must also emphasize freedom from harmful effects. Another consideration is economics. This not only means low cost for the manufacturer but also benefit to the user, and it addresses accountability for conservation and environmental issues (the cost of a quality society).[4]

A quality system must be more than a loose conglomeration of elements that produce quality; it must be a combination of elements that contributes to a specific purpose. In Table 1.1, the quality elements are physical properties, mechanical elements, human elements, time elements, economic elements, production elements, and market elements. It is also necessary to establish a way of expressing these quality elements, a way of measuring them, and a way of evaluating them. I call this system of addressing ways of constructing, expressing, measuring, and evaluating quality elements "quality engineering," a system that I feel must be put in place.[5] A powerful way to organize these quality elements into a system for these specific purposes is quality deployment, which will be described in the section "History of Quality Function Deployment," subsection "Deployment of Quality."

Quality Function Deployment

The corporate activities to achieve quality (quality planning and quality assurance) are the quality functions. It is necessary to clarify the quality functions of each phase from product planning through final scrapping and then to execute them fully. To do so, we must understand the *who, what, when, where, why,* and *how* of these corporate functions: What is the purpose of the function? Who has responsibility for performing it? and so on.

TABLE 1.1
Quality Elements

1. Physical property elements
   Exterior characteristics (size, length, weight, thickness)
   Dynamic characteristics (speed, pulling force, strength, brittleness)
   Physical properties (air permeability, heat retentiveness, thermal stability, elasticity)
   Optical properties (transparency, opaqueness, luminosity)
   Acoustic properties (tone, sound-blocking capability, audio output, signal-to-noise ratio)
   Information-related properties (redundancy, quantity of information, accuracy)
   Chemical properties (corrosion resistance, nonflammability, explosion resistance)
   Electrical properties (insulation properties, conductivity, induction)
2. Mechanical elements
   Efficiency (energy efficiency, ease of handling, automation)
   Safety (freedom from harmful effects, foolproof design)
   Versatility of function (multifunctionality, diversification through combining functions)
   Portability (portable, fixed)
   Experience of users (amateur level, professional level)
3. Human elements
   Image (high quality, name brand)
   Uniqueness (custom-made, imported, natural)
   Familiarity (traditional, newfangled)
   Sensory qualities (finish, feel, taste)
   Sense of fulfillment (intellectual fulfillment, emotional fulfillment)
   Trend toward *super* quality (service, features not found in other products)
4. Time elements
   Resistance to the elements (resistance to cold, humidity, dust)
   Effects of time (continuity of effect, immediate effect)
   Durability and maintenance (useful product life, failure rate, repairability)
   Disposability
5. Economic elements
   Advantages (low price, low maintenance cost)
   Premiums, extras
6. Production elements
   Operation factors (man-hours minimized, rework minimized, no special skills required, flexibility of operating standards)
   Raw materials (flexible quality tolerance, storability, inspectability, adaptability to process)
   Yield (high yield, ease of reworking, convertibility to other products)
7. Market elements
   Timeliness (fashion, seasonality)
   Product variety (wide selection)
   Trust
   Reason for purchase decision (personal criteria, opinion leaders, third-party evaluations)
   Life cycle (long life cycle, short life cycle but utilitarian)

Source: Shigeru Mizuno, "Quality Engineering," *Engineers* 251 (July 1969):2–7.

1. What is the purpose of the function? (Why)
2. What is the object of the function? (What)
3. Where will it be carried out (at which phase)? (Where)
4. At what time is it done? (When)
5. Which department is in charge of performing it? (Who)
6. In what way will it be done? (How)

If any of these questions is unanswered, that will have a detrimental effect on the quality function. After clarification of each quality function, appropriate control methods must be determined. Expressed differently, quality activities require accurate and effective execution. When problems arise, the causes must be discovered and eliminated; and if it becomes necessary, the quality function activities may require modification to improve the quality function itself. This activity should be called the *quality control function*; but since it is difficult to differentiate with accuracy quality functions from the activities that control them, both will be labeled "quality function."

It is also important to determine the *who, what, when, where, why,* and *how* of the control activities. These are the control items, the individual responsible for them, control frequency, area, purpose of the control, and the corresponding methodology. Clarification of these control items is not limited to the control items per se but includes other issues related to control. In effect, we standardize the task of controlling, and applicable items are documented in a control standard.

From the meaning of quality as a "task" comes an indication that there are "quality functions." There is also "quality deployment" itself, which by definition is the deployment of quality functions. Ideally, these terms must be distinguished, but when there is no need to do so, the definition of quality deployment and the deployment of quality functions (thus narrowly defined) are simply called quality function deployment (QFD).

TWO APPROACHES

Generally, there are two approaches to studying a problem. They are described below as they apply to quality control and quality planning.

The Analytic Approach

The analytic approach is commonly used in quality control to analyze cause and effect, and the cause-and-effect diagram is an excellent tool for this purpose. Statistical methods, too, determine the degree of effect (contribution) a particular cause may have; that is, they weigh the significance of the cause. The analytic approach to quality control effectively identifies the cause of the problem and eliminates it. It leads to upgrading the product or process to which it is applied. Since in this approach causes are evaluated by their effects, it is like a walk upstream.

The Design Approach

After the manufacture of the product has started, the analytic approach is effective for handling defects and improvements. But what about the development of new products? It requires a new method that provides a specific means to attain the goals. This is called the design approach. For example, examination of the engine or fuselage of a propeller-driven airplane would not be likely to lead to the concept of a jet plane. The conception of the jet came from the need for an engine more efficient than a reciprocating engine, in order to produce faster air flow. This design approach is the basis of Gerald Nadler's work system design method, and iterations of this approach are now known as function deployment.[6] Product function deployment uses a tree diagramming method that, when applied to the design approach, determines the means for achieving the specific end. Thus, it is tantamount to traveling downstream.

Product function deployment has been used in value engineering and value analysis for some time. The term "function" has two meanings: the purpose of the product and what it does. The term further divides into the basic function (required to give the product meaning) and secondary functions (to accomplish the purpose of the basic function). Take the example of a butane cigarette lighter. Its basic function is "to produce a flame." Secondary functions are "to discharge gas" and "to ignite gas." A function tree (function systematic diagram) shows the deployment of functions to primary, secondary, and tertiary levels, which indicate how the purpose is linked to specific means to achieve it. Figure 1.1 is the function tree for the butane lighter.[7]

The analytic approach alone does not effectively turn the quality functions and problem solutions into well-coordinated activities across departments and product development phases. This means that it is inadequate for total quality management (TQM) activities to progress into integrated activities that span product planning all the way to final scrapping. In this progression, the design approach systematizes these activities and thereby attains wide usage in TQM.

In the computer field both analysis and synthesis are regarded as

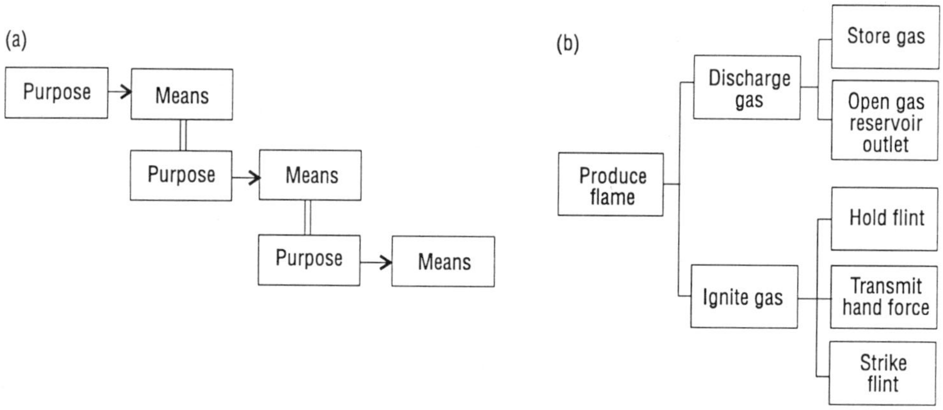

FIGURE 1.1
Function tree for butane cigarette lighter

important; they are the same two approaches as described here. Since quality control uses computers, adoption of these two approaches makes an ideal system.

HISTORY OF QUALITY FUNCTION DEPLOYMENT

Deployment of Quality Functions

A correct understanding of QFD requires a return to its origins.[8] Quality deployment and deployment of quality functions began in 1965–1967 when Yoji Akao and Katsuyoshi Ishihara were partially applying it in the field of quality control. Details of the procedural concepts are found in the cases discussed in the Appendix. To promote TQM, they deployed narrowly defined quality function deployment, that is, quality functions were deployed to achieve quality. Based on the work of Ishihara (at that time with Matsushita Electric's component division), who was the first to apply function deployment to clarify quality tasks, TQM was initiated companywide at Shimpo Industries,[9] winner of the 1965 Deming Prize for small and medium-size companies. At Shimpo, the quality assurance tasks of the sales department, for example, were for the most part nonexistent, making it almost impossible to determine needs from the analysis of data. From the results of functions deployed to five levels of detail, it was evident that half or less of the activities required to assure quality were implemented.

Even earlier, under the framework of TQM, Toyota Motors presented its version of clarifying quality assurance tasks in the form of a chart known as the quality assurance activities table. In association with Yasushi Furukawa, I was involved with the introduction of TQM at Toyota. One problem was the inability to make a clear determination of the activities required to assure quality. The table identified the tasks critical to quality assurance for each phase: planning, design, prototype building, production preparation, and production. The table delineated the assurance items related to quality, the operations for assurance, the individuals responsible for assurance, and so on. It was standardized as a part of the quality assurance regulations, and adherence to it was mandatory.

At that time, deployment of quality functions had not yet been applied to quality control, and the quality assurance activity table could not be properly called a QFD matrix. But a considerable effort was expended to create it, and it was used effectively. Although I cannot claim that it was cross-functional management delineating the activities between departments, deployment of functions for quality was indeed thorough, and for each phase the activities between departments were clarified. Cross-functional management began with the quality assurance activities table.

Toyota implemented cost control activities in the same manner, clarifying at each step the tasks appropriate to quality assurance activities. Although developing a quality assurance activities table based on items for quality assurance is a common practice, it does not necessarily clarify the needs of individual departments. By the deployment of functions, every essential task must be systematically identified.

Deployment of Quality

Until QFD, the quality characteristics of each phase, such as the planning quality, design quality, manufacturing quality, and delivery quality were established as independent entities. It is important, however, that the product design respond to the users' demands for quality, which, although previously emphasized, were difficult to assure because there was no positive way to do so.

In 1972, Mitsubishi Heavy Industries' Kobe shipyard was the first to use a quality chart to delineate critical responsibilities in order to accommodate product quality in the promotion of TQM activities.[10] I also participated in the introduction of quality control at this facility. The nature of its business was production to order, one ship at a time. The talented engineers utilized several technologies, and under these circumstances were not convinced that quality control programs would have a real effect. Still, even their most qualified engineers were not fully confident of product quality, particularly the relationship between the quality of the finished product and the quality of its components. Mitsubishi was not content with building giant ships profitably; its quality policy was to build "sophisticated" ships, advanced ships with high added value. Lacking was a consensus on the quality specifics of the ship. It was necessary to clarify what was meant by the quality of a ship, how quality could be produced, and what were the aims of its mechanisms and components. Based on the existing engineering technology, these points were not clear, so the quality deployment system offered additional values. For either a single product, such as a ship, or wide-variety, small-lot production, quality deployment is a powerful tool. The idea for the quality deployment chart or quality chart has been tailored by each successive company user. Shigeru Mizuno, Yasushi Furukawa, and Norikazu Mizuno led the way at Mitsubishi Heavy Industries' Kobe shipyard. Later, great success with quality deployment was achieved at the internal combustion engine division of Kubota, Ltd., and at Kayaba Industry, Ltd.

STRUCTURE OF THE QUALITY CHART

For discussion, the quality chart, which deploys the quality functions and indicates the goals and methods for accomplishing quality control tasks, will be called the quality function deployment chart. In it, quality itself is deployed, and the area that displays the relationships among the quality elements is called the quality deployment chart. A function deployment chart is created from an ordinary tree diagram, and the cause-and-effect diagram is also useful. Furthermore, the relationship between one level of quality elements and those of the next level is illustrated in a two-dimensional matrix. In fact, showing the entire system in this format is quite effective. Function deployment is unique because, unlike a list of ideas, it is complete and clearly identifies the relationships among its elements. Even with this system it is necessary to be sure that no quality elements are overlooked, and therefore to have a list of them, as in Table 1.1. For reference here, both the quality function deployment chart and the quality deployment chart will be broadly defined as the quality chart. As will be seen, there are several different quality charts with variation of content and purpose.

At Mitsubishi Heavy Industries' Kobe shipyard, product quality deployment refers to "hard" quality, and the corresponding charts are HQ charts. Charts referring to deployment of the functions are called "soft quality," or SQ, charts. Together, upon completion, these two become the quality assurance system.

Function Tree

As explained earlier, in value analysis and value engineering, a function tree or function systematic diagram depicts the link between the purpose and the working implementation of the quality functions. Since 1972, members of quality control research groups in the Osaka area, under the direction of Yoshinobu Nayatani, have advocated a group of quality tools for managerial and staff personnel with successful results. These tools are the New Seven QC Tools (also called Seven Management Tools for QC or Seven Management and Planning Tools for QC), which are a companion to the more familiar Seven QC Tools that include the Pareto chart and the cause-and-effect diagram. The function tree is one of the new tools, and its use is not limited to QFD; *hoshin* deployment and other activities also make use of its power.

Bill of Materials

In production planning, the product type and quantity for a specific period are established for a material requirements plan, in order to determine the types and quantities of raw materials and parts. The list of the construction and content of the parts for building the final product is commonly called a bill of materials. A parts deployment determines the components and required quantities. There are two approaches: the first deploys parts from the broadest level to detail levels with a tree diagram, and the second starts at the detailed level and proceeds to broader categories. The first is referred to as an explosion of the parts; the latter, as an implosion.[11] At any rate, the purpose of parts deployment is to calculate the required quantities of parts and raw materials, and as such is not a deployment of quality. Still, the methodologies are similar and it merits mention.

FMEA and FTA

Two tools developed in the United States are failure mode and effects analysis (FMEA) and fault tree analysis (FTA). These tools, as a part of reliability engineering, analyze product failures.

With FMEA, the mode of failure, effects of failure, potential cause of failure, corrective measures, and other data from the past are tabulated for identification of potential failures. This analytic approach typically implodes from greater detail to less detail. FTA, in contrast, looks for undesirable phenomena and explodes the potential causes of such failures into detail. This deployment is typically the *design approach.*[12]

These processes are not merely qualitative deployment. FMEA estimates the probability of a failure, the severity of its effects, and the probability of detecting a defect caused by the identified failure in order to prioritize the riskiest potential failures. FTA predicts the probability of occurrence of the phenomena causing the failures.

Failure is the negative aspect of quality; just because a product is defect-free, it cannot necessarily be called a quality product. To assure that both design quality and manufacturing quality meet the customer-demanded quality, one must not stop with the elimination of failures; broader issues must be analyzed and deployed. In failure analysis, process FMEA gathers and evaluates data from the manufacturing process in order to prevent defects. These techniques are highly effective, but it is necessary to go beyond the collection of data on failures; quality data must include data to improve process capability, reduction of cycle time, and so on. In other words, improved quality comes with effort, and that is why quality function deployment and analysis must be performed to the fullest extent. Thus, while these failure analyses are a necessary part of the TQM activities, it is emphasized that they comprise only a part of QFD.

Quality Deployment Chart

The quality deployment chart varies with its purpose and use, and serves the multiple functions of a quality chart, a quality deployment chart, a quality relationship matrix, a demanded-quality deployment chart, and so on. In this volume, it will be used as a quality deployment chart. The terms in this book are arranged as shown below.

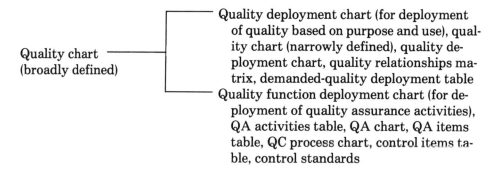

Quality chart (broadly defined)

- Quality deployment chart (for deployment of quality based on purpose and use), quality chart (narrowly defined), quality deployment chart, quality relationships matrix, demanded-quality deployment table
- Quality function deployment chart (for deployment of quality assurance activities), QA activities table, QA chart, QA items table, QC process chart, control items table, control standards

The quality deployment chart shows the correlation between demanded quality and the engineering required to achieve it. (This definition comes from the internal combustion engine division of Kubota, Ltd.)

From the manner in which companies handle their engineering technology, it is immediately evident that the relationship of quality characteristics between the product and its component mechanisms (subassemblies) and parts is unclear. For example, an industrial machine has a noise problem. Which part is causing the noise and which part needs improvement in order to reduce the noise become clear with the application of engineering technology. Without a systematic way to study such problems, effective corrective measures cannot be taken. Companies are currently applying their engineering technology to products, but they establish the quality characteristics for the final product, for subassemblies, and for parts separately, almost without regard to their interrelationships. As defined here, the quality deployment chart raises the level of technology (design engineering) through standardization.

Figure 1.2 is a quality deployment chart developed by Mitsubishi Heavy Industries' Kobe shipyard for a large-scale diesel engine. In this example, each level of quality detail has a number corresponding to the applicable engineering standard. Quality deployment often clearly delineates the dimensional and material specifications for nonessential parts, but those for critical parts are not always standardized. Figure 1.3 indicates the necessity of sorting out the relationships between each quality characteristic and the components of the product. A matrix of quality deployment and parts deployment performs this function.

In order to design product quality and take it to the manufacturing stage, it is critical to clarify the relationships between the characteristics the user requires for the product (substitute characteristics), the quality characteristics at the time of design (design characteristics), control characteristics during the manufacturing process, inspection characteristics, and others. Unfortunately, with either engineering technology or conventional quality control, the above relationships are inadequately researched and the resulting quality characteristics are independently derived from past experience only. Use of the quality deployment chart facilitates an understanding of the relationships of these quality characteristics at each phase of TQM activity (step deployment), with determination by a logical process. The quality deployment chart also leads to improvements in the current practice of engineering technology, including design engineering, production engineering, and measurement and inspection engineering, followed by standardization of these improvements.

The quality deployment chart is not confined to quality control; it applies to deployment of the quality activities for value engineering,

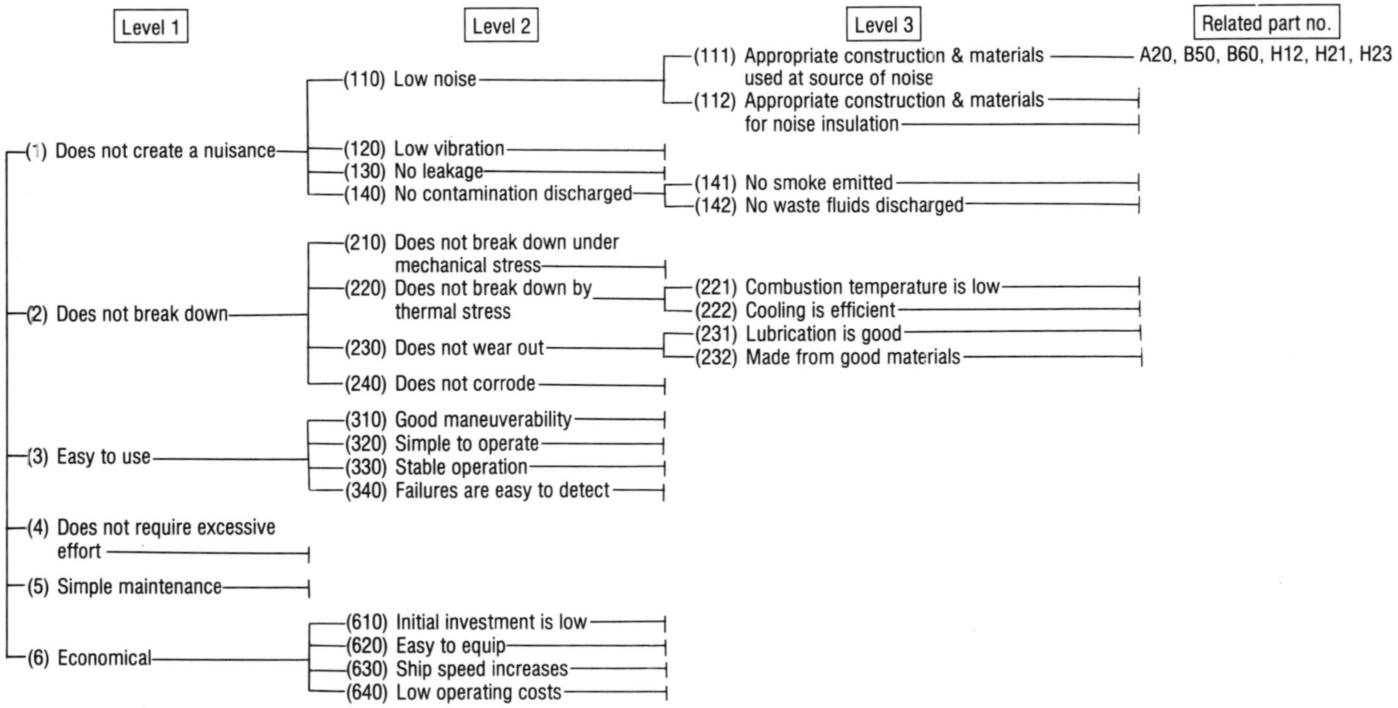

FIGURE 1.2
Quality chart for large-scale marine diesel engine

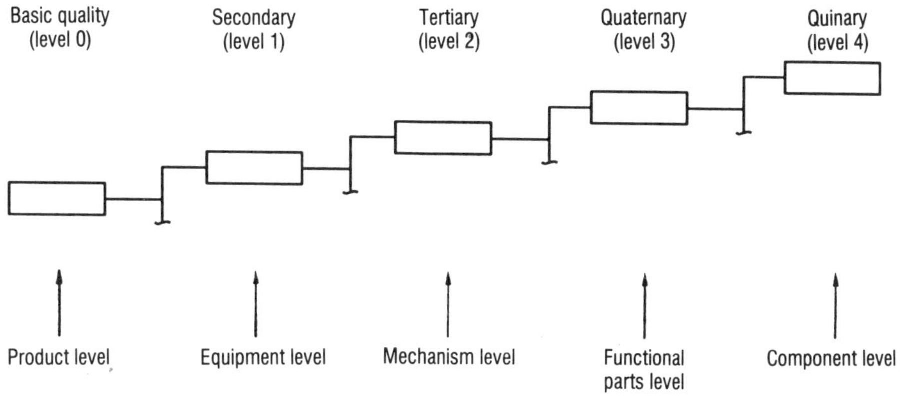

FIGURE 1.3
Relationship between each quality element and product components

to failures in reliability engineering, and to bills of materials for production quantities. When applied to quality control, it is particularly helpful for deploying user quality, which is the highest level. The quality deployment chart is no mere summary of results from analyzing quality; its purpose is deployment of the design approach to clarify what is not easily seen through conventional engineering technology and analysis, that is, the correlations between the quality characteristics of each component and part. Of course, the chart must also include items identified in conventional engineering practice. Then, through analysis, the quality elements and quality characteristics are weighted.

Quality Function Deployment Chart

The previous quality assurance activities table generally treats quality assurance items as "compliance with quality standards." In actual design and manufacturing, however, these items require further deployment for use. The QC process chart is a table of control methods including control characteristics and sampling and measurement methods for manufacturing processes, and the individuals responsible for them. Actually, the QC process chart precedes the quality assurance activities table, but the best results come from linking them together. This is done by achieving customer-demanded quality through showing items corresponding to standards for the manufacturing plant. These include assurance items and standards for each phase of the design, manufacturing process, raw materials and appropriate handling, and inspection in charts that also show the relationships. Specifically, the chart required adds the quality characteristics and the associated standards to the QA items from the quality assurance activities table. This chart is a QA chart or QA items chart (see Chapter 7, section "Communicating Quality").[13] Some manufacturing locations use a QA chart that combines the QA items chart and the QC process chart. In May 1977 I discovered a QA data sheet and an inspection method sheet at a Pratt & Whitney jet engine facility in the United States. The QA data sheet listed quality-specific requirements and inspection locations and procedures. The inspection method sheet specified the sampling method, the equipment to be used (including model number), and the exact locations to be measured.

The QA items chart should, of course, be based on the quality deployment chart. The chart is not limited to quality characteristics and performance values; degree of importance, prototype and trial run problems, claims data, process capability values, and internal and external quality data are to be included. It is especially effective because it indicates exactly what will happen when quality characteristics are not met. Thus, the QA items chart merges quality deployment and the quality functions to deploy it. It is the bridge to join the two.

THE ROLE OF THE QUALITY CHART

The Relationship to Engineering Technology

From the design standpoint, Osamu Hirao[14] attempted the deployment of quality for automobile engines in 1968. It also was applied to the design of homes by the design methods subgroup of the Architecture Planning Committee of the Japan Architecture Society[15] in 1968. This activity occurred two years after Akao's initial endeavors at deployment of quality. It seems that application to general use has been slow.

In the deployment of quality, quality elements should be selected systematically, not at random, by fully analyzing and studying the quality-related data. Even a comprehensive examination of product quality through engineering technology may be inadequate. For this purpose, the quality elements table is appropriate. Also, an engineering analysis of failures may be inadequate for quality control. For example, there is a need to initiate more rigorous studies of human error.

Frequently during the design, prototype, and manufacturing phases related to engineering technology, the relationship between quality characteristics and their relative importance is unclear. In some extreme cases, in spite of quality changes through the processes, there are no intermediary specifications. Final product specifications become the standard for the manufacturing processes. Thus, from a statistical point of view, the determination of part tolerances is often illogical.

Recently the term "quality analysis" has been used frequently; however, except in the case of identifying the cause of a failure and improving the quality of products by eliminating that failure, the analytic approach alone is never adequate to discover new quality characteristics and to develop a new product that possesses them. I have used and advocated the importance of "analysis of quality" since before 1960 to refer to selecting and quantifying critical quality characteristics for design quality.[16] Analysis of quality corresponds to analysis of processes, in which the relationships between quality characteristics and the factors of the manufacturing processes are described. Quality deployment and quality analysis are both needed, and analysis is required to determine the relationship of each quality characteristic deployed and to weigh its relative importance.

Professor Yasushi Furukawa speaks of the logical connection between quality and technology. This refers to the complex system of linking customer-demanded quality to the QC process charts and to the manufacturing process through after-sales service, of reviewing and solving engineering bottlenecks, and of quality deployment that is based on customer demands for quality. The high technology at companies that do this requires a system to make best use of it, and Professor Furukawa has worked long and hard to select and administer such a system.

In quality analysis some examples have been published of technical improvements that result from using statistical analysis such as multivariate analysis in association with mechanical models such as output analysis, noise analysis, and tolerance analysis.[17] It is necessary in such cases to make certain that all the necessary quality elements are included by performing quality deployment in advance and to review the relationships among them. With chemical products it is important to conduct quality deployment for the chemical characteristics and physical characteristics, such as the size and shape of crystals, in order to analyze the relationships. Professor Furukawa has developed an analysis of the logic of multivariate analysis and systems engineering that links quality deployment and analysis, and has proposed a "relation chart" to indicate the interrelationships of quality.

Evaluation of Relationships among Quality Characteristics

It is necessary to identify the quality characteristics, in order to be assured at each step of the quality control activities and to define the relationship among quality characteristics, such as use characteristics and substitute characteristics, control characteristics, and inspection characteristics. In the past, these characteristics were often selected indiscriminately, and the resulting control charts were not useful. This situation is frequently caused by inadequate preliminary deployment of the relationships of various quality characteristics, resulting in the use of control characteristics that have an insignificant relationship to the quality characteristics of the finished product. If the process capabilities are seen as a group of process capability elements reduced to individual quality elements or steps, it will be possible to predict the process capability of a new product. In this way, predicting quality becomes possible.

I advocated the need to evaluate the interrelationship of quality characteristics among many steps in 1966.[18] In 1972 Yoji Akao discussed the system of quality deployment in detail, divided it into 17 steps, and deployed it in the form of the QC process chart.[19] (These steps are given in Chapter 3.) There is a quality deployment chart for each step of quality. At the first step, when researching market quality, it is necessary to make a demanded quality chart. A typical sales point for a product is usually a qualitative term like "easy to use." If sales requests to the engineering department are based on such a quality characteristic, engineering cannot understand the substitute characteristics and, therefore, will not respond to the request immediately. It is necessary to deploy such a sales point and to transform it into something that can be further evaluated. For example, "easy to use" in regard to wallpaper can be deployed into such quality items as "does not wrinkle when glue is applied" and "does not stick at the corners." Technically, these items can be transformed into characteristics such as "does not stretch or shrink excessively when wet." In this way, the quality of one's own product and those of competitors can be compared. It should be emphasized that the quality deployment chart is particularly important to the sales department.

Quality deployment is also needed for manufacturing equipment and machinery. Tolerance and looseness should be studied for precision, manufacturing specifications, quality of all the installed machinery, the drive section, power transmission section, control devices, and so on. It should also review how operating conditions, such as change in temperature, would affect the quality of the product machined on it. The improvement of process capabilities can be achieved only through such activities. Mere reporting of the process capability index is not enough.

In the construction industry it is necessary that quality deployment be performed and that items be considered with reference to quality assurance and the point to be checked. Further, the service activities of distribution, maintenance, and repair require quality deployment.

Control Standards

As an important part of TQM activities in Japan, many companies are enthusiastically pursuing "clarification of control items." As far as I am aware, Teijin (recipient of the Deming Prize in 1961) was the first corporation to perform these activities systematically. I was involved in the introduction of TQM at this company. In an effort to improve the efficiency of the organization, control items for each level of management, control method, and control data were studied and summarized into a control items chart. Then systematic control activities were based on the chart. These data not only show control items but also cover all the control activities that I consider "control standards."

Quality function deployment is necessary for establishing control standards, but it should be stressed that quality deployment is just as important. (Quality function deployment in this context is defined later as deployment of quality-related job functions.) The common tendency of managers is to focus on cost as the major control item. However, quality itself should be included as a control item to make managers feel personally responsible. This is one area that general TQM activities do not adequately emphasize. As for cost, as shown in Figure 1.4, various control items should be the responsibility of different levels of management. For quality, low-level quality elements should be included in the control items of lower-level managers, and the high-level quality elements should be assigned to high-level managers. In this way, again for the sake of quality, management personnel of various levels participate in creating truly "total" activities.

For the departments in a company, the functions shared among them are clearer when relationships resulting from deploying the quality function chart for quality assurance activities are reviewed. Also, the interrelationship of activities within a department that has multiple responsibilities must be studied. For example, for quality assurance activities and activities to increase sales, the sales department must perform quality function deployment, and the relationships among the results of such deployment are evaluated by using a matrix to identify the relationships. In one reported case, this mode of evaluation resulted in an understanding of the importance of quality assurance activities by the sales personnel, who naturally have an interest in increased sales.

Through parts deployment and phase deployment, the evaluation of the quality of finished products, subassemblies, and components is now carried out properly, and quality evaluation in each phase is cor-

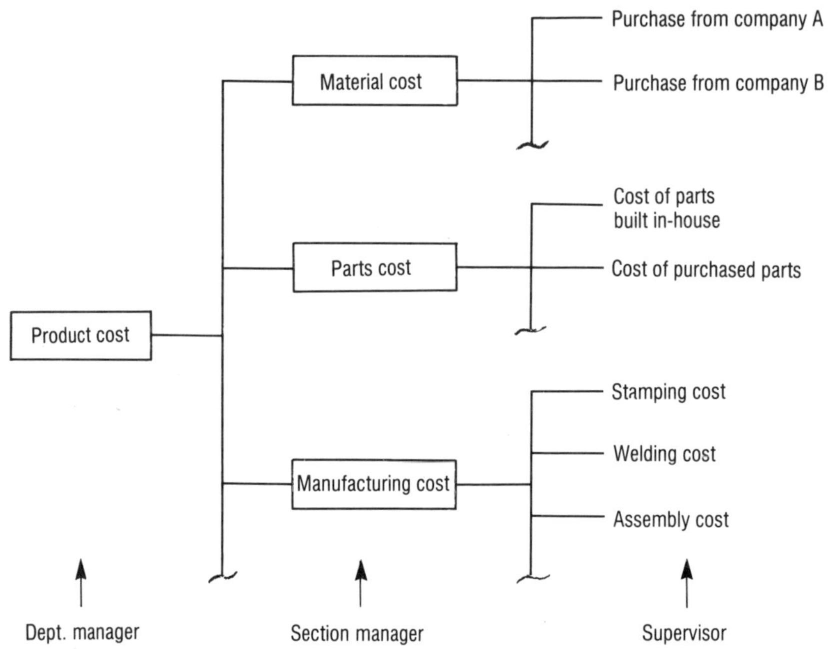

FIGURE 1.4
Control items for management job levels regarding product cost

rectly performed. In new product development, quality evaluations like these have particular importance. In an actual case, a quality deployment chart was constructed from the detailed evaluation of parts and steps for products developed in the past, and research addressed in detail areas in which quality problems were found, in order to concentrate on causes of cost increases and schedule delays. Then corrective measures were developed to prevent recurrence of these problems in the next generation of products, planning charts were constructed, and the corrective measures were implemented. Actions made it possible to avoid the problems experienced with past products.

Quality System

The Subcommittee on Organizational Quality Control of the Japan Standards Association[20] performed a trial of quality functional deployment utilizing the planning-programming-budgeting system, which is one of the scientific methods of complex decision making. In this project, the eighth-level work unit objectives were deployed as shown in

Table 1.2. It is an effective and interesting method to implement quality function deployment; however, it lacks reality, and in actual situations it appears that reviews through normal function deployment and the function tree would adequately serve the purpose. One of the achievements of the Quality System Study Group of the Union of Japanese Scientists and Engineers (JUSE) was publication of Toshiaki Chazono's *Claims Handling System.*[21] A Japan Society of Quality Control (JSQC) group, led by Yoji Akao, intensively studied quality systems and reported a new computer system for quality deployment.[22] Also, Yasushi Furukawa and his group[23] have formulated models for quality control systems. The deployment of quality and quality functions, and a systematic utilization of quality systems, has begun.

Classifying and storing information on quality are becoming increasingly important to industry, especially where product liability prevention is concerned. Thus it is important to perform deployment of quality and quality functions as part of overall TQM activities. An integral part of TQM activities in this new era of quality, deployment of quality and quality functions as a new trend in quality control have taken on a very significant meaning.[24]

Review of Engineering Standards

A relationship with engineering technologies is one of the important roles of the quality deployment chart. By deploying parts and phases for quality, areas lacking design technology or manufacturing

TABLE 1.2
Example of a QC System

Work unit	*Examples of contents*
8th (objectives)	To re-create high quality that satisfies customers
7th (total output)	System to plan product that satisfies customers
6th (programs)	Information, education, & advertising program to satisfy customers
5th (final product)	Customer information, market research, market development
4th (work-in-progress)	Determine research items, secure source of information
3rd (section-level jobs)	Research & collection of information, discovery of products that customers desire
2nd (element operation)	Dialogues, education, sales
1st (actions)	Scheduling, personnel, expenses

technology can be better evaluated. This suggests that the quality deployment chart can be used for evaluating quality characteristics of components to satisfy the conditions under which the final product is used as well as the manufacturing methods and conditions. Also, the quality deployment chart serves to organize engineering data for the design, preproduction, and production phases. Engineering standards or engineering documents are summarized into a quality chart; and through assignment of a number to the quality element at each level, they support the search for engineering information.

The effectiveness of the quality deployment chart in quality evaluation has often been mentioned. It is also effective for a design review, which is regarded as one of the effective modes of quality assurance in the development and design stages. The quality deployment chart is also a powerful tool in the configuration management[25] of documents and records for design changes made to support quality assurance.

QUALITY FUNCTION DEPLOYMENT AND MANAGEMENT

The quality function does not concern merely the activities of engineering.[26] Important nonengineering or nontechnical activities exist even in the development phase (the source), as well as in the post-manufacturing sales and service phases. Market research for new product development and advertising and public relations for sales are examples. None of these activities is unrelated to product quality. Therefore, deployment of quality and quality functions does have a significant meaning in these phases.

The Yaesu Book Center reported an example in which quality characteristics were determined through deployment of quality and quality functions at its bookstores, so that sales operations could be carried out appropriately.[27]

I found the lecture,[28] on high-technology management, given by Professor H. E. Riggs of Stanford University at the Central Japan Quality Control Symposium, sponsored by Central Japan Quality Control Research Committee, very interesting. Professor Riggs summarized four functional strategies concerning high technology.

1. Market strategy
2. Sales strategy
3. Product strategy
4. Manufacturing process strategy.

Deployment of quality and of quality functions will be helpful for formalizing strategies for the product and for the manufacturing process. Similarly, quality can be considered for marketing as well. Therefore, the deployment of quality and of the quality functions will be helpful for marketing and sales.

In the past, effective methods of quality control in sales activities have been developed through the efforts of many people. On this basis, deployment of quality and of the quality functions are expected to become effective activities in sales.

Quality function deployment provides an effective method for establishing a quality information system, also an important activity in TQM. Quality information is a crucial indicator of the efficiency of quality management. It is also related to the control items for each position. For this reason, I feel that quality function deployment is significant because it provides an important method for quality management.

While cross-functional management,[29] discussed in the section of this chapter "Quality Problems Today," is implemented as management for each objective, such as quality, cost, and delivery (QCD), a strong effect occurs only when it is applied comprehensively rather than on an individual basis. Each department – design, manufacturing, or sales – should implement management controls within its own organization; such management can be called companywide quality control only when it exhibits comprehensive power. Similarly, cross-functional management, or interdepartmental management laterally connecting these divisions, should be implemented not only individually for each objective but also under a comprehensive management system. Only then does TQM produce results.

In collaboration with Professor Yasushi Furukawa[30] and others, I have experimented with the simultaneous management of QCD, under the name QC-PERT and PERT-QC, for the development phase and individual production. This is done by using a comprehensive control chart that includes control items such as quality, cost, and production volume (delivery) in the daily schedule table based on PERT.

Comprehensive management of QCDS (Safety added) has been implemented by Shimuzu Construction at its construction sites in accordance with the daily schedules. In addition, based on a proposal made by Shunzo Nakagawa and others, management activities integrating *hoshin* management and cross-functional comprehensive management are now implemented with all-out efforts at construction sites by integrating individual plans and schedules based on deployment of the policy at the top and the policy provided by the supporting divisions. Through this, *hoshin* management and cross-functional management finally become capable of showing their comprehensive power. This is an activity worthy of attention. In any case, quality function deployment will play an important role as the foundation of these TQM activities.

Thus, the deployment of quality and the deployment of quality functions are useful, directly or indirectly, for solving problems of quality control activities. Today the construction industry can no longer secure an order based solely on the hardware aspects of its product. For example, today construction firms not only erect office buildings, but also must introduce potential tenants to the party who ordered its construction. In other words, the quality not only of the hardware (the quality of a product) but also of software or user merits (the quality of the total business experience) is being sought.

A manufacturer of carbon electrodes for electric furnaces is increasing its sales by providing potential users of its products – manufacturers of specialty steel furnaces – with appropriate operational conditions for their furnaces by taking relevant electrical measurements. A manufacturer of a steam trap provides potential customers with an energy saving comparison of its product and the competitor's, in order to demonstrate the superiority of its product and how to use it. These examples show that no longer can sales be based on the product alone; rather, they must include the software of application technology, that is, how to use the product. Obviously, quality function deployment has a significant meaning, especially for management in such an environment.

NOTES

1. A. V. Feigenbaum, *Total Quality Control* (New York: McGraw-Hill, 1961).

2. Shigeru Mizuno, "Outline of QC Process Diagram," *Quality Control* 26 (April 1975):4–9.

3. J. M. Juran, *Quality Control Handbook* (New York: McGraw-Hill, 1954, 1962, 1974).

4. Shigeru Mizuno, "Quality Cost in the New Era of Quality," *Quality Control* 26 (July 1975):9–13.

5. Shigeru Mizuno, "Tasks of Quality Engineering," pts. 1 and 2, *Quality Control* 17 (August 1966):1–3 and (October 1966):1–4.

6. Gerald Nadler, *Work Systems Design* (Homewood, Ill.: Richard D. Irwin, 1967).

7. Masatoshi Tamai, *Function Analysis* (Tokyo: Sangyo Noritsu Junior College [Sanno College] Press, 1967).

8. Shigeru Mizuno, "Deployment of Quality Function," *Quality* 6, no. 2 (1976):3–8.
9. Shimpo Industries, Ltd., *Company-Wide Quality Control* (Tokyo: JUSE Press, 1970).
10. Yasuyuki, Suzuki, "Attempt of Design Improvement for Large Marine Diesel Engine," *Quality Control* 23 (May 1972):16–20 (spec. iss.); Koichi Nishimura, "Designing Ships and Quality Chart," *Quality Control* 23 (1972):71–74.
11. Japan Management Engineering Association, *Management Engineering References* (Tokyo: Maruzen, 1975), p. 120.
12. Shigeru Mizuno, ed., *Product Liability Prevention Planning* (Tokyo: JUSE Press, 1975).
13. Yoji Akao, "New Product Development and Quality Assurance," *Standardization and Quality Control* 25 (April 1972):7–14.
14. Osamu Hirao, "Attempted Principles of Automotive Engine Planning," *Internal Combustion Engines* 7 (1968):4–12.
15. Subcommittee on Designing Methods, Architecture Planning Committee, Japan Architecture Society, *Methods of Designing* (Tokyo: Shokokusha, 1968).
16. QC Research Group, Union of Japanese Scientists and Engineers, *Beginner's Quality Control Text* (Tokyo: JUSE Press, 1959).
17. Yasushi Furukawa, "Process Analysis," in *Reports on the 5th Quality Control Symposium*, ed. by Union of Japanese Scientists and Engineers (1967), pp. 71–93.
18. Mizuno, "Tasks of Quality Engineering."
19. Akao, "New Product Development and Quality Assurance."
20. Japan Standards Association, Subcommittee on Organizational Quality Control, "Systematic Approach for Systematic Reevaluation of Quality Control," pts. 1–7, *Standardization and Quality Control* (November 1971–July 1972).
21. Toshiaki Chazono, "Attempt at Claims Handling by System Matrix," *Engineers* no. 297 (May 1973):32–37.
22. Hisakazu Shindo, Yojo Akao, and Takashi Shirachi, "Quality Deployment Computer System QECS-1," *Quality* 8, no. 1 (1978):33–39.
23. Yasushi Furukawa, Mizuno Norikazu, Yoji Kubota, and Hiroshi Iimori, "Theoretical Analysis of Quality Control Organization," *Ninth Reporting Session of the Japanese Society for Quality Control* (Tokyo: JSQC, 1976), pp. 20–23.
24. Shigeru Mizuno, "Quality Deployment: New Trends in Quality Control," *Engineers* no. 346 (July 1977):1–5.
25. R. K. Ruzicka, "Documentation: Configuration Management," in *QC Handbook*, 3rd ed. (New York: McGraw-Hill, 1974), pp. 19–21.
26. Shigeru Mizuno, "Concerning Quality Deployment," *Quality*

Control 33 (1982):412–418; "Management and Quality Control," *Quality* 11 (1981):67–73; "Quality Planning," *Quality* 8 (1978):208–215; and Shigeru Mizuno and Norikazu Mizuno, *Check List for Quality Activities* (Tokyo: Taxation Accounting Association, 1984).

27. Zenjiro Kawai, "Lecture Series: Quality Control of Many Industries, XVII: Specialty Store Issue, 2. Quality Control at Yaesu Book Center," *Quality Control* 34 (1983):520–523.

28. Kiyoshi Kawakami, "Report: The 5th Central Japan Quality Control Symposium, Aims and the Effects of the Management System in the High Technology Field," *Engineers* no. 415 (1983):30–34.

29. Shigeru Aoki, "Cross Functional Management as Management for the Top," *Quality Control* 32 (1981):204–210, 298–303, 401–405.

30. Shigeru Mizuno and Yasushi Furukawa, "PERT and QC," *Quality Control* 14 (November 1963):17–19 (spec. iss.).

2

The Concept of the Quality Chart and Its Beginnings

Akira Takayanagi

INTRODUCTION

The purpose of this chapter, as the title suggests, is to introduce the "chaotic" process that eventually led to systematization of the concept.[1] Thus this chapter primarily addresses concepts, and the reader will find certain terms that have not yet been standardized. When they are standardized, eventually by the Japanese Society for Quality Control or by other organizations, they should of course be used. This chapter follows the conventions of normal use.

At the Kobe shipyard of Mitsubishi Heavy Industries, "quality chart" is generally a concept that includes (1) the quality chart (Q chart), (2) the quality assurance chart (QA chart), and (3) the quality assurance level chart (QL chart). In this chapter, in numerous instances the term "quality chart" encompasses these three types of charts. The confusion arises from the fact that in the process of establishing the QA system, the topics were defined by stratification after they were completed. The differences across the Q chart, QA chart, and QL charts are summarized below.

The *quality chart (Q chart)* is a chart in which true quality (demanded by customers) is systematized according to functions and the relationship between these functions and quality characteristics (substitute characteristics) is indicated.

The *quality assurance chart (QA chart)* is a chart that shows methods (such as specifications and standards) of linking true quality to be assured to quantifiable quality characteristics and, further, to assure that quality.

The *quality assurance level chart (QL chart)* is the QA chart with the addition of an assurance level and the names of responsible personnel.

In actual use, combining the Q chart and QA chart or the QA chart and QL chart is feasible, and it appears impossible to differentiate the three completely. The concept of the quality chart arose from the promotion of quality control. However, not only QC in a narrow sense but also integrating and systematizing the value engineering function tree, system theories based on computer applications, and other factors contributed to a better understanding and provided a reference for effective and meaningful discussions on a subject that now has a common language.

THE KOBE SHIPYARD OF MITSUBISHI HEAVY INDUSTRIES

Before proceeding to the details of a quality control system based on the quality chart applied to production of single products built to order, an outline of the Kobe shipyard will provide an understanding of the background. The concept of the quality chart was developed from 1970 to 1973, and the organization described in this section represents its status in 1973. The organization of the Kobe shipyard is typical of a plant that manufactures a single product only when an order is received. Shown in Figure 2.1 are its twenty departments handling eight products, including ships and nuclear-powered equipment. The shipyard employs approximately 10,000 people. Figure 2.2 lists the major products and the customers for them. One unique characteristic of the plant is that the most orders come from customers having technological capabilities equal to or higher than the manufacturer.

Given these circumstances, it was a concern that merely copying quality control systems that were effective in the process and mass-production industries would have limited use. However, many significant changes have occurred in all areas and the interest in, and demand for, quality by the general population continues to grow strongly. To respond to these new trends, an upgrade of the quality control systems for the manufacture of made-to-order single products is required. The Kobe quality chart came into existence out of the process of promoting divisionwide quality control activities based on recognition of this trend.

CONTROLLING THE DESIGN PROCESS AND QUALITY

Figure 2.3 is an outline of a control system that centers on the quality of the design process. In the figure, the area surrounded by a bold line represents the design department, which is in contact with

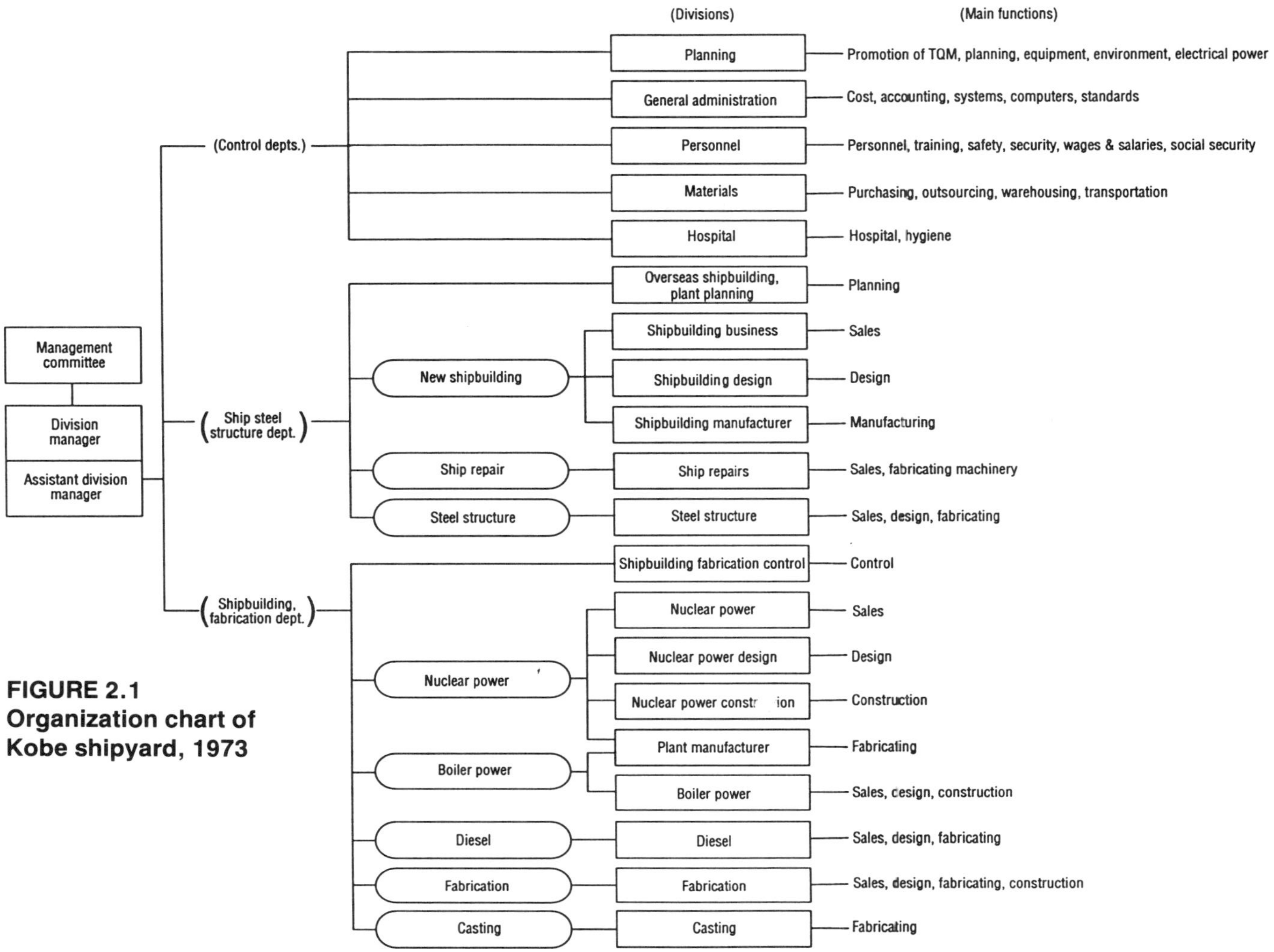
(Divisions)
(Main functions)
Management committee
Division manager
Assistant division manager
(Control depts.)
Planning
Promotion of TQM, planning, equipment, environment, electrical power
General administration
Cost, accounting, systems, computers, standards
Personnel
Personnel, training, safety, security, wages & salaries, social security
Materials
Purchasing, outsourcing, warehousing, transportation
Hospital
Hospital, hygiene
(Ship steel structure dept.)
Overseas shipbuilding, plant planning
Planning
New shipbuilding
Shipbuilding business
Sales
Shipbuilding design
Design
Shipbuilding manufacturer
Manufacturing
Ship repair
Ship repairs
Sales, fabricating machinery
Steel structure
Steel structure
Sales, design, fabricating
(Shipbuilding, fabrication dept.)
Shipbuilding fabrication control
Control
Nuclear power
Nuclear power
Sales
Nuclear power design
Design
Construction
Plant manufacturer
Fabricating
Boiler power
Boiler power
Diesel
Diesel
Sales, design, fabricating
Fabrication
Fabrication
Sales, design, fabricating, construction
Casting
Casting
Fabricating

FIGURE 2.1
Organization chart of Kobe shipyard, 1973

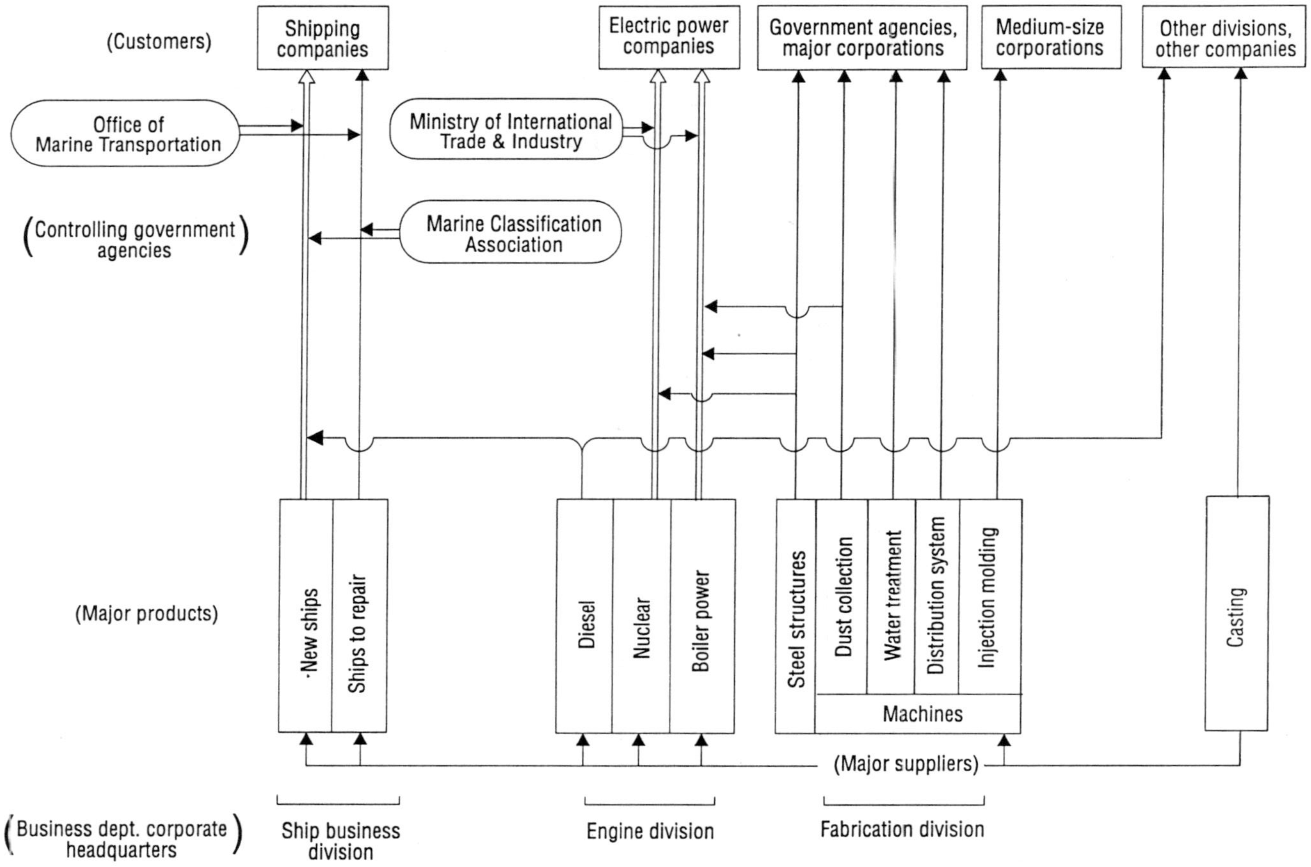

FIGURE 2.2
Major products and major customers

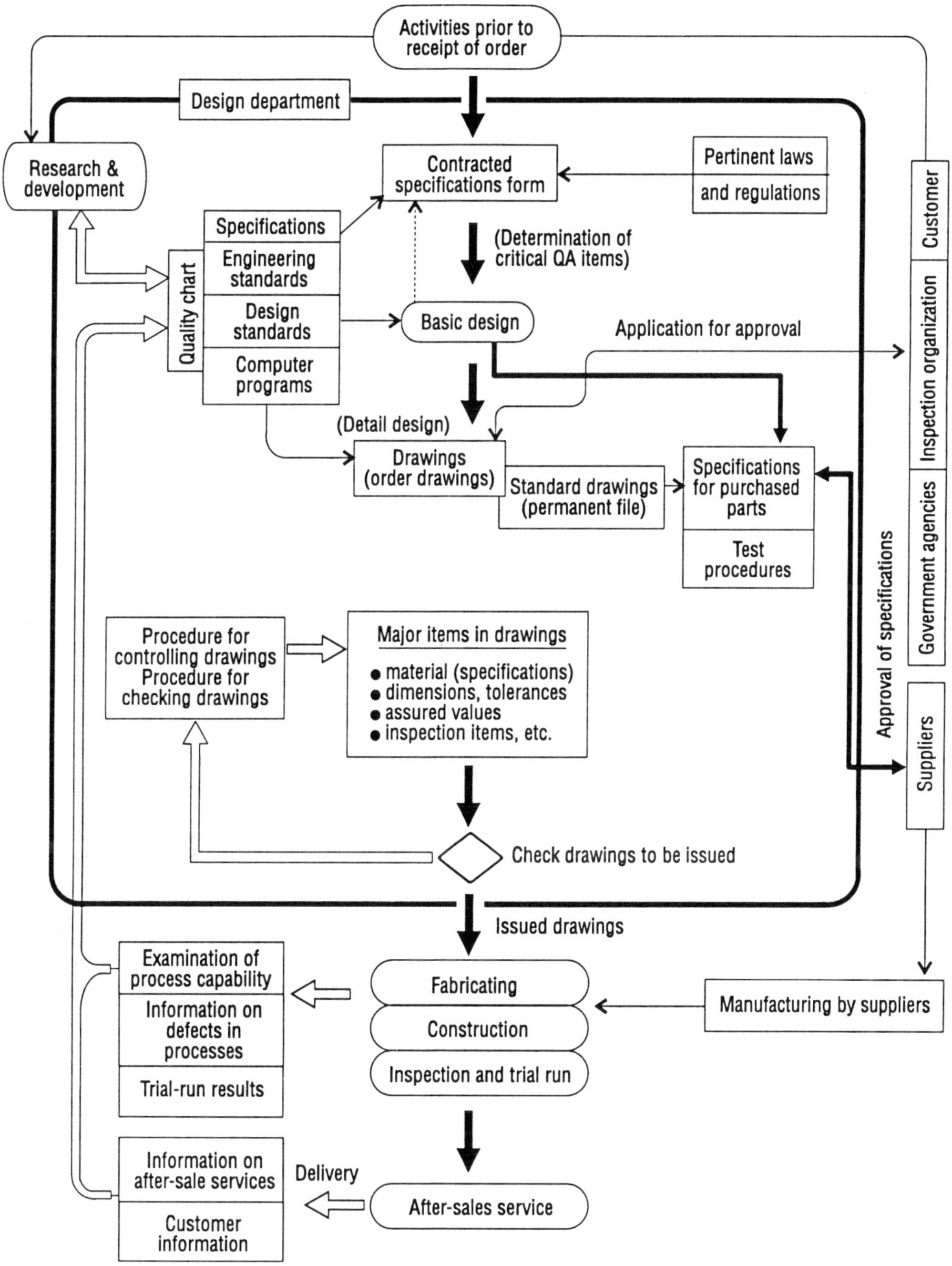

FIGURE 2.3
System for control design process

other departments outside the bold line. Three points summarize the quality control activities of the design department.

First, *control activities for the accumulation and utilization of technologies* are designed to upgrade the level of research and development technology to reflect customer requirements positively and to obtain information regarding failure both of the process and after delivery. The data are accumulated in the engineering standards and computer programs for later use.

Second, in *verification and communication of detailed quality assurance items*, the application procedure for approval verifies in detail customer requirements for quality. The drawings and media communicate precisely to the subsequent processes.

Third, in *activities to improve issuing of drawings*, the drawings are checked for ease of comprehension and to minimize changes. The quality chart appears in the upper left part of Figure 2.3. It is the basis for various standards, including specifications, engineering standards, design standards, and computer programs. It is a good indication that the quality chart has an important place as a common link. It emulates the human brain, and into it must be fed all the important information to be sorted for use in the entire system. Although the format and content of the quality chart are not yet final, because it is now in the conceptual and preparatory stages, I hope that at least the concept of the subject is understood.

MANUFACTURING PROCESSES AND TARGET QUALITY

Figure 2.4 summarizes the manufacturing process for single-product manufacturing with the operation sheet (which brings together functions closely associated with the process design), a sample of which is Figure 2.5. It lists the individual parts for each operation, with information on machinery, operating standards, jigs and tools, checkpoints, standard machining time, and other parameters. A copy of this operation sheet for each segment of operations is given to the workers as operating instructions. Standard time is used for production scheduling, efficiency measurement, cost distribution, and so on, and is applied to cost scheduling and ultimately to quality.

The control system in Figure 2.4 routes the feedback in two separate directions. On the left are quality circle activities, and activities for staff personnel appear on the right. These activities, however, are not quite as clear-cut, for in fact they complement each other to promote the program by closely linking the two groups. When addressing data collection in single-product manufacturing, how it is collected and

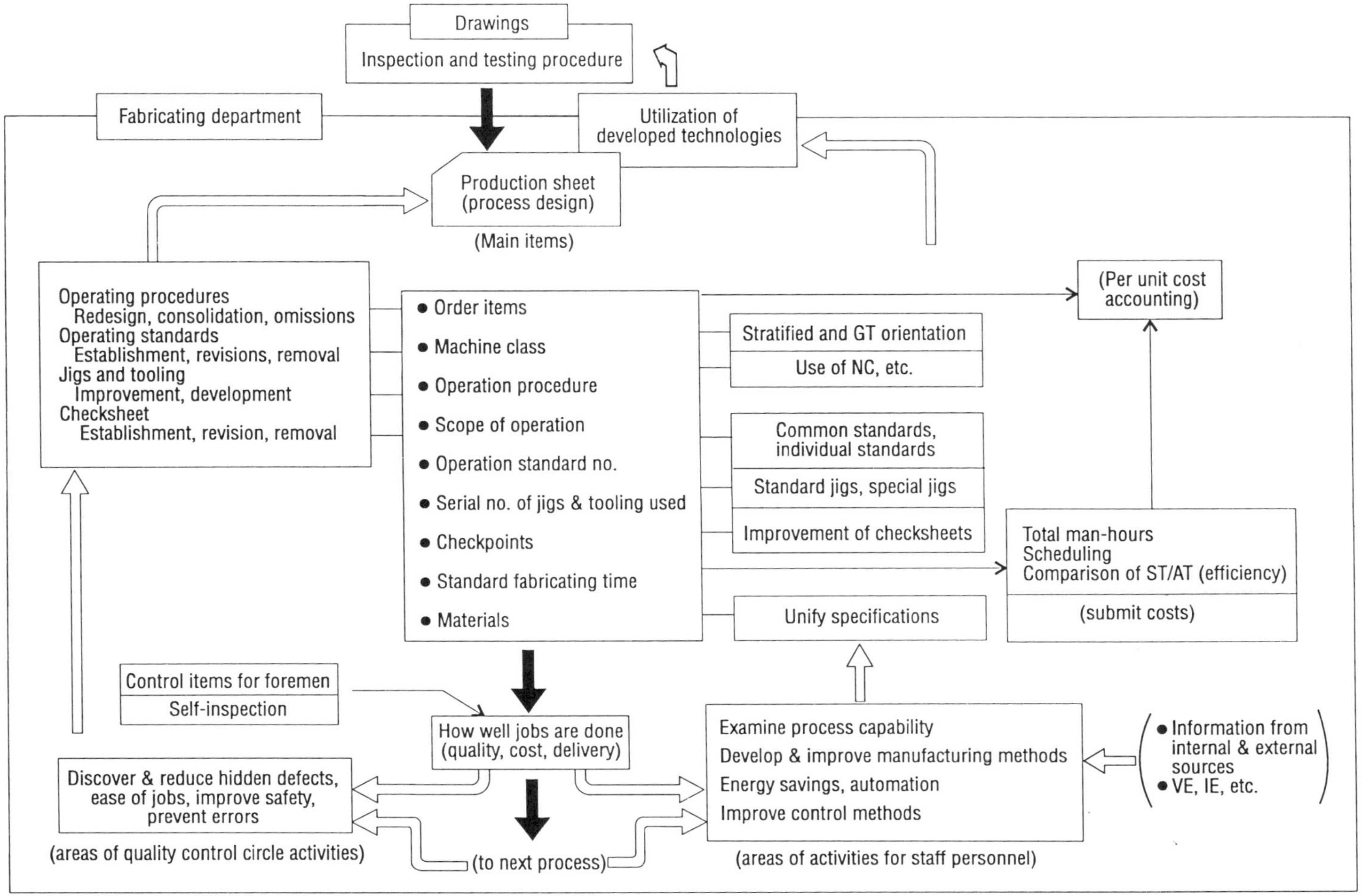

FIGURE 2.4
System for control of manufacturing processes

Original operating sheet / Remarks	※※※※	Order 7-809415	Item -0200	Spec.	Ordered by: SC1		Project Name: 7RND90				Card no.	Delivery
	Related sect.				No.	Operation	Machine class	Time per unit	Preparation time	Details of operation		
	※※※	Part name & rough sketch	Drawing no.	Code	※	※						
		Cylinder jacket 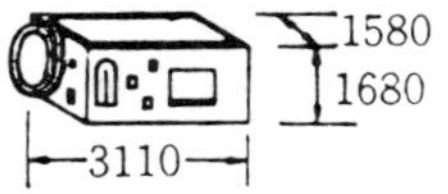	61-509870	1-3	1 ※	43 ※	13	×× ×	× ×	Top section: 1154, surface finished to 00 mm left		
			Quality of wood	Qty	※	(NC) ※				File, lower surface, 510 ϕ, and 425 ϕ finished to 00		
			FC25	7	※	S ※		× ×		Other surfaces rough grind to xx mm left		
			Material		※	※				Check for porosity		
	Mfg. sect. D				※	※						
	※※※	Part name & rough sketch	Drawing no.	Code	※	※						
					※	※						
			Quality of wood	Qty	※	※						
					※	※						
			Material		※	※						
					※	※						

NC machining methods	
Machine	
Tape no.	122
Checksheet	48

※※※	Part name & rough sketch	Drawing no.	Code	※	※						Finish all 4 sides correctly, so that I.D. is straddled properly (finish all parts to same dimensions)
				2 ※	43 ※	1	××	×	×	×	
		Quality of wood	Qty	※	S ※		××	×			
				※	※						
		Material		※	※						Checksheet 48
				※	※						
※※※	Part name & rough sketch	Drawing no.	Code	※	※						
		61-50987	01-3	3 ※	43 ※	13	×	×	×	×	I.D. up/down
		Material	Qty	※	(NC) ※						O.D. finish completely
		FC25	7	※	S ※		×	×			

FIGURE 2.5
Sample operation sheet

sorted are essential to quality control. While it is easy to talk about single-product manufacturing, it is difficult to practice. It cannot be analyzed by the simple N = 1 type of data theory.

In normal quality control, samples are taken from products that are continuously produced, and control of the entire population is based on data taken from such samples. However, in large, single-product manufacturing, machining one surface can take 10–20 hours, and collecting one piece of data from such a process is of no value. But by detailed analysis, surfaces and lines produced in machining operations can be translated into flatness, out-of-roundness, and so on, and variance can be clearly specified. This clarifies problems such as (1) how to establish operating conditions to meet the specifications, and what should be improved and how; and (2) finished products that do not meet specifications (inadequate process capabilities). In order to satisfy specifications, efficiency must be substantially compromised.

As the relationship between specifications and efficiency is quantified in this manner, the relationship between specifications and higher-level quality characteristics follows.

An example of a question that must be answered is how to select which will be most affected by overly stringent specifications (requirements for machining precision): performance, safety, or noise level (in many cases, they affect two or more characteristics). Another likely question is whether they affect only the ease of assembly. All of these must be quantified to improve efficiency. Figure 2.6 summarizes the relationship among these factors. When by analysis these factors are treated as a link between manufacturing and design, inevitably their link with "target quality" must be identified by tracing from the "downstream" processes to "upstream processes."

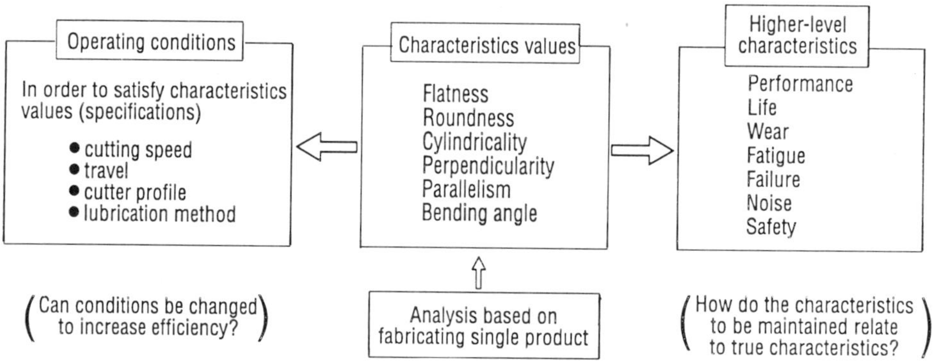

FIGURE 2.6
Method of collecting and using data

THE CONCEPT OF THE QUALITY CHART: IMPORTANCE RATINGS

Thus far the discussion has focused on the manufacturing processes. It is necessary to include the flow of the entire control system, however, from product planning all the way to delivery and after-sales service. Although an oversimplification of the system, Figure 2.7 summarizes it. A large-scale product under actual manufacture involves a diversification of specialized areas such as machinery, electrical control, steel structures, instrumentation, building, and others, and there is a limit to the extent of the familiarity with them a single individual can have. Consequently, specific actions on the left side of the diagram can be implemented with relative ease when required; however, overall actions appearing on the right side are not so easy. Also, when specific actions prove to be effective for known characteristics, the possibility exists that their effects on other characteristics may not be understood or may be overlooked. For this reason, it is necessary that the center area labeled "target quality" be systematically reviewed and well-balanced activities be conducted through specific actions.

One of the basic concepts of quality control implementation is management by prioritization. To perform management by prioritization, it is necessary first to establish firmly, in a systematic procedure, critical machinery, parts, processes, and quality characteristics, and to link them with such factors as inspection plans and quality assurance agreements for purchased machinery and tools. Of course, management by prioritization has long been practiced, but the manner in which priorities are assigned is not necessarily logical or systematic. Without correction of this deficiency, it is quite possible that certain vital elements will be missed, with a resulting biased control. Specifically, if past failures are emphasized too much and excessive weight is assigned, the entire system can easily become unbalanced or the preventive measures can be insufficient. In searching for these problems and by trying to solve them logically and systematically, the need to focus on "target quality" inevitably emerged.

THE CONCEPT OF THE QUALITY CHART: PURSUING QUALITY LOGICALLY

Another idea to consider is a logical concept. Assuming that quality control is the control of quality and, therefore, quality to be controlled must be clear, what is the quality of a ship, a boiler, or a diesel engine? It could be argued that quality control cannot be performed without clear definitions. In a single-product, made-to-order manufacturing op-

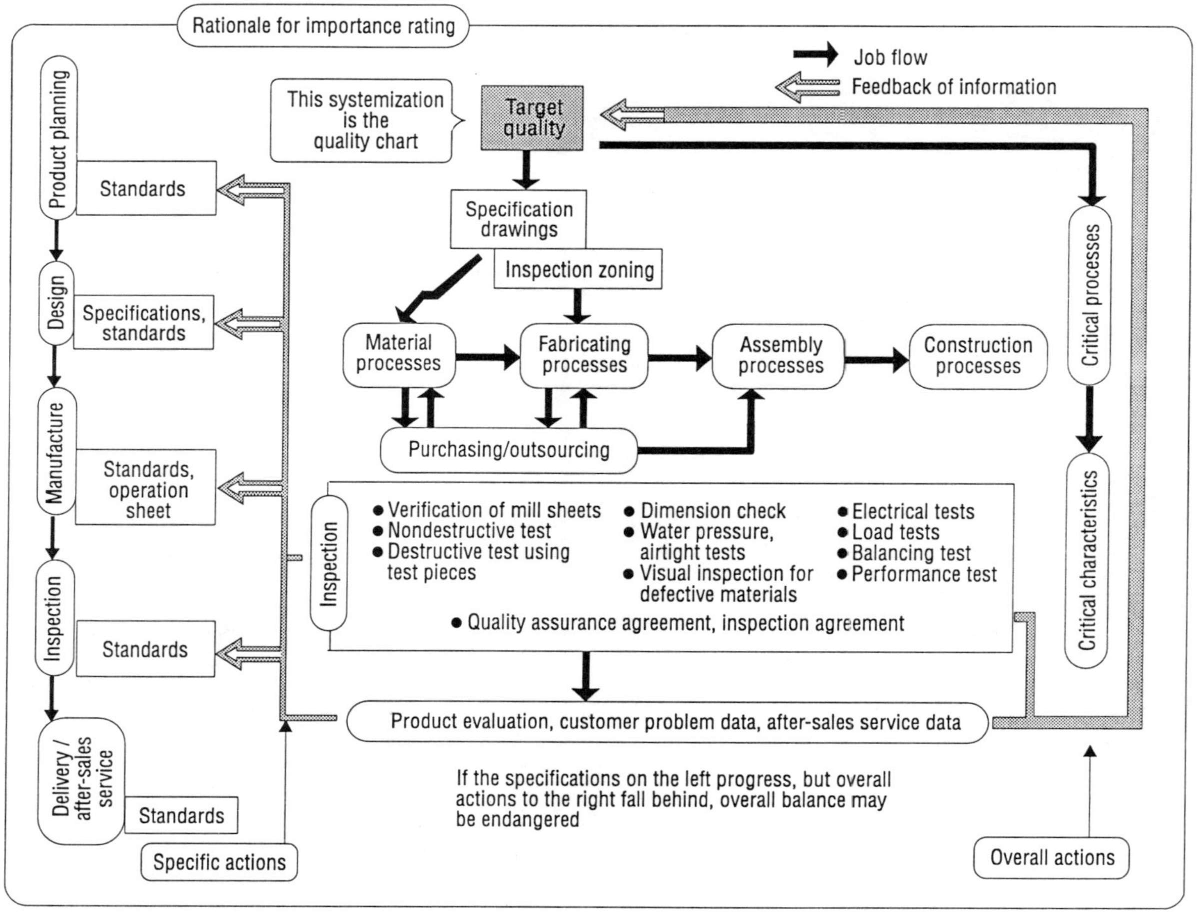

FIGURE 2.7
Concept of quality chart

Source: Yoji Akao, "New Product Development and Quality Assurance—A System of Quality Deployment," *Standardization and Quality Control* 25 (April 1972):9–14.

eration, specifications and grades vary for each product, so that such an argument must be based on a comparison of quality between product 1 and product 2.

Figure 2.8 summarizes that argument. Such an argument pertains to the very root of the concept of quality control, but it is too academic and not suitable for discussion at a manufacturing plant. Also, those who are involved in quality control know from past experience (or think they do) what it is all about, and therefore are inclined to consider the results as not worth their effort or as not easily accomplished. However, to respond to customer demands as they reflect the times and also to develop and improve quality, to prevent predictable failures, and to evaluate suggestions for value engineering are subjects too important not to be addressed, on the assumption that design engineers are aware of them. In fact, minor quality problems have created the need for modification, so preventing their recurrence is urgent. From these discussions comes a recognition of the necessity to systematize quality itself. To understand the subject leads to focus on design for a period. It is executed with the three steps shown below, although they are a bit abstract.

1. True quality of the product being designed is clarified.
2. Targets to satisfy true quality (functions) are quantified. This means setting quality characteristics and their assurance values.
3. Assurance values thus determined are achieved. Materials to be used, dimensions, profile, and so on are established by using

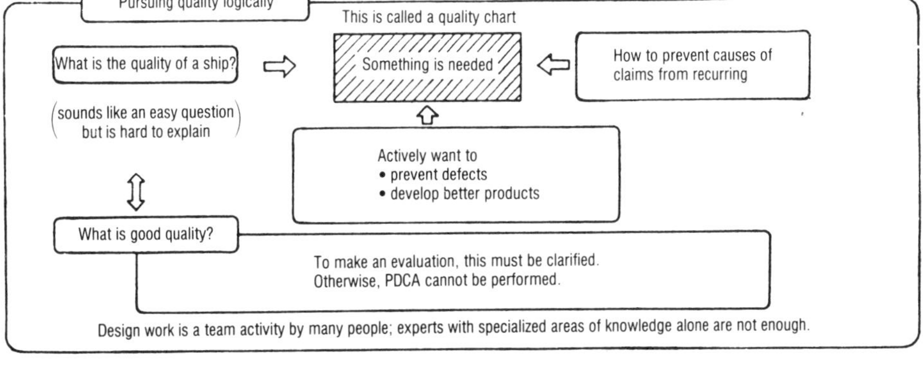

FIGURE 2.8
Concept of quality chart

Source: Yoji Akao and Yamada Ryoji, "A System of Quality Deployment and Case Studies—Computer Research Group Report No. 1," *Quality* 7, no. 3 (1977):30–37.

drawings, specifications, and other items to the extent where actual manufacturing is possible.

When these steps are reversed, the components are assembled into functional parts, which are assembled into machines and equipment, which is arranged to function satisfactorily as an integral product.

"Design" can thus be defined as a process of coordinating the deployment of functions (true quality) and assurance of functions with some combination of parts. It is summarized in the diagram below.

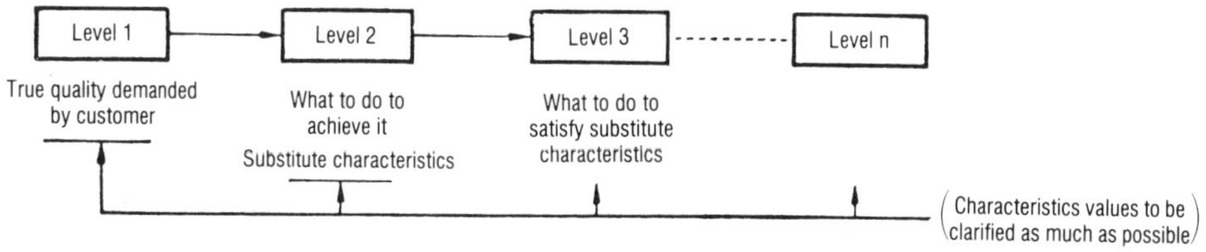

THE CONCEPT OF THE QUALITY CHART

Following the logic up to this point, the outline of the quality chart and its purpose can now be pictured. The chart thus conceived was given the name "quality chart" and was placed at the center of the quality control activities. It also was defined.

> The Quality Chart is a chart in which true quality (demanded by the customer) is systematized around functions and the relationship between these functions and quality characteristics. Such a quality chart is the basis for systematically promoting quality control activities.[2]

This definition was created during development of the chart and, therefore, changes as the methodology develops. For this reason, it is a tentative explanation rather than an established definition. The quality chart has different uses for different products, with no uniform format being used throughout the entire organization of the Kobe shipyard. Figure 2.9 is one of the formats. During completion of the quality chart, it was clear that, in design-related departments, a quality control system based on some overriding viewpoint is required. There was confidence that QC activities could be systematized for the operations, including production, outsourcing, and inspection.

DEPLOYMENT OF THE QUALITY CHART

What has been summarized is basically justification of the necessity of the quality chart to promote quality control at a manufactured-

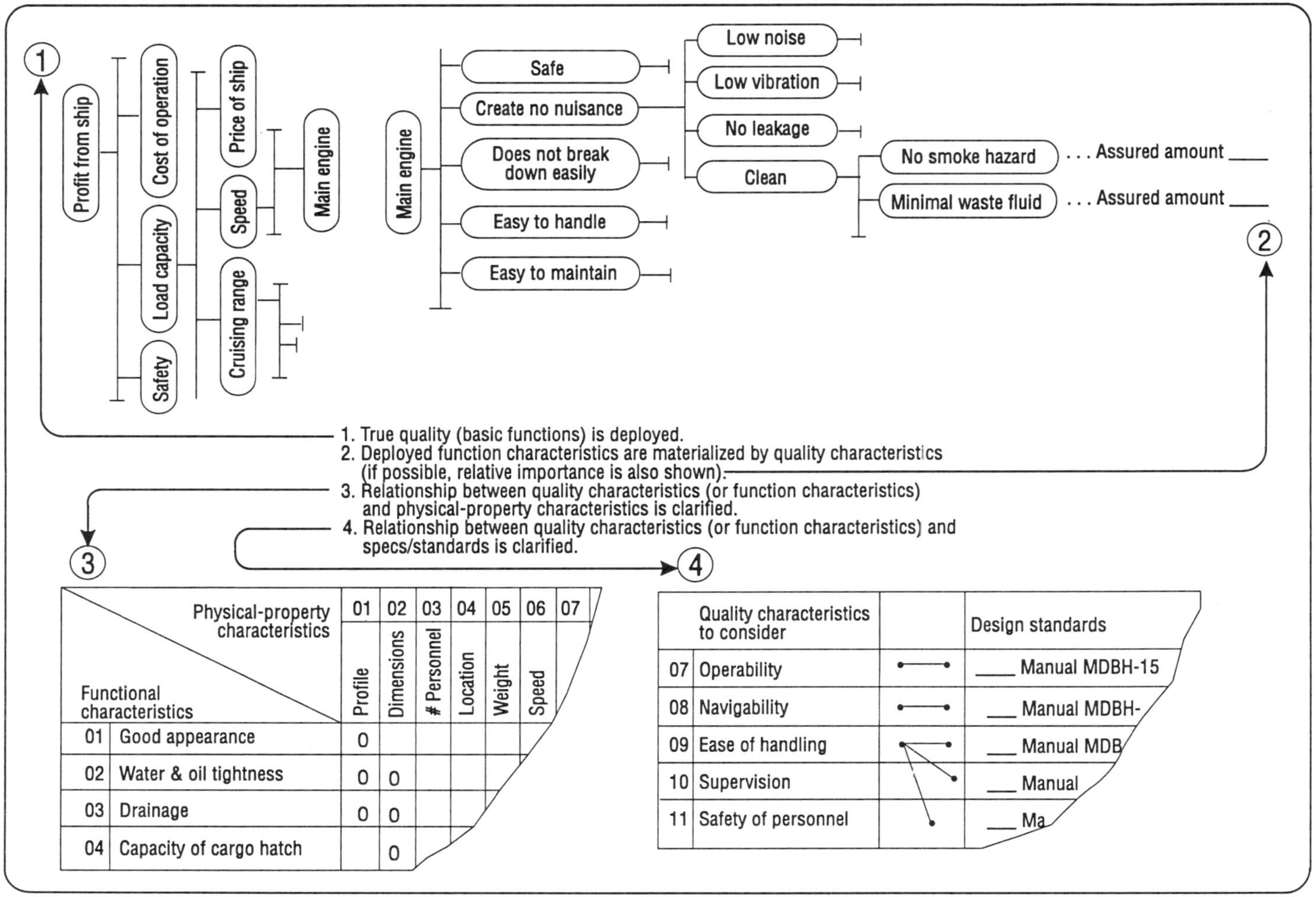

FIGURE 2.9
Deployment of quality chart with an example

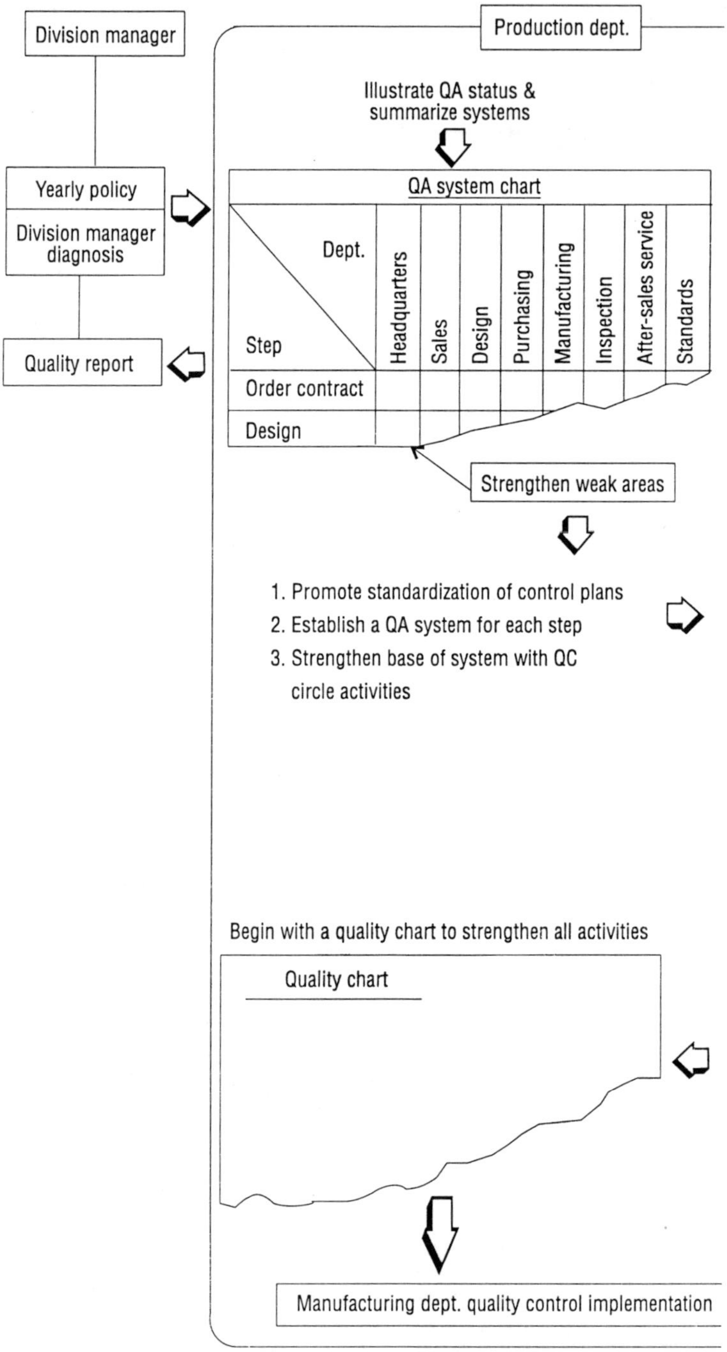

The implementation procedures for 8 departments, including new ship building and atomic power, & the policies & diagnosis of the division manager & quality report are summarized & made part of the standard *TQM Promotion Manual.*

FIGURE 2.10
Procedure for improving the quality assurance system (concept diagram)

Clarify activities & the person responsible to achieve assurance functions

QA activities table			
Step		Quality assurance task	Person responsible
Before receipt of order	Comprehensive plan	1. Participation in long-term corporate planning 2. Establishment of development & improvement policies	
	Collect information	1. Gather & analyze market data 2. Gather & analyze technical data	
	Prototype & design improvement	1. Plan prototypes 2. Build prototypes	
Receive order	Quotation & negotiation of specs	1. Grasp customer needs 2. Establish sales promotion	
Design	Basic plan	1. Confirm contract quality 2. Establish basic plan	
	Detail design	1. Detail design 2. Confirm customer-demanded quality with approval drawings	
Production	Process planning	1. Prepare QC process chart 2. Prepare operating standards	
	Inspection planning	1. Establish inspection standards & items 2. Establish inspection classifications	
	Manufacture/ construction	1. Perform operations 2. Perform self-inspections	
	Trial	1. Perform trial run 2. Evaluate trial results	
After delivery	Service	1. Implement service plans 2. Supply parts plan	
	Handling claims	1. Obtain claim information 2. Register critical quality problems	
Comprehensive evaluation		1. Diagnose quality 2. Diagnose system 3. Quality report	

manual

Summarize system & standardize

to-order plant. It is time to address how the quality chart can be further deployed and utilized. First, do not be overly concerned about the format – proceed on the basis of unique features of each product.

Figure 2.9 illustrates the deployment of the quality chart with an example of how it is used. This one is for ships. Its link to the manufacturing processes is described in detail in works by Kiyokazu Kawai[3] and Yoshiaki Tajiri.[4] The way the quality chart is deployed and used in the works by Kawai and Tajiri is different from Figure 2.9.

Second, promote the quality chart selectively and efficiently. The deployment of the quality chart to full scale for large shipyards and atomic plants is a large-scale, time-consuming, and costly effort. Also, when deployment disregards the cost and time required, the products could change and the efforts would be wasted. In addition, maintaining such a quality chart, which actually is a gigantic standard, would be a heavy burden. Such an exercise must be performed on a selective basis.

There are three areas for emphasis.

1. Areas that have presented quality problems and have not been sufficiently analyzed
2. Items with high frequency of use: for example, items on the checklist that are links and thereby require complete assurance, and items to be organized for use during training
3. Areas where customer complaints have been reported.

CONCLUSION

We have discussed the process leading up to the quality chart and the necessity for promoting quality control in built-to-order products. Since the descriptions concentrated on the quality chart, its relationship to the entire quality control system is still vague. To compensate, Figure 2.10 is a concept diagram of the procedure for establishing the whole system. The procedure develops the activities from the QA chart in the upper left corner to the QA activities table on the right side. Because of weakness in the main structure of the system, the reader should now understand why the quality chart was added as an important part of the procedure.

These activities occurred in 1970–1973, a period of high economic growth. The effort to modify the entire system of quality control in the days when "the more you build, the more you can sell" was not necessarily without criticism. However, the oil crisis at the end of 1973 changed the way the world looked at quality control, and at that time various antipollution programs were initiated. They contributed to the heightened recognition of the importance of quality control. It is our wish that these activities to utilize the quality chart at the center of quality control, which began at the Kobe shipyard of Mitsubishi Heavy Industries, spread to other companies and assist in the upgrade of quality control.

In concluding this chapter, I extend my deep appreciation to those who provided guidance, including the late Drs. Shigeru Mizuno and Tokichi Yura, and Drs. Furukawa, Nayatani, and Norikazu Mizuno.

NOTES

1. Koichi Nishimura, "Design of Ships and Quality Chart," *Quality Control* 23 (May 1972):71–74 (spec. iss.); Yasuyuki Suzuki, "Attempt at Design Improvement Activities for Large Marine Engines," *Quality Control* 23 (May 1972):16–20 (spec. iss.); Akira Takayanagi, "Quality Control Activities for the Concept of Production to Order Quality Chart," *Quality Control* 24 (May 1973):63–67 (spec. iss.); Kazuhiko Kanai and Yuko Hasegawa, "Control of Design Quality of Ships Based on the Quality Chart," *Quality Control* 24 (May 1973):68–72 (spec. iss.); Yasuyuki Suzuki, "Systematic Improvement of the Quality Control System for Single-Product Production," *Quality Control* 24 (May 1973): 38–42 (spec. iss.); Kazuhiko Kanai and Shinsuke Akagi, "Analysis of Cause of Design Change by the ZDALT System," *Quality Control* 24 (May 1973):29–34 (spec. iss.); Kiyokazu Kawai, "Quality Control for High Tensile Steel Pipes," *Quality Control* 25 (May 1974):39–44 (spec. iss.); Yoshiaki Tajiri, "Deployment from the Quality Chart to Process Design and QC Process Chart," *Quality Control* 25 (May 1974):69–73 (spec. iss.).
2. Takayanagi, "Quality Control Activities for the Concept of Production to Order Quality Chart."
3. Kawai, "Quality Control for High Tensile Steel Pipes."
4. Tajiri, "Deployment from the Quality Chart to Process Design and QC Process Chart."

3

Quality Deployment System Procedures

Yoji Akao

INTRODUCTION

This chapter discusses quality deployment by addressing selected procedures that are commonly considered necessary.[1] Actual cases require different approaches. Different types of businesses may use different procedures, with new ones added to the basics in the future. No single procedure is adequate for every case. Rather, the addition of management modifications of procedures occurs in the operations of each firm. The procedure of quality deployment here comes from an actual example of quality function deployment studied by the Research Committee of the Japanese Society for Quality Control and, to make the application straightforward,[2] it is presented in a structure to address issues rather than to elaborate procedures. Regularity and comprehensiveness were addressed in anticipation of future computerization. At this time a priority system was developed by constructing the quality deployment system based on earlier experiments that resulted in removal of part of the system (Figure 3.1).

Charts (1) through (3) are the quality charts, as narrowly defined. Many companies used the QC process chart (process control chart) on site, but since the job site or production engineering group itself created this chart, frequently it was not associated with user demands. The quality deployment system necessitates involvement of the entire company.

Charts (7) through (13) are the quality deployment charts, or quality charts as broadly defined. They are marked Quality Chart A, Quality Chart B, or I, II, and so on, for purposes of identification. Item (13) is similar to what is normally called the QA chart. Here the system structure will be explained mostly through the example of the automotive headlamp (it is not an actual case history).

Step numbers are applied to the procedures, as in Table 3.1. Each important step in quality deployment is identified with the number 1, 2, and so on.

SETTING OF PLANNED QUALITY

Demanded-Quality Deployment

Step 1: Determination of the Appropriate Product

To start, before quality is set, it is vital to know what is demanded in the market for which the product is intended. Both overt and latent demands must be identified. In the case of agricultural equipment, for example, the structure of agriculture in the specific area and the life-style of the farmers must be analyzed to determine the needs in the particular area and the factors to make their jobs easier and more convenient. If the product is transportation equipment for export, it is necessary to analyze the industries of the country targeted for export to determine what types of loads will be carried. In this way, it is first determined what should be manufactured. To identify latent demands, the construction of a demanded-quality deployment table, explained here, is helpful.

Step 2: Collection of Market Data and Construction of Demanded-Quality Deployment Table

This step determines the functions that the product as defined should possess.

1. Identify the user. If the product is agricultural equipment, is it for dry fields or irrigated paddies? If it is toiletries, are they for men or for women?
2. What is its expected function? As Dr. J. M. Juran pointed out, the user expects a fan to produce a cool breeze at a comfortable level, and an iron to eliminate wrinkles completely and quickly while making sharp creases in trousers. Particularly when it is a new product, the expected functions must be clearly defined.

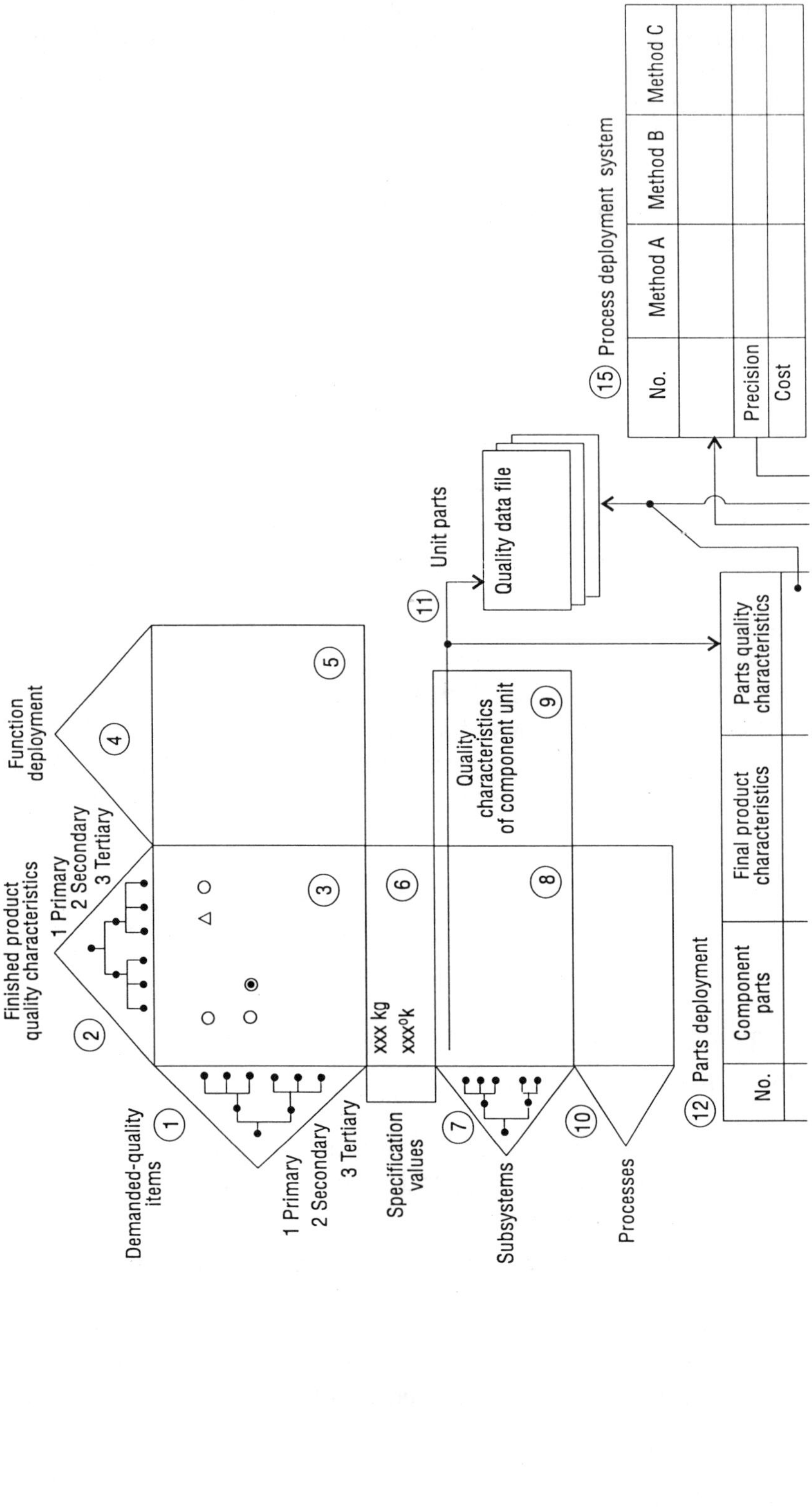
Demanded-quality items
1 Primary
2 Secondary
3 Tertiary
Finished product quality characteristics
1 Primary
2 Secondary
3 Tertiary
Function deployment
Specification values
xxx kg
xxx°k
Subsystems
Quality characteristics of component unit
Processes
Unit parts
Quality data file
Parts deployment
No.
Component parts
Final product characteristics
Parts quality characteristics
Process deployment system
No.
Method A
Method B
Method C
Precision
Cost
1
2
3
4
5
6
7
8
9
10
11
12
15

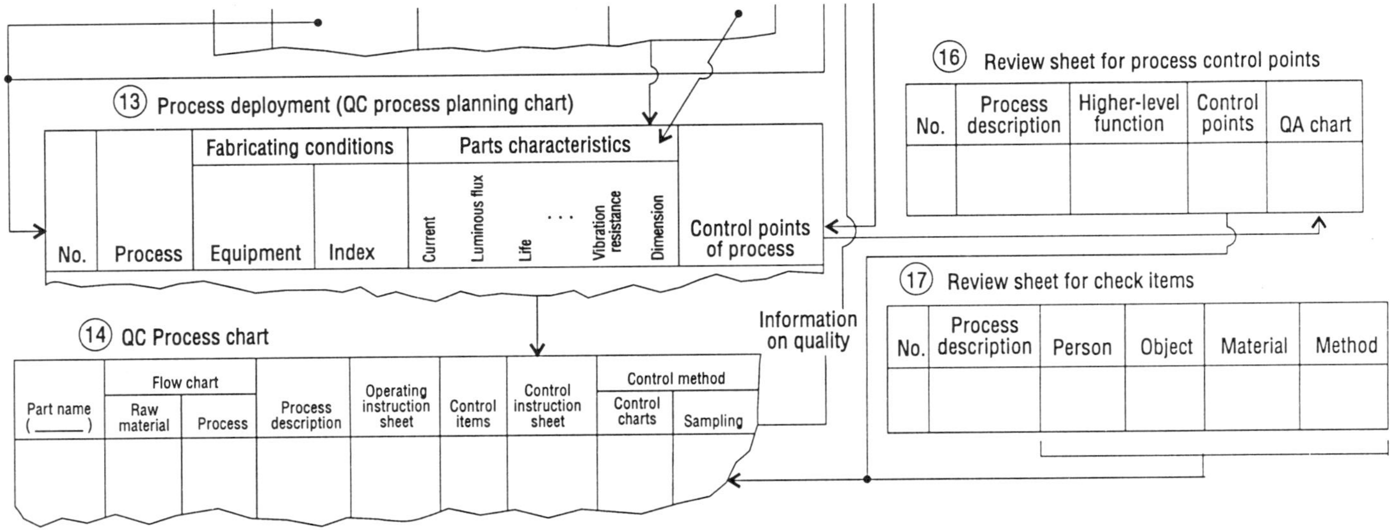

FIGURE 3.1
Quality deployment system

Source: This figure was originally developed for this book. It is also included in Y. Akao, ed., *Quality Function Deployment—Integrating Customer Requirements into Product Design* (Cambridge, MA: Productivity Press, Inc., 1990). The translation used in this edition is original and has not been published previously.

TABLE 3.1
Steps to a Quality Deployment System

Setting of Planned Quality

I. Demanded-quality deployment
1. Determination of the appropriate product
2. Collection of market data & construction of demanded-quality deployment table
3. Competitive analysis & determination of sales points

II. Quality characteristics deployment
4. Construction of quality characteristics deployment table
5. Competitive analysis of quality characteristics & reliability
6. Construction of quality chart
7. Claims analysis
8. Setting of planned quality & design quality
9. Evaluation for product development decisions

Engineering Technology Deployment and Setting of Design Quality

III. Deployment to engineering technology
10. Construction of the function deployment chart

IV. Deployment to subsystems
11. Construction of the subsystem deployment chart
12. Analysis of claims, quality characteristics, reliability, PL (product liability), & cost
13. Setting of design quality & selection of critical-to-safety parts & critical-to-function parts
14. Improvement by VE & FMEA
15. Establishment of quality evaluation items
16. Design review

Detail Design and Production Deployment

V. Parts deployment
17. Construction of parts deployment chart

VI. Manufacturing method deployment
18. Research & deployment of manufacturing methods

VII. Process deployment
19. Deployment to process control points (preparation of QC process planning chart)
20. Establishment of quality standards, operating standards, & inspection standards
21. Design review & evaluation of prototypes

Deployment to Initial Flow Process Control

VIII. Deployment to shop floor
22. Preparation of the QC process chart
23. Addition of process control points by reverse function deployment
24. Management by priority
25. Deployment to outside suppliers
26. Active cause-&-effect analysis
27. Feedback to model change or development of next generation products

3. What are the preferences of the user? What is the usefulness expected? "Additional" or secondary qualities of a product are now growing in importance.

When a product is used for a long time, it is desirable that the user develop an attachment to it. To achieve this effect, the user's true demands require identification. A demanded-quality deployment table, as shown below, is advisable. It is constructed in six steps.

1. Assemble the quality items demanded by the users, both verbal and written. Do not confuse these with characteristics values; the preference is qualitative verbal data. To the extent possible, sensory data should be expressed as language data.
2. Write each item on a separate piece of paper (adhesive removable notes serve this purpose well).
3. Group them in a KJ-like (affinity diagram) method (see Figure 3.2).
4. With these items considered as third-level items in detail, group them into similar categories through descriptive headings at the primary and secondary levels.
5. Identify which items are at the primary level of detail for demanded quality. Add second and third levels of detail.
6. Assign reference numbers (see Figure 4.1). Summarize as shown in Figure 3.3 (write them in the center and leave the right column blank).

During the initial application of quality deployment, try the following to understand its purpose. Instead of Step 1 in the procedure, have people from sales, service, planning, designing, testing, complaint handling, and so on form a group of up to 10 and then brainstorm a list of user demands for the product. Then proceed to Step 2 and create a demanded-quality deployment table. This method is more straightforward. Figure 3.2 illustrates this method at the midpoint of completion. However, since this list was created by internal people, organize a team as early as possible to include sales, development, and engineering people to visit users and identify their hidden demands through direct communications with them. Modifications must be based on direct communication with the users. The best approach is to compare a list thus created with another list based on the brainstorming session. The users' hidden demands will not be known from the simple question "What do you expect of the product?" It is easier to discover the true desires by observing actual or trial use of the product and to have users compare it with similar competitors' products.

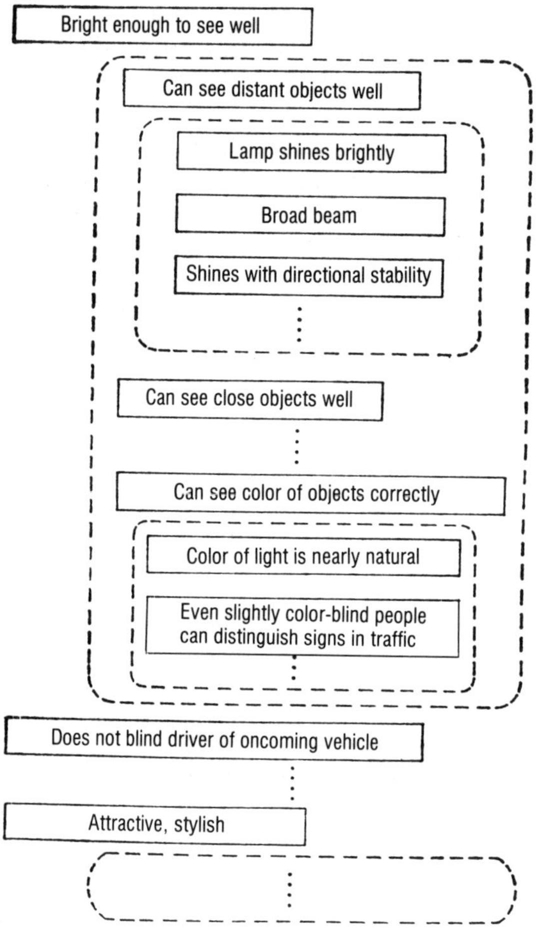

FIGURE 3.2
Group of demanded-quality items

During the creation of this list, the verbatim statement of the customer is not merely passed on. Rather, from it latent or unspoken demands are derived and expressed as simply as possible. Quality characteristic values and component parts are not entered here. Engineers must be careful about mixing in quality characteristics and values. If component parts are included, the tree diagram created might go to many, many levels of details. Regardless of system product complexity, in evaluation for human use, three to four levels of items cover the product in most cases.

The basic approach is to express the objectives in detail but without further subdivision to the fourth or fifth level or beyond. Also, expressions are not restricted to the noun plus verb format used in value

Demanded quality: Primary	Secondary	Tertiary	To be used for comparison with competitors' & other products, for quality chart, etc.
Bright enough to see well	Can see distant objects well	Lamp shines brightly	
		Broad beam	
		Shines with directional stability	
		Light does not scatter	
	Can see close objects well	Low beam is bright enough	
		Broad beam	
		Shines with directional stability	
	Can see well even under adverse conditions	Can see well in poor weather conditions	
		Coordinates with steering wheel	
		Can see well even when vehicle bounces	
		Direction of beam correct under no-load condition	
(Additional items)			

FIGURE 3.3
Demanded-quality deployment table

engineering (VE), such as "A does B." The deployment of the product functions is not the issue; it is a thorough analysis of users' demands. Deployment of product functions as performed in VE is important in Step 10 of the procedure.

When the list is first created, the temptation is to add new items and to revise the list frequently. This requires a considerable amount of time and should be stopped before too much time is expended. An extra column in the list would be useful for later additions. Assigning numbers to added items at this point will accommodate later referencing. Modify the demanded-quality deployment table as appropriate to improve the product. Simple statements in the above procedure facilitate grouping in the same manner as used in the affinity diagram. Perhaps another method for this procedure could be developed in the future. In fact, classifications by quantification, cluster analysis, and factor analysis have been tried. The right side of the demanded-quality table is available for other uses, such as comparisons with competitors, the next step in the construction of the quality chart. Chapter 4 explains this activity.

Step 3: Competitive Analysis and Determination of Sales Points

Regarding competitive or similar products, use the right-hand column of the list of demanded-quality deployment items to determine which product features should be emphasized (see Figure 4.4). Including columns for a comparison of price, volume, and design would help. From this comparison, the sales points for the product to be promoted are derived. In this deployment phase the competitive comparisons must be subjected to evaluation not only by the development personnel but also by others in engineering, sales, and planning.

To determine the sales points, place emphasis on critical items by assigning points, as in Chapter 5. (From Figure 5.3, evaluation points such as found in Figure 5.4 can be derived.) The current product is compared against competing products, as they currently exist, for each demanded-quality item, and is assigned points. When selecting the items that will become sales points of the product, points are totaled, resulting in an overall upgraded evaluation of the product (quality target). Cost and production volume are compared. In some cases, total points for certain items may fall below those for competing products.

From this evaluation, the items that receive more points than competing products become the sales points for the product. At this stage sales personnel with responsibility for the product should be chosen (when and if the product successfully materializes). In many instances a Pareto analysis is adequate to select the critical items as the sales points. One company reports that many sales points, as initially established, resulted in an increase of product cost and the number of critical items eventually had to be reduced.

In Chapter 5, numerous types of clothing and raw materials and the demanded-quality deployment table are combined into a matrix, as in Figure 4.5, for comparison with each other. It makes it easier to reevaluate the product mix and to re-sort and reconstruct the programs for new product types. Also, the sales group can make multiple uses of it.

Quality Characteristics Deployment

Step 4: Construction of Quality Characteristics Deployment Table

Previously, engineers established quality characteristics, in many cases, from their personal technical experience. However, the objective identification of product quality requires expression in scientifically measurable characteristics. Such characteristics are substitute characteristics, and on their own merit most of them do not reflect the genuine demands of the users. True quality must first be identified against fitness for use; it is for this purpose that the demanded-quality deployment table was created in Step 2. The next need is to transform the demanded quality into measurable quality characteristics. To accomplish this, construct a quality characteristics deployment table. The engineering group has the primary responsibility for this exercise. The quality characteristics deployment table is constructed in six steps.

1. Using Figure 3.4, list the quantitatively definable characteristics for each of the lower-level demanded-quality items in the demanded-quality table.
2. Write each on a separate piece of paper (adhesive removable notes are ideal).
3. Group them with the use of the affinity diagram (see Figure 3.2).
4. Treating these as approximately third-level characteristics, group them into similar categories by adding descriptive headings to the primary and secondary levels.
5. Identify the characteristics details at the primary level. Make adjustments by adding secondary and tertiary levels of detail.
6. Assign reference numbers and summarize in a table, as shown in Figure 3.5 (leave the bottom space open).

The list of Figure 3.4 is also called a quality table. Because some characteristics appear in more than one demand, duplication can be avoided by building a tree for characteristic items such as shown in Figure 3.5. This assists the grouping of product quality characteristics. Even with an existing system good enough to group characteristics, it is better to start anew. Examination from a technological standpoint is also necessary, but the technical people must recognize that the demanded-quality characteristics chosen are important to the users. Generally, items that have not been previously considered are often found. Note whether items listed were included in the past. New terminologies may be introduced for items at the primary and secondary levels. These terms apply to classification rather than to characteristics, and by definition many of them may never have been used previously.

Quality characteristics deployment as described plays a significant role in the definition of quality assurance characteristics, product evaluation characteristics, control characteristics, and inspection characteristics.

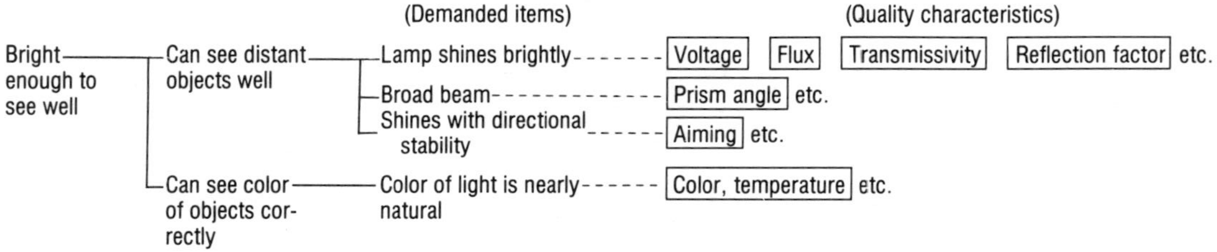

FIGURE 3.4
Deployment of quality characteristics

Quality characteristics (substitute characteristics) — Primary	Flux distribution								Safety	
Secondary	Flux distribution value				Flux of light				Automatic aiming	
Tertiary	Distribution value	Lens size	Low beam/ high beam angle	Aiming angle	Brightness of light source	Transmissivity	Reflection factor	Color temperature	Redundancy angle	(Additional items)
(To be used for comparison with competitors' & other products, & for quality chart, etc.)										

FIGURE 3.5
Quality characteristics deployment table

Step 5: Competitive Analysis of Quality Characteristics and Reliability

Use the bottom section of the quality characteristics deployment table to make an analytic comparison of the planned product and competing products (see Figure 5.8). Based on information supplied by the sales department, the engineering department makes an in-depth analysis. If collecting competitive information in detail takes too long, whatever information is available could support an analysis. It will then be clear which information is missing. Remaining activity is to continue the investigation while proceeding through the steps and completing the competitive data collection until Step 8 is reached. For existing products the following parameters must be clearly defined for each characteristic value: the mean, standard deviation, specification currently in use, process capability index, and distribution. The same is required for information credibility.

Step 6: Construction of Quality Chart

Deployment of user demands has now been fulfilled in the demanded-quality deployment table and quality characteristics deployment table. However, a review of the two tables independently will not reveal how they are interrelated. Only when they are displayed two-dimensionally as a matrix will they effectively have significance as a quality chart. Some quality charts currently in use are deployed, as shown in Figure 3.4, in a one-dimensional arrangement from user demands to control characteristics. However, the use of a matrix is preferable because it avoids many duplications that would otherwise result from this method. The quality chart can be defined, in a narrow sense, as a list that transforms quality demanded by consumers (language data) into substitute characteristics.[3] Figure 3.6, therefore, better serves the purpose.

The quality chart is constructed in four steps.

1. Create the demanded-quality deployment table.
2. Create the quality characteristics deployment table.
3. Juxtapose the two tables in order to relate the item lists to each other.
4. Assign symbols to items according to the appropriate relationship.
   ◎ Strong relationship
   ○ Average relationship
   △ Weak relationship.

Quality characteristics (substitute characteristics) / Demanded quality	Flux distribution										Life				Safety			
	Flux distribution value				Flux of light						Efficiency						. . .	. . .
	Flux distribution value	Lens size	Low beam/ high beam	Aiming angle	Brightness of light source	Transmissivity	Reflection factor	Color temperature	Electric power	Voltage	Air tightness	Filament strength	Characteristics of sealed-in gas	. .	. . .	. . .	Level of redundancy	Angle to vehicle in front
Bright enough to see well																		
Can see distant objects well																		
Lamp shines brightly	○	○	△	△	○	◎	◎	○	◎	○								
Broad beam	◎	○	△		△	△	△		△									
Shines with directional stability			△	◎														◎
Light does not scatter	◎																	
Can see close objects well																		
Low beam is bright enough	○	○	◎	△	△	◎	◎	○	◎	○								
Broad beam	◎	○	△		△	△	△		△									◎
Shines with directional stability	◎																	
Can see well even under adverse conditions																		
Can see well in poor weather conditions	○		△															
Coordinates with steering wheel																		◎
Can see well even when vehicle bounces																		◎
Direction of beam correct under no-load condition																		◎

Characteristics value	JIS requirement	160 ϕ	1°	± 4° (up/down, left/right)	7.5 cd/mm²	0.9 min	0.9 min	3000° K	37.5/ 50 W	12.8 V	0.2 atmos. pressure	SAE % impact 95° min	Ar 80% N20%	. . .	. . .	. . .	. . .	5°
Headlamp																		
Unit holding mechanism																		
Left retaining ring																		
Right retaining ring																		
Left mounting ring																		
Right mounting ring																		
Bolt																		
Unit																		
Lens	◎	◎				◎			△									
Reflector		○					◎		△									
Bulb			◎		◎	○		◎	◎	◎		◎						

FIGURE 3.6
Quality chart and subsystem deployment chart

Source: This figure was originally developed for this book. It is also included in Y. Akao, ed., *Quality Function Deployment—Integrating Customer Requirements into Product Design* (Cambridge, MA: Productivity Press, Inc., 1990). The translation used in this edition is original and has not been published previously.

Determination of the strength of relationships can involve several phases, from actual experience to the use of statistical methods, to arrive at the correct ones. It is realistic to begin with an easy method reflecting the actual situation and to proceed gradually to a more sophisticated model. For this purpose multivariate analysis is also effective. Hopefully, more exacting methods will soon be established. The quality chart in Figure 3.6 is constructed through Step 8 from the above procedure.

Step 7: Claims Analysis

For current products and similar competing products, past claims are analyzed against the quality chart. Check marks in the appropriate part of the matrix reveal marginal frequency. Since Figure 4.6 makes use of only the demanded-quality deployment table, and since only the marginal frequency of the right-hand column appears, it is also best for the characteristics chart to show the marginal frequency at the column bottom of the chart. When an importance rating such as a, b, or c is assigned to each item, score the ratings using the method shown in Figure 5.2 to determine their relative importance. (See Figures 5.4 and 5.9.)

During claims evaluation, the items found deficient in the process of demanded-quality deployment or quality characteristics deployment should be added in the space outside the columns. The demanded-quality deployment table is constructed not only on claims information but also on information from unspoken demands of the consumers, an equally important consideration.

One method commonly used in the development programs is the collection of claims items and introduction of a new or improved product incorporating a solution to each claim. This at least prevents failure of the product but is a passive solution. Even if the product does not fail, customers will be unhappy with its use unless it incorporates their demanded functions. Consequently, when the issue is the quality a new product should possess, it is important to begin planning from the demanded-quality deployment table.

Items in the demanded-quality deployment table are, in a sense, those that could be potential defects or complaints, so it could also be called a list of anticipated claims. It could be used as a check when collecting complaint information and conducting market research and market surveys. A quality chart covers demanded items and characteristics quite thoroughly but has a tendency to become too general. The Pareto principle must be applied to problems associated with these items and characteristics, and the concept of priority or importance rating must also be applied. This is why analysis based on facts such as claims is important.

Assigning priority to demanded-quality items and quality characteristics identifies opportunities for new developments and improvements, and a few significant items receive the emphasis of attention. It is also important to define "critical," "not so critical," and "not important" defects clearly, by examining the antonyms of the demanded-quality items.

Step 8: Setting of Planned Quality and Design Quality

In the quality chart each quality characteristic is examined against all the demanded-quality items relating to it, that is, according to area of product use. Then a level of planned quality is set. For example, in Figure 4.1, in the case of the canvas covering the connector between two passenger rail cars, which "must not tear from wind pressure," "must not tear from pushing and pulling on the inside," and "must not tear from the shock of starting and stopping," the current product can be compared with the competitive products for a quality level to establish a target or planned quality. Then, in the lower part of the quality chart, the boundary values that will ensure that the demanded quality from which the quality characteristics were converted is met are recorded as quality characteristics. For both the vertical and the horizontal modes, what are the minimum value kg/cm^2 to be studied and the design quality to be established? Traditionally such decisions have been based on the personal experience of engineers, and thus on their ideas. Figure 3.6 is an example of a decision reached in this manner.

For a more detailed evaluation, it is best to combine, as in Figure 3.7, the list comparing competing products, based on the demanded-quality deployment table constructed in Figure 3.6, and the list derived from the quality characteristics deployment table completed in Step 5. The adequacy of the standard specification for the characteristics $X_0 \pm \triangle X_0$, as determined by the method explained, is evaluated as shown below.

1. Compare $X_0 \pm \triangle X_0$ (fourth step in the figure), as tentatively established, and the standard specification that already exists in the company. Compare it with $i = 1, 2, \cdots, k$, where k is the number of competitors. (See Figure 5.8.)
2. Following the arrows on the chart, verify the adequacy of $X_0 + \triangle X_0$, in light of the current product's performance and targets set. These come from the demanded-quality deployment table discussed in Step 3 and comparisons with competitors.

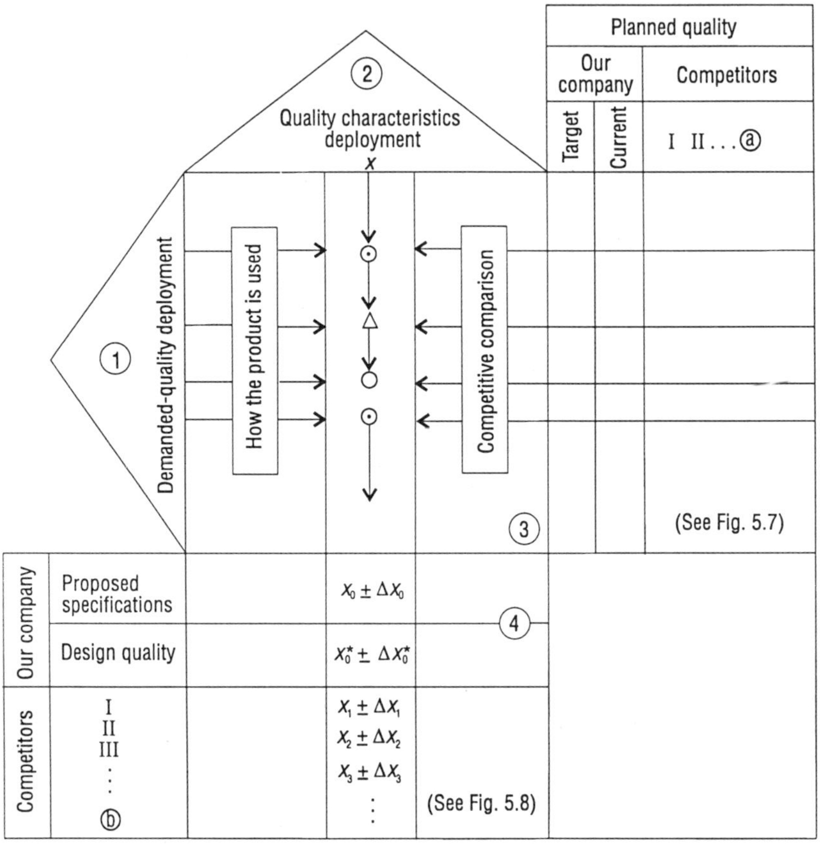

FIGURE 3.7
Setting of planned quality

3. Refer to the characteristic value X compared with the value of the current product, the process capability, and the process capability index.
4. Evaluate the circumstances for prevention of recurrence through claims analysis (Step 7).

A comprehensive standard specification, $X_0^* \pm \Delta X_0^*$, based on the procedure above is set up and is made the proposed design quality. When the process capability does not satisfy this specification, corrective measures must be taken immediately to find possible solutions. The design quality also serves as an important measure to verify quality.

Step 9: Evaluation for Product Development Decisions

Before R&D and design activities begin, study the adequacy of the proposed design quality, using information obtained from the evaluation above. This is the initial design examination. It is also necessary to conduct an internal survey, primarily to determine the adequacy of the project concept. Factors involving corporate policies concerning the projection of changes in social and economic climate; one's own policies; one's own distribution network, level of technological capability, production capacity, and sales network; plans of competitors; trends in consumer preference; and so on must be discussed. Such discussions lead to definition of quality policy and design quality (target quality). (See Figure 5.2.) Since quality deployment is the issue, the method of evaluation and design appraisal will not be discussed.

DEPLOYMENT TO ENGINEERING TECHNOLOGY AND SETTING OF DESIGN QUALITY

Deployment to Engineering Technology

Step 10: Construction of Function Deployment Chart

Demands for the final product and appropriate characteristics have now been established. From the viewpoint of engineering technology, the important decision is the choice of technology to apply in order to fulfill the demands. Traditionally, development has been the domain of the engineering department and has centered on the engineering technologies therein. The consideration of quality is always paramount, with engineering technologies applied to achieve the quality targets. But in quality deployment it is important to deal with quality as an area of the control technology.

An extensive activity of value engineering (VE) is function analysis, since deployment of functions will have a significant role in connecting to engineering technologies. In VE, the objective is to define the functions of a product by using a verb plus object, such as "the product *does something*." Since demanded-quality deployment is truly the transformation of language data from the users, in some cases it does not of its own accord represent the product function. Therefore, when multiple purposes of the product are evident from the demanded-quality deployment, its functions are deployed into first, second, and third levels of detail based on achievement of demanded quality (the function tree or systematic diagram). The classification of the basic functions in Figure 5.7 is an example of this deployment. In order to develop engineering techniques, the functions are transformed into a mechanism and connected to the engineering technologies.

The roles of the function deployment chart and the mechanism deployment chart differ from the demanded-quality deployment table. For this reason, the transformation of user requirements into engineering technologies, followed by construction and deployment of systems, requires quality charts, as shown in Figure 3.8. In other words, it involves research of the functions and mechanisms in the chart for the

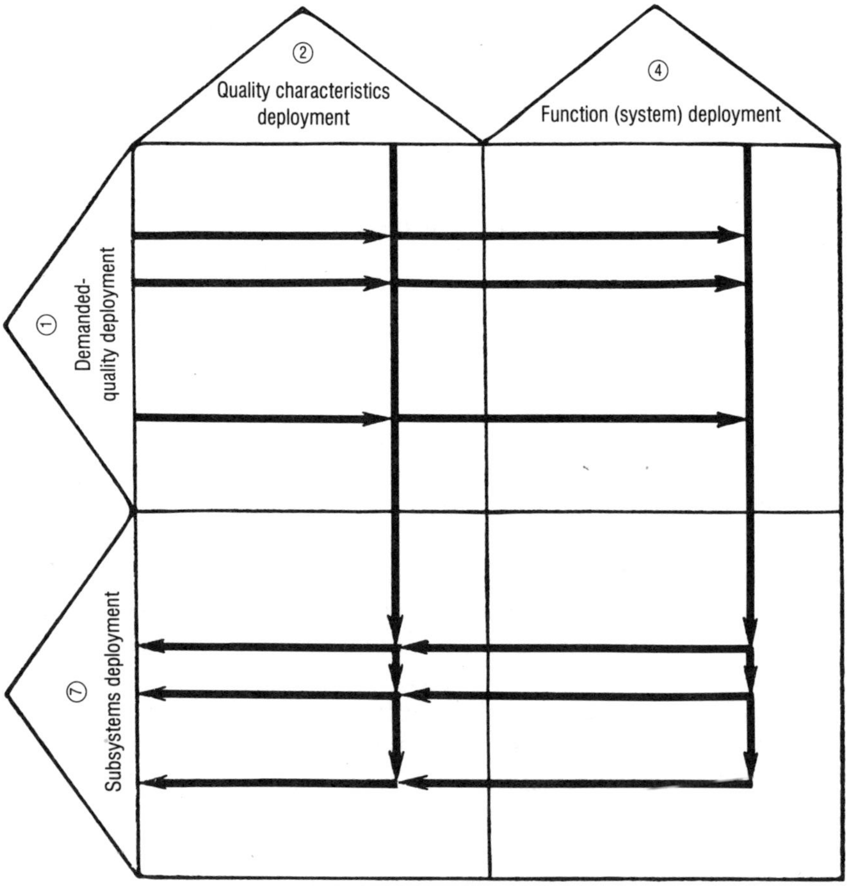

FIGURE 3.8
Transition to engineering technologies through function deployment

product to satisfy the requirements of demanded-quality deployment. This process is the transformation from language data of the users to engineering technologies. Further, the system is based on the function deployment chart. If necessary, prepare a quality chart for the characteristics deployment table and function deployment chart.

Deployment to Subsystem

Step 11: Construction of the Subsystem Deployment Table

Assembled mechanical products consist of several subsystems, component units, and detailed parts. Each has its own quality characteristics; however, in many cases it is not clear how they relate to the final product. Clarification of the relationship between them is important.

When the subsystems have been organized to perform the functions of the final product, prepare a subsystem deployment table in the form of a tree, and construct a matrix, as indicated by (7) and (8) in Figure 3.1 or by Figure 3.8, encompassing the characteristics deployment table and function deployment chart. The lower area of Figure 3.6 is an example of a case study. Also show how the quality characteristics of the final product and functions relate to each other.

The deployment of subsystems, in the example of an automobile, separates into such units as the brake system and power transmission system. The transmission system further divides into the clutch, transmission, differential gear, etc., all of which are composed of more detailed components. Because the tree for this subsystem expands to a large size, the deployment does not extend to the final component units but stops at the third (or fourth) level of components. Then the exercise of deployment into more detailed parts begins again with the most vital component units. In this method it will not become too complicated and readily divides into segments for assignment to several people. In this volume the routine designations of assemblies and subassemblies are called "component units."

In section (9) of Figure 3.1 is a list of the quality characteristics of the component units. The example of an electric light bulb includes such characteristics as beam of luminous flux, life, vibration resistance, and dimensions. One approach is to enter the characteristics in section (8) of the chart. The ideal approach is the preparation of a matrix of the bulb characteristics and the quality characteristics of the final product. In this instance, a simplified procedure avoids the complex structure of a matrix (quality chart) for each component unit. The recommendation is to store the quality information on the component parts in a separate file (11).

Step 12: Analysis of Claims, Quality Characteristics, Reliability, Product Liability, and Cost

Write the frequency of claims in section (8) of the subsystem deployment table in Figure 3.1, reference the claims analysis described in Step 7, and count the complaints for each component unit.

Analyze the existing data for quality characteristics (9) and compile them to clarify the process capability and process capability index. In addition, compile the reliability data for each component. In the reliability deployment of (2) and subsystems of (7), a combination with FTA is possible. Based on the analysis, priority is given to vital items so as not to dissipate efforts.

Study product liability thoroughly. Reassess it in relationship to relevant ordinances and regulations. Also, because many claims arise from product misuse and abuse, perform research on how the product is used at (1) in the chart, and thoroughly evaluate its safety.

Step 13: Setting of Design Quality and Selection of Critical-to-Safety and Critical-to-Function Parts

Assemble all the evaluations, research, and discussion, and reevaluate the projected quality of Step 8. Then establish the design quality of the final product and of the subsystems, and the quality characteristics of the component parts. Consider the factors of process capability, ease of manufacture, and cost effectiveness.

Now select the critical parts by use of the analysis in Step 12. From the critical parts, designate the product liability items as critical-to-safety parts and identify the parts with an **(S)**. Review these parts again in terms of the effects of the appropriate regulations and make necessary additions. Designate the parts that do not affect safety and security, but could cause the product to stop functioning, as critical-to-function parts by marking them with an **(F)**. These parts are subjected to special control after such classifications are assigned.

Parts for which insufficient process capability exists, or those with low reliability, are identified for proper evaluation and improvement.

Step 14: Improvement by VE and FMEA

From a cost analysis of the component units in the subsystem deployment table in Step 12, parts having a high cost, those having considerable variance between the target cost and estimated cost, and those with a high potential for cost reduction are subjected to value engineering (VE) in order to reduce their cost.

Critical-to-safety safety and critical-to-function parts with a high claims rate are subjected to FMEA or FMECA (failure mode effects and criticality analysis). To do this, list the parts that constitute component units and identify their failure modes and effects in order to take preventive measures.

It is advisable that a team involved in the program perform the reviews and research. During the analysis, the quality deployment may advance to the next step. VE is to be performed concurrently, as far as Steps 17 and 18. It is recommended that at an early phase, suppliers review the components for which they are responsible. A small group of parts or elements often governs the reliability of a product. Consequently, critical parts and materials are to be subjected to a reliability test beginning with the prototype stage.

Step 15: Establishment of Quality Evaluation Items

Even in a corporation that has its own system of product quality evaluation and testing, the engineering department traditionally determines the quality evaluation items; consequently they do not always reflect the actual use of the product by the customer. Items for assessment of product quality and test methods must be comprehensively based on the demanded-quality deployment table, characteristics deployment table, and function deployment chart. This area is not adequately addressed with statistical analysis, including reliability tests and sensory tests. It will be necessary to develop more effective methods related to quality deployment.

Step 16: Design Review

After completion of the basic design from these steps, conduct a design review with the data of the VE and FMEA analyses. When a problem is found, feed it back to each step for reconsideration. New product success often depends on the efforts made at this step; therefore, when necessary, major design changes must take place. It will prevent the need for changes in later phases of the basic design. Cooperation with vendors should begin no later than this step.

DETAIL DESIGN AND PRODUCTION DEPLOYMENT

Parts Deployment

Step 17: Construction of Parts Deployment Chart

Prepare the parts deployment chart in (12) for the component units that have been deployed into subsystems according to (7) of Figure 3.1 and described in Step 11, and prioritize component units in either Step 12 or 13. In other words, deal with the higher-priority units first. This exercise is conducted efficiently by dividing the job into component units and assigning them to teams or groups responsible for them. By progressive deployment and accumulation of the results, the exercise eventually will be assimilated into the entire system. Activity for which FMEA has been performed should be related to the FMEA analysis table.

Deploy the product into component parts similar to the component units in Table 3.2 and translate the final product characteristics to which each of the components is related into the quality characteristics of the component parts necessary to achieve final product characteristics. An electric lamp serves as an example of a component unit. It further breaks down into its component parts such as the bulb, filament, and shade. It must be clear how each part relates to the other final product characteristics. For example, wire diameter and length readily come to mind as quality characteristics of the filament. However, since the filament is attached to the bulb, the correct approach, if the filament goes bad, is to consider the effect on the bulb. To secure "brightness of light source" and "color temperature," items like "material," "wire diameter," and "wire length" must be adopted. To do this, the quality of the final product must be transformed into the quality of the parts. Then the effect of a filament position on the angle of primary and secondary filaments is noted here.

In fact, the parts deployment chart should be a quality chart matrix covering quality characteristics for each individual part and the final product characteristics. The process has been simplified here. Based on information components clarified previously, a detailed design can now begin.

It is recommended that a quality assurance chart be made at this

TABLE 3.2
Parts Deployment Chart for Component Unit ⑫*—Electric Bulb

No.	*Component part*	*Characteristics of final product*	*Quality characteristics of part*
1	Bulb	Transmissivity	Material thickness
		Volume of bulb	Dimension, shape
2	Filament	Angle of primary & secondary filaments	Location of primary & secondary filaments
		Brightness of light source	Composition, diameter, length
		Color temperature	Composition, diameter, length
3	Shade	Value of flux distribution	Location, shape, dimension
4	Metal base	Air tightness	Adhesion to glass
		Dimension	Dimension
		Retention strength	Dimension
5	Terminal	Retention strength	Dimension
		Dimension	Dimension
		Material	Dimension

*See Figure 3.1, ⑫.

Source: This table was originally developed for this book. It is also included in Y. Akao, ed., *Quality Function Deployment—Integrating Customer Requirements into Product Design* (Cambridge, MA: Productivity Press, Inc., 1990). The translation used in this edition is original and has not been published previously.

time. As will be discussed in Chapter 7, "Communicating Quality to the Manufacturing Phase," a QA chart details the effect of unmet design targets on system-level characteristics by clarifying the relationship between them. Figures 7.1 and 7.2 describe this relationship. The QA chart allows critical quality assurance points in the design to be passed to the manufacturing phase.

Manufacturing Methods Deployment

Step 18: Research and Deployment of Manufacturing Methods

One of the important activities in the production preparation phase is the research of manufacturing methods (operating methods). The quality deployment of the preceding step is an effective connection of quality objectives initiated from user demands. The deployment of methods to achieve these objectives, that is, deployment of manufacturing methods (discussed in the section "Deployment to Engineering Technology" of this chapter), is also important. In this process, manufacturing methods to achieve the target quality at minimum cost are selected as an optimized balance between quality and cost.

In the actual execution of this step, in order to select a manufacturing method, it must be clear to what degree the most important characteristics must be fulfilled, as determined by quality deployment. The determination of the precision and cost requires testing of available manufacturing methods. Based on the precision and cost, curves are plotted to arrive at the most cost-effective method to achieve the required precision. The manufacturing engineering department sets the tolerances of other parts as required by the selected manufacturing method, as allowed by the process capability of that manufacturing method, and as related to how the part will be used. The product design department, in many cases, sets the dimensional tolerances of parts. This action often produces a lower process capability index that leads to excessive rejects or an "overquality" effect.

The examination of the process capability is one of the important issues in this phase. The ease of manufacture prior to production is also important, and sufficient consideration to this subject is required in the prototype stage. This phase of the program requires VE activity.

Process Deployment

Step 19: Deployment to Process Control Points (Preparation of the QC Process Planning Chart)

The quality demanded by the users has been deployed to the quality characteristics of the individual parts. It is now necessary to deploy them to control characteristics of the processes selected to manufacture the parts. This requires preparation of the QC process planning chart (13) of Figure 3.1, which is the process deployment chart for manufacturing processes. Normally, the manufacturing engineering department performs the process design for new parts manufactured in-house. This activity involves industrial engineering evaluation of the equipment, manufacturing conditions, man-hours required, and so on, and the preparation of a process planning chart based on the results. This chart, in many cases, shows only machining conditions; but it also must be determined how the process affects any of the parts characteristics after completion of machining. This becomes the basis for setting the process control points.

The part referred to in Table 3.2 is the filament sample, for the manufacture of which a QC process planning chart is prepared. However, since the case study here addresses a simple vendor-supplied product, Figure 3.9 illustrates the QC process planning chart for the electric bulb. For example, an inquiry into the control points for the degassing process might lead to focus on the degree of vacuum and gas pressure. The way to determine control points is to consider which end product or subsystem characteristics (or part, in this case, of a light bulb) will be affected if a problem occurs in the degassing process. Luminous flux, life, and vibration resistance could be affected, as indicated by the ○ and ◎ in Figure 3.9. Therefore, we conclude that to control the degassing, degree of vacuum and gas pressure should be control points. Note the use of a matrix to transform the quality characteristics of a product, subsystem, or part into process control points.

Step 20: Establishment of Quality Standards, Operating Standards, and Inspection Standards

The parts deployment of Table 3.2 establishes the quality characteristics of individual parts. The set quality standards now reference the process capability, and quality standards based on the results of certain control classifications of processes now exist for work-in-process and for semifinished products. Operating standards are prepared to meet established quality standards. Finally, the action of relating them to items of quality deployment in Step 15 determines the inspection parameters. From this inspection activity the methods to set the inspection standards evolve.

Step 21: Design Review and Evaluation of Prototypes

Following the on-paper completion of designing quality into the product for production comes the final stage of paper planning, the design review. It includes an intensive quality analysis of the test results of several prototype units. Conduct as many types of tests as possible relating to how the product is actually used in the market. If the product is totally new, it may be difficult fully to establish its quality characteristics. At this phase prepare a defect item list and review the quality information again to determine, by the use of the quality chart and subsystem deployment chart of Figure 3.1, whether targeted quality objectives have been achieved. At this time establish feedback of information to all the steps of quality deployment.

No.	Process	Manufacturing conditions: Equipment	Manufacturing conditions: Index	Parts characteristics: Current	Luminous flux	Life	Antivibration	Dimension	Others	Process control points
1	Forming of flare	Flaring machine	2–3 sec					○	○	I.D. & O.D. material thickness, dimension, crack, scratch
2	Forming of stem	Stemming machine	″					◎	○	Dimension, dumet color, interior distortion, temperature
3	Forming of mount	Mounting machine	5 sec	◎	◎	◎	◎	◎	○	Distance between L.C.L. & filament
4	Sealing	Sealing machine	3–5 sec					○	○	Appearance, dimension, distortion
5	Degassing	Degassing machine	″	△	○	◎	○		○	Degree of vacuum, gas pressure
6	Basing	Basing machine	2–4 sec	△	△	○		○	○	Warp, eccentricity
7	Aging	Aging machine	90 sec				○		○	Voltage, time
8	Final inspection	Current checker		± 7%						(± 7% 4.0/3.1A)
		Projector								
		Light flux meter			± 10%					(± 10% 850/625 lm)
		Life tester				600/700				
		Vibration tester					JIS D 1601			(JIS D 1601 4G class 8 hr)

FIGURE 3.9
Headlamp bulb ⑬* process deployment (QC process planning chart)

Note: See Figure 3.1, ⑬.

Source: This figure was originally developed for this book. It is also included in Y. Akao, ed., *Quality Function Deployment—Integrating Customer Requirements into Product Design* (Cambridge, MA: Productivity Press, Inc., 1990). The translation used in this edition is original and has not been published previously.

DEPLOYMENT TO INITIAL FLOW PROCESS CONTROL

Deployment to Shop Floor

Step 22: Preparation of the QC Process Chart

Prepare a QC process chart from the QC process planning chart. Unlike the latter, the former specifies control standards for use on the shop floor. For a specific control point (check item and control item), specify who should take the samples, how many samples should be taken, when and with what kind of measurement method data are to be taken, who should take what action against abnormalities, and so on. Examine the QC process planning chart beforehand to differentiate the above information from the control points to be selected (see Figure 3.10 for an example).

In regard to product quality or how well the product is made, in many instances factors lie outside the "upstream" in the chain of deployment. Consequently, the people involved directly in manufacturing activities on the shop floor must address these subjects. It is an appropriate subject of discussion for improvement by shop floor staff and QC circles. The QC process chart should reflect the results of these reviews and discussions. This action assures that the quality of products and quality of design are secured, and promotes the development and manufacture of products that offer true quality to users.

Step 23: Addition of Process Control Points by Reverse Function Deployment

As mentioned, the shop floor becomes passive when deployment comes only from upstream. To bring the know-how of the shop floor personnel to the contents of the QC process chart, see the method in Chapter 10.

This step clarifies the functions of one's own process and reconfirms that, through reverse function deployment, functions of "higher level" equal what this process should accomplish. Quality assurance will be made more effective by setting control points with deployment from upstream and will relate better to QC circle activities on the shop floor.

By following these steps, intended quality has now been deployed, like the central nervous system, from design to engineering to the shop floor. In a modern manufacturing plant where several people build one product, the responsibility of the individual workers can become unclear. If individuals were responsible for one entire item, they would do their best to turn out a good product. It is quite normal that when

Part name (stem)	Flow chart: Raw material	Flow chart: Process	Process name	Operation instruction sheet	Control items	Control instruction sheet	Method of control: Control chart, etc.	Method of control: Person responsible for daily operation	Method of control: Person in charge of operation	Method of control: Measurement by sampling	Inspection items	Inspection method
Glass tube	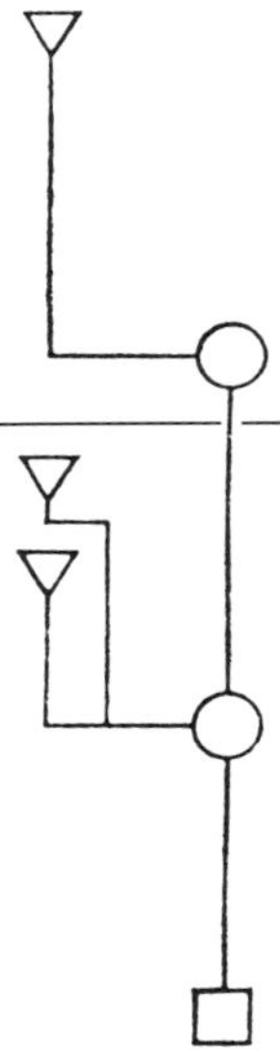				O.D.		Checksheet					
					I.D.					n = 5/incoming lot		
					Material thickness							
					Finished dimension		↑			Gauge n = 5/hr		
			Flare forming		Crack, scratch		↑			100%		
Guide-wire					Dimension		$\bar{x}$-R (checksheet)					
Glass tube					Dimension		↑(↑)			n = 5/incoming lot		C_p
					Preheating temperature		x					Thermo-color
			Stem forming		Enclosing temperature		↑			At startup		
					Annealing temperature		↑					
					Dimension		$\bar{x}$-R (checksheet)			At startup, n = 5		C_p
					Dumet color					100% visual		
					Interior distortion					At startup, n = 5		Simple distortion gauge

FIGURE 3.10
Headlamp bulb QC process chart

roles of individuals regarding quality are obscure, sensitivity and a feeling of responsibility for quality are lost. Only when the function of each part and element is clearly defined for quality assurance from the user's standpoint is the barrier between plant workers and product user removed. The idea of "one complete product, one worker" helps to clarify the role of each individual operator in achieving quality targets.

One of the important aspects of quality deployment is to build a system that permits this to happen.

Step 24: Management by Priority

Step 13 explained the importance of placing priority on vital points. To carry out the system of deployment described, prioritization must be applied to all the program steps. Obviously, it must be based on facts supported by statistical analyses. Since products as addressed here have many characteristics and factors, multivariate analysis is effective for this purpose. In the case of a machine-assembled product, use stratification and gather a considerable amount of information through stratified totaling.

Place an **(S)** by processes and parts related to critical-to-safety parts, as specified in Step 13, and mark critical-to-function parts with an **(F)**. Careful management is necessary for items so marked. Include these marks in drawings and, if possible, note which quality factors of the final product are affected.

Refer to Chapter 8, section "Control System for Critical-to-Function Parts and Processes." Many companies have adopted the practice of deploying targets for loss reduction caused by defects from department to section to subsection, as is the practice in management by objectives. It is often observed that people are satisfied when the defect rate within their own subsection has fallen to 0.5% or 0.1%. However, even if monthly defect rates decrease considerably, it does not mean that the problem with defective parts has been eliminated. Any defective unit, even with a low rejection rate, can become a major catastrophe.

As seen in Step 13, resolving this situation requires a special control by establishing **(S)** and **(F)** ratings for parts affecting safety and security, and the clear identification of major points throughout the manufacturing process. This increases the manufacturing cost to some degree. The next step is to rationalize the control system throughout and to conduct comprehensive value engineering activities to reduce cost.

For reliability, as many vital elements as possible should be subjected to analysis through reliability tests in the initial stage of development. Usually, though, the actual situation is made clear only after product life has been completed. Even after other problems have been solved, problems of reliability must be analyzed and reviewed on a continuous basis. It is advisable to relate them to fault tree analysis and to failure mode and effects analysis. Proper corrective measures, based on sufficient analysis and study, will address the problems of misuse and abuse.

Step 25: Deployment to Outside Suppliers

Many companies rely on outside suppliers for raw material and parts, so establishing good systems within one's own company alone does not guarantee proper quality assurance. It is important to relate the company systems to those of outside suppliers through a linked QC process chart, such as is used by automotive manufacturing plants. In other words, the practices of QC process chart deployment for the company are applicable to outside suppliers. Of course, it is preferred that quality deployment described here be applied directly by the outside suppliers.

Step 26: Active Cause-and-Effect Analysis

For an assembled product, the effect of assembly processes on critical characteristics of the product can be easily identified. However, with progression "upstream" to machining processes and then further to casting processes, it becomes difficult to identify the cause and effect in various factors. Also, chemical processes may require experiments in many cases. As a result, design of experiment methods, especially the orthogonal array, is valuable. An analysis of the contribution ratio is important and should be used, as in a Pareto analysis.

From the initial flow phase, it is important not only to gather and analyze claims within and outside the company but also to collect data on actual use of the product, thereby identifying, at an early stage, the effect of factors through multivariate analysis. Control points for quality assurance then become clear. There is a major difference in the level of quality deployment between the methods explained above and a simple brainstorming session or personal experience.

Step 27: Feedback to Model Change or Development of Next Generation Products

More companies are developing their own quality information systems. The major purpose of such a system is to gather claims and defects from various processes and to feed them back to the departments of origin. The quality deployment system analyzes and then synthesizes. Quality information systems could further be refined by utilizing a comparable quality network. Efforts are in process to computerize such a system.

Graphs show the quality information claims, reliability, number of design changes, and so on; and from these graphs inadequacies of the quality deployment system are analyzed. Research into the degree of user satisfaction with the product takes place. It is important to develop it into a system for the next generation of new products that satisfies customers while also being profitable. The quality deployment system should be improved gradually through revisions until it becomes satisfactory, rather than trying to perfect it in a single effort.

The above steps have emphasized assembled and manufactured goods. Some adjustments must be made when applying QFD to chemical processes. While it is relatively easy to progress from subsystems to component units to parts deployment to process deployment in assembling and manufacturing processes, when using QFD on chemical processes, deployment from Step 3 to 6 to 10 to 13 to 14 is more suitable. Processes are best handled by a tree diagram that classifies the individual operations and equipment.

CONCLUSION

This chapter introduced methods of quality deployment as a system organized for easy application while relating it to actual company case histories up to 1977. The entire system was divided into several integrated "modules." It is important to modify them with assignment of segments to many people working together. It is recommended that the system be applied within a company, that problems resulting from it be identified, and that a tailored system be established for the purposes of that company.

It requires a great amount of work to conduct reviews and evaluations from the earliest phases. However, actual situations have been reported in which the further upstream they originate, the more effectively market complaints are reduced. Implementing quality deployment grasps the entire situation. It will become possible to involve design engineers from outside suppliers at the planning phase, thus minimizing claims resulting from improper planning and designing.

SUPPLEMENT: DETERMINING PLANNED QUALITY—METHODS FOR SETTING AND TRANSLATING IMPORTANCE LEVELS

The Importance Level Questionnaire Method

In the sections describing the steps of quality function deployment, the methods by which importance levels are set were not discussed. I recommend the use of the questionnaire method described below, a method that has been widely used since the first edition of this book was published. This method will be explained using the demanded-quality deployment chart shown in Figure 3.6.

The average demanded-quality deployment chart used in Japan has 8 primary items, 20 secondary items, and 80 tertiary items. Thus there would be more questions in a survey of tertiary items than would be appropriate in questionnaire studies. Because of this, studies are done on the secondary level, as is shown in Figure 3.11.

Consider, for example, question I in Figure 3.11, regarding the method by which to calculate the level of user interest (i.e., the level of importance) of demanded-quality items. In this example the demanded quality "can see well even under adverse conditions" has little effect on the choice of headlamp – it shows that any headlamp is acceptable. The levels of importance are set to be the averages of the data obtained through a questionnaire study involving a large number of subjects, and are written in as the levels of importance in Table 3.3.

Determining Planned Quality

In question II of Figure 3.11, regarding the method of comparing quality levels with those of other companies, A scores 5 (very good), B scores 3 (fair), and C scores 2 (poor) on the quality "can see well even under adverse conditions." The averages of the data obtained in the questionnaire survey are written in the "competitive comparison" column in Table 3.3.

Planned quality is set strategically, based on such factors as the levels of importance of various qualities from the perspective of the users, comparisons with competing products, and so on. Because the product of the firm given in Table 3.3 is rated 3 in "can see well even under adverse conditions" while competitor products A and B both score 4, it is clear that on this dimension the product of the firm is inferior. In order to make this a "feature" of the product, the firm determined to raise the score on this to 5, and thus set the planned quality to 5. When it did so, it set the improvement ratio (the "level-up" ratio) at 1.67 (i.e., 5/3). Although the level of importance from the perspective of the user was not high (only 3), the firm decided to advertise and make appeals to the public based on this feature, and set this characteristic as "critical sales point ◎." The others were set similarly. The ○ indicates a regular sales point.

Prioritization Perspective of the Company

The quality level of "can see close objects well" for the firm scored 5. Compared with the 5 of competitor A and the 4 of competitor B, the

This questionnaire will ask you two kinds of questions. There are items on these pages we would like you to consider as well as a column for your answers. Please answer both types of questions at the same time.

Question I: The items listed below may influence your selecting a product or manufacturer of a headlamp. In column I, please rank how much of an influence these items have on your purchase decision. Please circle the appropriate value.

Question II: Who makes the product you are currently using? Please fill in the manufacturer's name.

Company A: manufacturer's name ( )
Company B: manufacturer's name ( )
Company C: manufacturer's name ( )

In column II, please evaluate the pluses and minuses of using each manufacturer's product.

Item	Column I	Column II
	No influence at all / Minor influence / Some influence / Strong influence / Very strong influence	Very bad / Bad / Fair / Good / Very good
Can see well even under adverse conditions	1 2 3 4 5	A 1 2 3 4 5 B 1 2 3 4 5 C 1 2 3 4 5

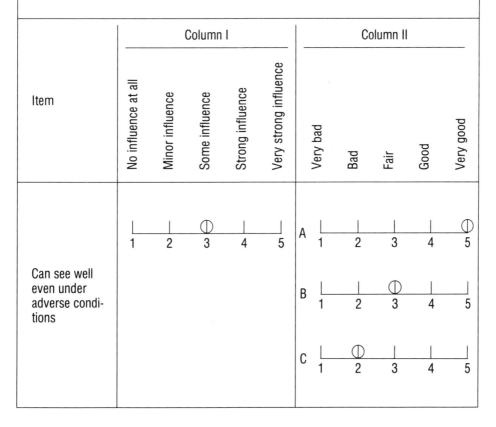

FIGURE 3.11
Questionnaire

TABLE 3.3
Planned Quality Table

Demanded quality		Planned quality								
			Comparative analysis			Planning			Weight	
				Competitors						
Primary	Secondary	Level of importance	Our company	Company A	Company B	Planned quality	Level-up ratio	Sales point	Absolute weight	Demanded-quality weight
Bright enough to see well	Can see distant objects well	4	4	4	3	4	→ 1.0		4.0	5.0
	Can see close objects well	5	5	5	4	5	→ 1.0	○	6.0	7.5
	Can see well even under adverse conditions	3	3	4	4	5	→ 1.67	◎	7.5	9.4
Does not give blinding glare	Does not blind driver of oncoming vehicle	4	5	4	4	5	→ 1.0	○	4.8	6.0
	Does not blind oncoming pedestrians	3	4	4	4	4	→ 1.0		4.0	5.0
	Total								80.0	100.0

firm did as well or better. Were the firm to set the planned quality level at 5, all it would need to do to achieve this level is to maintain the status quo. Although the level of importance from the perspective of the user is high, rating 5, there is no need to put rigorous effort into further development. In contrast, although the level of importance of "can see well even under adverse conditions" does not rate highly (scoring only 3), the firm must raise the quality level by a factor of 1.67, and has set this as a critical sales point. Naturally it is important to put greater efforts into developing this feature than "can see close objects well."

In this type of case, the method shown below is used to calculate the level of importance that includes allowance for the objectives of the company.

$$\text{Absolute weight} = (\text{level of importance}) \times (\text{improvement ratio}) \times (\text{sales point})$$

Here the sales point is given a value of 1.5 for ◎, 1.2 for ○, and 1.0 if it is left blank (no symbol). In the case of "can see close objects well," the level of importance = 5, the improvement ratio = 1.0, and the sales point = 1.2. Thus the absolute weight $= 5 \times 1.0 \times 1.2 = 6.0$. Similarly, the absolute weight for "can see well even under adverse conditions" is $3 \times 1.67 \times 1.5 = 7.5$. The other absolute weights are calculated similarly.

When the absolute weights above are totaled, the sum is 80.0. Normalizing this to 100%, "can see close objects well" is scored at 7.5%, and "can see well even under adverse conditions" is scored at 9.4%. These values are called the "demanded-quality weights (includes the objectives of the firm)." In contrast with the initial importance levels of 5 and 3, attaching demanded quality to these two, after converting to demanded-quality weights the latter becomes higher than the former. This is because the firm must increase the level of the latter by a factor of 1.67, and because it has been established as a critical sales point. The development efforts of the firm will focus on the issues with highest demanded-quality weights.

Translating Importance Levels

We will use the quality table (Table 3.4) to discuss the method of translating the secondary demanded-quality importance levels into secondary quality characteristic importance levels. Although various methods exist by which to perform this translation (including the independent distribution method, the proportional distribution method,

TABLE 3.4
Conversion of Degree of Importance

Primary	Secondary	Primary / Secondary	Flux distribution: Flux distribution value	Flux distribution: Luminous flux	Life: Efficiency		Safety: Redundancy	Demanded-quality weight
Bright enough to see well	Can see distant objects well		◎ 20.0	◎ 20.0			○ 10.0	5.0
	Can see close objects well		◎ 30.0	○ 15.0			○ 15.0	7.5
	Can see well even under adverse conditions		△ 9.4				◎ 37.6	9.4
Does not give blinding glare	Does not blind driver of oncoming vehicle		◎ 24.0	△ 6.0			◎ 24.0	6.0
	Does not blind oncoming pedestrians		◎ 20.0	△ 5.0			○ 10.0	5.0
	Total		413.6	193.2			376.6	491.70
	%		8.4	3.9			8.1	100.0

and methods using fuzzy logic), below we will discuss only the independent distribution method.

The ◎, ○, and △ showing the strength of relationships in the quality table are assigned numeric values – for example, 4, 2, and 1, respectively – and the numeric values in cell in a row are multiplied by the weight of that row. For example, in the case of "can see distant objects well" the calculations would be as shown below.

◎ · · · (4) × 5.0 = 20.0; ◎ · · · (4) × 5.0 = 20.0; ○ · · · (2) × 5.0 = 10.0

After assigning points to the other rows in a similar manner, totals are found by summing vertically over each characteristic's column. For example, the calculation for "flux distribution value" would be 20.0 + 30.0 + 9.4 + 24.0 + · · · = 413.6. The other columns are calculated similarly. Summing these totals gives a total of 4,917.0 for the table, and after normalizing this to 100%, the value for "flux distribution value" is 8.4%, the value for "luminous flux" is 3.9%, the value for "redundancy angle" is 8.1%, and so forth. The focus on quality assurance is allocated according to the order of these quality characteristic importance levels.

It should be noted that although those items more strongly desired by the customers have higher demanded-quality importance levels, the underlying characteristics are not necessarily the most highly ranked. Because of this, rather than looking only at the demanded qualities, it is best also to make a function deployment chart, to calculate the levels of importance of the functions, and to create and use the translated quality characteristic importance levels as well.

Downstream Translations of Importance Levels

The quality characteristic levels of importance can similarly be translated into subsystem levels of importance in a matrix that relates quality characteristics to subsystems. QA charts are drawn up for the critical components identified, and the emphasis placed on these parts in quality assurance should be communicated from design into manufacturing.

By using the process deployment chart in Figure 3.9, the parts importance levels can be translated into process importance levels, with emphasis being placed on the processes that rank the highest in process importance level.

It must be noted, however, that the translation processes above are only first approximations, and are not absolute. It is important to look at the results technically; when there are doubts, studies must be performed to look at such factors as the assumed strengths of relationships. Moreover, it is important to use substantiating data whenever possible.

NOTES

1. Yoji Akao, "New Product Development and Quality Assurance–a System of Quality Deployment," *Standardization and Quality Control* 25 (April 1972):9–14; Yoji Akao and Ryoji Yamada, "A System of Quality Deployment and Case Studies–Computer Research Group Report (no. 1)," *Quality* 7, no. 3 (1977):30–37.

2. Akao and Yamada, "A System of Quality Deployment and Case Studies."

3. Akira Takayanagi, "Quality Control for Production of Subcontracted Products at Our Company (no. 1), Quality Control Activities for Sub-contracted Products–On the Concept of a Quality Chart," *Quality Control* 24 (May 1973):63–67.

Reference

Akao, Yoji, ed. *Practical Application of Quality Deployment for New Product Development.* Tokyo: JSA, 1987 (in Japanese). Translated into English as *Quality Function Deployment–Integrating Customer Requirements into Product Design.* Cambridge, Mass.: Productivity Press, Inc., 1990.

PART II
Deployment of the Sales, Planning, and Design Stages

4

Deployment of Demanded Quality Based on Sales Examples

Sampei Kobayashi

INTRODUCTION

A unique aspect of today's market is that trends change dramatically, accompanied by a significant diversification of consumers' tastes. In addition, there is a demand for high levels of functionality, reliability, and safety.

Traditional quality control that emphasizes preventing the recurrence of problems cannot keep current with today's needs. It is important to establish a strong quality assurance system that places priority on the market by gathering and understanding market demands and to incorporate those demands into the design goals by creating production specifications responsive to the product users.

SIGNIFICANCE OF DEPLOYMENT OF DEMANDED QUALITY BY THE SALES DEPARTMENT

To place top priority on the market means to implement quality assurance activities at every phase, beginning with identification of demanded quality; proceeding to planning, design, manufacturing, inspection, and sales; and ending with after-sales service. The entire effort is based on the needs of consumers who actually use the product. Identification of demanded quality is extremely important because with it starts the process of quality assurance. It serves as a stage for the design group. From company to company different departments are given the responsibility of gathering information and of determining how it is related to design; however, collection of information is an appropriate task for the sales department because it has daily contact with customers. How should collected customer information be effectively communicated to the design group? Sending bits and pieces of information to the design group as they are obtained could cause some essential items to be missed, or the relationship among items and their level of importance to be unclear. Therefore, this mode is not effective. This is why involvement of the sales department in deployment of demanded quality is significant. It is important that sales not only communicate to the design group information as it is gathered but also edit the list for easier understanding.

At Dynic Company, the demanded-quality deployment table became a means of systematically communicating quality to the design group. The following section presents the background, methodology, and utilization of the demanded-quality deployment chart as used by the sales department.

DEMANDED-QUALITY DEPLOYMENT TABLE

What Is the Demanded-Quality Deployment Table?

The demanded-quality deployment table identifies the quality items demanded by the customers in their original form (voice of the customer) for such steps as distribution of products (including those that are in the process of development), secondary fabrication, consumption by the end user, disposal, and other actions. They are deployed to a secondary and tertiary level with the items systematically linked together.

Figure 4.1 is an example of the chart for the fabric connecting the bellows that joins one train car to the next. In the chart, the demanded quality in the stages of sewing the fabric after it is shipped to the bellows manufacturer and installed in the train is deployed to the tertiary level, which systematically links various items. The left half of Figure 4.1 is the demanded-quality deployment table, and the right half illustrates a usage of the charts that will be explained later.

Background and Introduction of the Demanded-Quality Deployment Chart

Dynic handles a product range that includes cloth for book covers, interior decorating, and apparel. The company is unique in being (1) a typical wide-variety, small-lot manufacturer and (2) a manufacturer of raw materials whose products undergo a secondary manufacturing process.

In wide-variety, small-lot production, technologies and information have a tendency to expand because products that undergo several steps of secondary fabrication after they are shipped produce numerous targets for quality assurance. It has long been a challenge to avoid omission of essential information, let alone to accumulate it. Facing similar circumstances, Kobe shipyard of Mitsubishi Heavy Industries introduced the quality chart, which deploys quality from the standpoint of use and clarifies its relationship to quality characteristics and component parts. This new system has attracted much attention.

At Dynic, too, a method for clarification of the relationship among the demanded quality and characteristic values and raw materials (equivalent to parts) was applied to the quality assurance items chart (QA chart). Developed by Dynic engineers and the engineering staff, it was not effective because the segment pertaining to demanded quality was based on partial information sporadically provided by the sales department. Consequently, upgrading this area of the QA chart was necessary to make it effective as a design tool.

To make the sales department more effective in obtaining demanded quality and communicating it to the design group, the structure of quality deployment, in the form of the quality chart, was introduced to the sales department. A review began in 1975 and, following some trial and error, a format was established the following year, at which time reports on the special activities of the sales department were initiated.

How to Prepare a Demanded-Quality Deployment Table

The demanded-quality deployment table is most effective for new product development; however, it also applies to existing products. It is so important that although the sales staff is not normally familiar with this type of work, they should still create one. Future efforts will be easier with adoption of a standard format. The steps below were taken at Dynic.

1. Preparation of the demanded-quality deployment table for groups of products classified by how they are used. (It would be convenient if such a chart also corresponded to classification by product specifications.) Also, items can be made clear through classification by class, group, or type.

Destination	Registration no.	Department manager	Section manager		Drafted by
	K-0006				

Use				
Use	Class	Industrial materials	Design	11/28/75
	Group	Waterproof cloth	Revision (order)	Date
	Type	Fabric for connecting bellows	Division	Industrial goods sales division
			Designers	Sakurai, Matsuda

Phase	Demanded quality						Degree of importance
	No.	Primary	No.	Secondary	No.	Tertiary	
Sewing stage	1	Easy to sew	11	Easy to spread & cut	111	Light	C
					112	Nonsticky	B
			12	Easy to sew by machine	121	Easy to sew by machine	B
					122	Coating does not peel off	B
			13	Adhesives can be used	131	Does not deteriorate from organic solvents	C
In use	2	Protects passengers	21	Rainproof	211	No tears or holes	A
			22	No pressure change in tunnels	221	Airtight (no pinholes)	A
			23	Does not tear even with application of force	231	Does not tear from wind pressure	A
					232	Does not tear from pulling or pushing on the inside	A
					233	Does not tear from shock of starting or stopping	A
			24	Safe even in a fire	241	Does not ignite from small flames	A
					242	Fire does not spread if it catches fire	A
					243	Does not smoke if it catches fire	A
					244	Does not produce toxic fumes if it catches fire	A
	3	Strong and durable	31	Does not tear with repeated flexing	311	Skin does not tear when flexed	A
					312	Threads do not break when flexed	A
			32	Can be used in cold climates	321	Remains flexible in cold climate	A
			33	Resistant to environmental deterioration	331	Does not deteriorate from sunlight	A
					332	Does not deteriorate from rain	A
					333	Does not turn brittle from contact with machine oil	B
					334	Does not get dirty easily	B
					335	Dirt comes off easily	B

FIGURE 4.1
Demanded-Quality Deployment Table

Sales dept.	a. Comparison with competitor's products b. Comparison with our own products c. Complaint check d. Others ( )	Plant	Manager of plant			Drafted by
			1/16/76			
	Period from ________ to ________		Kyoto plant, engineering section			

Substitute characteristics

Thickness	Weight	Tensile strength	Tear strength	Elongation percentage	Fold/flex resistance	Flex failure resistance	Water pressure resistance	Cold resistance	Airtightness	Fireproofing	Weatherproofing	Antiblocking	Surface texture	Peeling resistance	Solvent resistance	Oil resistance	. . .	. . .	. . .
	○																		
												○	○						
													○						
														○					
															○				
							○												
									○										
		○	○		○														
		○	○	○															
		○	○	○															
										○									
										○									
										○									
										○									
					○	○													
						○													
								○											
											○								
											○								
																○			

2. Contribution of ideas on demanded quality by sales personnel through brainstorming and compilation of information with a KJ-like method (affinity diagram). Each individual item is written on a card, and similar items are grouped. A heading is attached to them to indicate the classification of that particular group of cards, and detailed levels are assigned to these card groups.
3. Expression of items should be as close to the raw data form (customers' own words) as possible, avoiding the use of characteristics values. The design department will transform the information into substitute characteristics and values.
4. Grouping separately by different phases, such as distribution after products have been shipped, secondary processing, consumption by the end user, scrappage, and other topics.
5. Addressing of reliability and safety, regardless of whether the customers directly demand them.
6. Numbering of each item for convenience of control and utilization.
7. Desirability of comprehensiveness. However, in order to avoid too broad a focus, the items in the chart must be weighted according to relative importance.

Importance of the Demanded-Quality Deployment Table and How to Use It

The importance of the demanded-quality deployment table lies, first of all, in the degree of initiative toward it. During its creation sales personnel become involved in the subject of quality and improve their knowledge of it. After its creation, the deployment chart provides opportunities for the sales department and design group to discuss subjects related to planning, including product policies, establishment of sales points, and contributions to better communications between the two groups. This is the second significant point of the chart. Further, if the sales group uses the chart effectively, it not only will result in an increase of sales but also will give sales personnel confidence in their quality control role. This is the third significance. The chart generally has two uses: (1) linking sales activities to design and promoting the establishment and revision of product specifications, and (2) establishing product and other policies within the sales department.

As is detailed in Figure 4.1, the left half will represent the demanded-quality deployment table and the right half the two above uses.

Actually, the application described in the following sections is included in the area of the chart that is to be filled in. The company retains a blank master form while providing working copies for each project.

ESTABLISHMENT OR REVISION OF THE DEMANDED-QUALITY DEPLOYMENT TABLE AND PRODUCT SPECIFICATIONS

Conventional Method

Figure 4.2 shows the conventional relationship between the sales department and the design department for the steps from demanded quality to product specifications. The sales department formerly relayed information to the design group through prototype reports, information cards, claim forms, and other means as information was

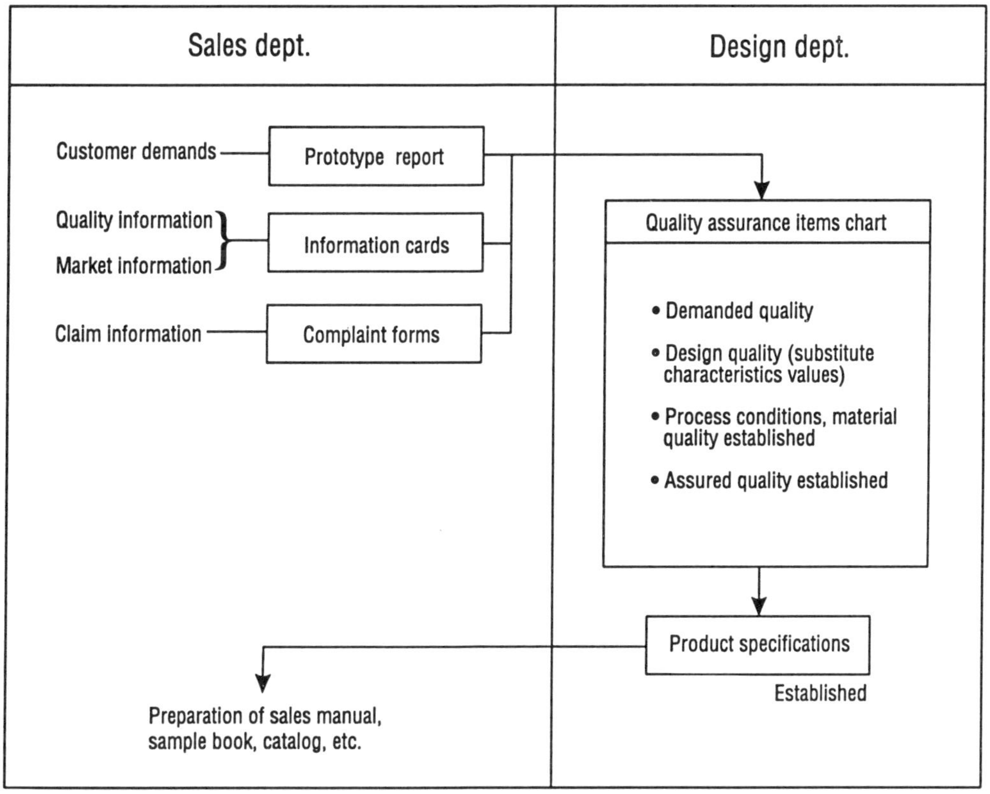

FIGURE 4.2
Creation of product specifications by conventional method

acquired. From this information the design group designed products and established or revised the product specifications. Also, the sales group conducted sales activities on the basis of product specifications as created. There were three problems with this traditional method.

1. The sales department merely handed over requirements of the customers, as they were received, to the design group, and did not take positive action to collect information. As a result, information was communicated in an unorganized manner that could not comprehensively indicate the use of the product in its market.
2. Because information sent by the sales group in this way was not comprehensive, and because the relationships among information items were unclear, the design group could not determine substitute characteristics and levels in a logical manner. The result was a waste of time and effort in development and improvement activities because such a trial-and-error sequence was not productive.
3. The design group, which has a tendency to include every characteristics value that comes to mind, then determined the product specifications. As a result, the sales personnel did not know which values were assured to what degree, and therefore could not indicate what would be the sales points. Even when products did satisfy designated specifications, many complaints were still reported.

How to Use the Demanded-Quality Development Table

In order to solve problems arising from the conventional method, there were two major improvements. The first was implementation of the demanded-quality deployment table as a means for the sales department to communicate demanded quality. Individual pieces of information are communicated as required, as in the conventional method; however, the difference is the sorting and summarizing of the information into a demanded-quality deployment table that is given to the design department. When the design department receives it, the members identify the relationship between demanded quality and substitute characteristics and return the table to the sales department with suggested product specifications. A chart in which demanded quality and substitute characteristics are listed is called a quality chart, as illustrated in Figure 4.1, using the connecting bellows fabric as an example.

The other improvement was the transfer of responsibility for establishing product specifications from the design group to the sales group. As in the past, the design department drafts the specifications, but the sales department first makes certain that items included in the demanded-quality deployment table are satisfied in the draft. Then the specifications are finalized at the initiative of the sales department.

Figure 4.3 explains this procedure with the connecting bellows example. Through the use of this chart, the communication of demanded quality, its incorporation into products, and establishment of product specifications now go smoothly and the level of marketplace acceptance has been improved.

HOW THE SALES DEPARTMENT USES THE DEMANDED-QUALITY DEPLOYMENT CHART

The demanded-quality deployment table also serves as information to assist the sales department in establishing product policies. Some of the representative uses by the sales group are (1) comparison with competitors' products, (2) comparison with one's own products, and (3) checking complaints. The table can be modified for other purposes as needed.

Comparison with Competitors' Products

Through a comparison with competitors' products, sales points are reevaluated and requirements are given to the design department to improve areas found inferior. What is usually compared is the level of individual product quality, but it would be interesting also to compare the "brand image" of various manufacturers.

Figure 4.4 illustrates an example of needlepunch carpet. In the past, sales points were vaguely expressed as "easy to install," but now it can be described in more concrete terms as "easy to fold over, and therefore can be installed on steps easily." This makes the salesman's job much easier.

Comparison with One's Own Products

Comparisons with one's own products make it easier to retain products that satisfy their original purposes and allow reevaluation of product line structure leading to streamlining and the development of new

(Text continues on p. 106)

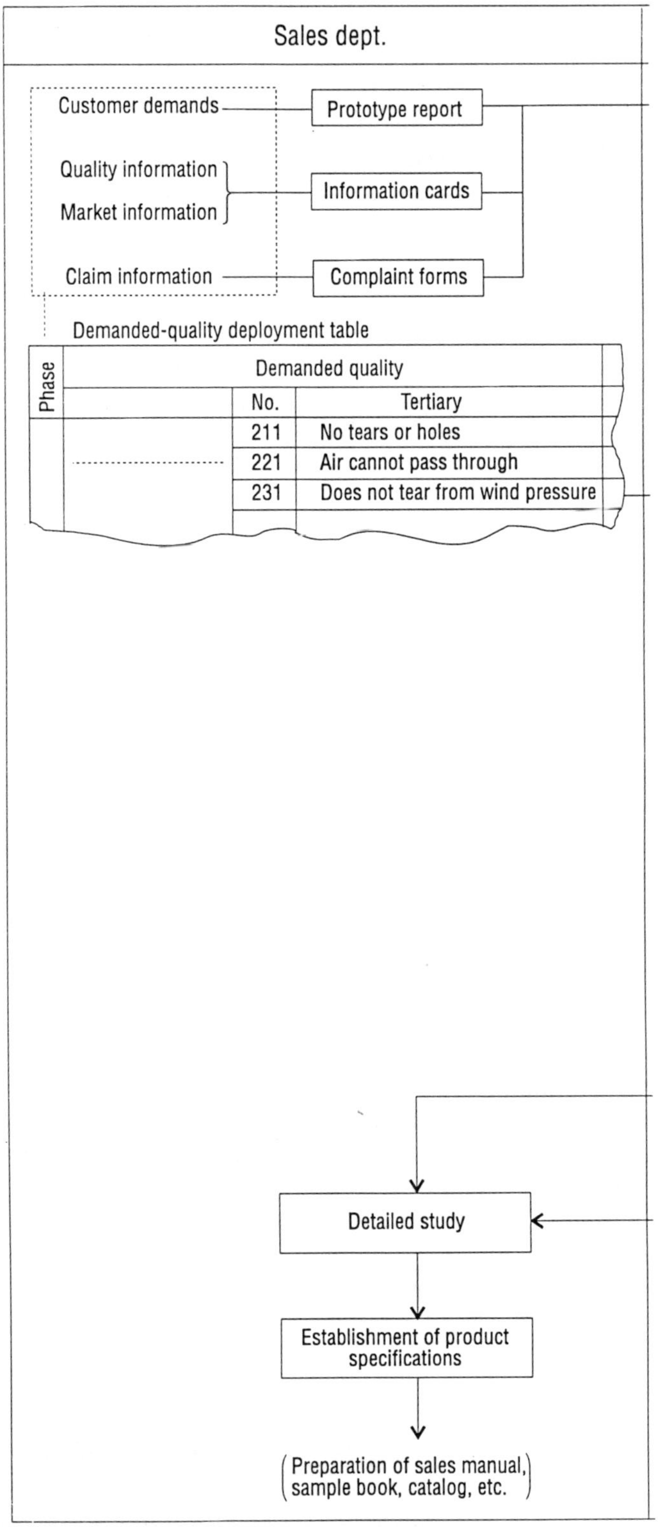

FIGURE 4.3
Establishment of product specifications by demanded-quality deployment table

Design dept.

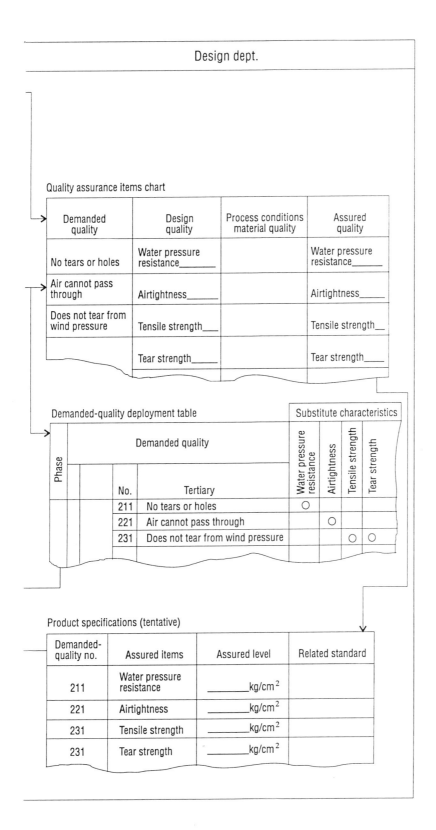

Quality assurance items chart

Demanded quality	Design quality	Process conditions material quality	Assured quality
No tears or holes	Water pressure resistance_______		Water pressure resistance______
Air cannot pass through	Airtightness______		Airtightness_____
Does not tear from wind pressure	Tensile strength___		Tensile strength__
	Tear strength_____		Tear strength_____

Demanded-quality deployment table

Phase			Demanded quality: No.	Demanded quality: Tertiary	Substitute characteristics: Water pressure resistance	Substitute characteristics: Airtightness	Substitute characteristics: Tensile strength	Substitute characteristics: Tear strength
			211	No tears or holes	○			
			221	Air cannot pass through		○		
			231	Does not tear from wind pressure			○	○

Product specifications (tentative)

Demanded-quality no.	Assured items	Assured level	Related standard
211	Water pressure resistance	________kg/cm^2	
221	Airtightness	________kg/cm^2	
231	Tensile strength	________kg/cm^2	
231	Tear strength	________kg/cm^2	

Destination	Registration no.	Dept. manager	Section manager		Drafted by	Sales dept.	a. Comparison with competitors' products b. Comparison with our own products c. Complaint check d. Others ( )	Plant	Manager of plant			Drafted by
	I-0001						Period from ______ to ______		Date			
									Plant section			

Use				
Use	Class	Interior design materials	Design	1/16/76
	Group	Floor materials	Revision (order)	Date
	Type	Needlepunch carpet	Division	Sales dept. for interior design materials
			Designers	

Phase	Demanded quality No.	Primary	No.	Secondary	No.	Tertiary	Degree of importance	Our company	Company A	Company B	Company C	
Application process stage	1	Easy to apply	11	Easy to cut	111	Cuts nicely	B	○	△	○	△	
					112	Can piece together	B	○	○	○	○	
					113	Cut end does not unravel	A	○	○	○	○	
					114	Cut in any direction	B	○	○	○	○	
			12	Easy to install	121	Easy to handle	C	○	○	○	○	
					122	Can fold over (stairs)	A	○	△	○	△	
					123	Easy to relax curl	A	○	△	○	△	
					124	Easy to lay on floor	B	×	×	×	×	
					125	Can be doubled over	B	○	○	○	○	
			13	Economical installation	131	Available in many widths	B	○	○	○	○	

FIGURE 4.4
Comparison with competitors' products

Destination	Registration no.	Dept. manager	Section manager		Drafted by	Sales dept.	a. Comparison with competitors' products b. Comparison with our own products c. Complaint check d. Others ( )	Plant	Manager of plant			Drafted by
	G-0002						Period from ________ to ________		Date			
									Plant section			

Use				
	Class	Clothing materials	Design	1/29/75
	Group	Core texture	Revision (order)	Date
	Type	Heat adhesive core texture	Division	Sales dept. for clothing materials
			Designers	

Phase	Demanded quality: No.	Primary	No.	Secondary	No.	Tertiary	Degree of importance	S8	S9	S110	S17	S29	7709	7756	8890	8856	8854	
Sewing process	1	Easy to sew	11	Easy to handle	111	Easy to cut	B	○	○	○	○	○	◎	◎	◎	◎	◎	
					112	Nonsticky	B	×	×	×	×	×	◎	◎	◎	◎	◎	
					113	Does not curl from heat	B	◎	◎	◎	◎	×	◎	○	○	○	◎	
					114	Nonelastic, nonwarping	B	×	×	×	×	×	◎	◎	◎	◎	◎	
					115	Easy to straighten out curl	B	◎	◎	◎	◎	◎	◎	◎	◎	◎	◎	
					116	No after-tackiness of resin	A	×	×	△	△	○	◎	◎	◎	◎	◎	
					117	Smooth to iron	A	△	△	○	◎	◎	◎	◎	◎	◎	◎	
					118	Can be overlapped to join	A	×	×	×	×	×	○	○	○	○	○	
					119	Hoffman press can be used	C	×	×	×	×	×	○	○	○	○	○	
			12	Nice finishing	121	Plastic does not outgas	A	△	△	○	○	△	○	○	△	△	△	

FIGURE 4.5
Comparison among DYNIC's own products

Destination	Registration no.	Dept. manager	Section manager		Drafted by	Sales dept.	a. Comparison with competitors' products b. Comparison with our own products c. Complaint check d. Others ( )	Plant	Manager of plant			Drafted by
	C-0001						10/1/73–9/30/76		Date			
									Plant section			

Use				
	Class	Business supplies	Design	2/21/77
	Group	Cloth for bank passbook covers	Revision (order)	Date
	Type		Division	Cloth sales dept.
		(Bank accounts, postal CDs)	Designers	Yamamoto, Onodera

Phase	Demanded quality: No.	Primary	No.	Secondary	No.	Tertiary	Degree of importance	10/73	10/74	10/75	10/76	No. of complaints	2 4 6 8
Secondary process phase	1	Good imprintability	11	Passes through printing machine easily	111	No curl		/	/	////		6	
					112	Squares up readily							
					113	No foreign matter mixed in		/	///	///		7	
					114	Adequate stiffness							
					115	Does not stretch during imprinting		/	/	/		3	
			12	Good ink transfer	121	Surface is flat							
					122	No variance in thickness		/				1	
					123	No paper particles escape							
					124	No pinholes				////		4	
					125	Does not get dirty		//	//	/		5	

In use	6	Allows name to be placed on it	61	Can write on with ballpoint pen	611	Can write on clearly					/		1	
					612	Ink dries well					/		1	
					613	Ink doesn't rub off					/		1	
			62	Can be typed on	621	Imprints clearly								
					622	Ink dries well								
					623	Ink does not rub off								
	7	Can use safely	71	Hands & clothing do not become stained	711	Color does not fade								
			72	Harmless	721	Contains no harmful substances								
	8	Nice appearance & feel	81	No appearance defects	811	Color matches sample			///	//	///		8	
					812	No uneven color or gloss			/				1	
					813	Stitching does not wobble								

FIGURE 4.6
Checklist of complaints

products, if needed. In other words, when there is no differentiation among products, some must be eliminated. If they are not satisfying demands, improvements must be made or, in some cases, new products must be developed. Figure 4.5 shows an example of a fabric used in Western-style clothing.

Use as a Checklist of Complaints

Complaints and requests for improvements are reviewed for items that require attention. This leads to improvements. Shown in Figure 4.6 is an example of the cloth used to cover bank passbooks. Data are collected for all varieties of the product for a specified period, but they can also be collected for individual product variations. In either case, a review of this information supports a further analysis of any claims. At Dynic, the sales department uses this method to identify problem areas and to request improvements from the plant. The plant takes on these critical quality problems and makes improvements.

In the checking of product complaints, newly identified items are added to the deployment chart as they are found. Thus the deployment is always up to date. Also, although this may be part of a staff responsibility, systematically reevaluating the entire demanded-quality deployment table can indicate weaknesses in products from the standpoint of quality assurance.

Other Ways to Use the Demanded-Quality Deployment Table

The methods described have been used in many of the case studies published in the past. Another way to utilize the chart is to divide the new product development process into segments, such as first prototype, nth prototype, production prototype, initial production stage, and so forth, and make a comparison at each step against the target quality. By using ◎ to designate completion, the advancement to completion can be shown by × → △ → ○. Also, when a certain item is being improved, as indicated by △ → ◎, other items might be marked ○ → ×, which could suggest too much effort has been placed on improvements, leaving other areas unattended. Another effective way to use the chart not normally associated with the sales department is that of communicating demanded quality to subcontractors for raw materials procurement and subcontracting work. Details of this approach are not covered here.

CONCLUSION

The demanded-quality deployment table has grown from the need to deploy demanded quality. With experience, unique ways to utilize it have been created.

Sales Department

1. Quality consciousness has increased as a result of taking on the responsibility of identifying demanded quality and establishing product specifications.
2. QA activities, including identification and communication of demanded quality, formerly sporadic, are now systematized and coordinated.
3. Understanding the relationships between demanded quality and product specifications, and demanded quality and sales points, has upgraded sales promotion activities.

Design Department

1. Communication of demanded quality is now systematic and is fully reflected in the design engineering.

But there are still problems to be solved.

1. Improving the methodology by better expressing sensory characteristics, and balancing fulfillment of requirements and the cost of doing so
2. Smooth operation of the system (speedup of the process) for new product development
3. Regular use of the system

In any event, the sales department's use of the demanded-quality deployment table has aroused its quality consciousness, and with the means to take action, the intent is to establish a systematic quality assurance system tied directly to the market being served.

In conclusion, appreciation is given to Professor Yoji Akao for his guidance and to the Computer Research Group of the Japan Society for Quality Control for the role they have played.

5

The Use of Prioritization in Quality Deployment at the Planning and Design Phases

Norio Kamisawa

During the planning and design phases, quality policies (*hoshins*) and quality targets are established, and sales points based on them are determined or, as needed, weak points are identified and followed by measures to strengthen them. Since customer needs form the basis of all these activities, the demanded-quality deployment table will deploy these based on functions. In order to select the themes that must be emphasized and to establish directions toward which technology, development, capital investments, marketing, and other areas should be aimed, the current status of a company is evaluated to set weights. One effective method is to weigh relative importance by using the demanded-quality deployment table.

Weighing the relative importance of various quality elements is part of any corporate strategy, and must be handled carefully. It can be supposed that in some companies deployment of demanded quality has become important to quality planning. It is likely that this activity is treated as confidential by these companies, so few examples of actual use have been publicized.

At Ishikawajima-Harima Heavy Industries Co., Ltd., assignment of relative importance based on past experience is checked against the demanded-quality deployment table. In this chapter, I offer a summary of the approach by giving examples of actual applications that have been made available to the public.

USE OF THE QUALITY CHART IN THE QUALITY ASSURANCE SYSTEM TO ASSIGN RELATIVE IMPORTANCE

A matrix in which the demanded-quality deployment table and characteristics deployment table are related to each other is, by narrow definition, the quality chart. Its purpose is to fortify the quality assurance system with reliability and comprehensiveness. Consider carefully where to position the quality chart in a quality assurance system by diagramming the system. Figure 5.1 is an example of a quality assurance system diagram. The bold lines indicate the route to design and build quality into the product, and the items in boxes are activities required to achieve this goal. Another description for it might be the quality information transformation route.

When addressing hardware quality issues, inspection data must be compared against design data (drawings are part of the design data). But at a completely automated plant, information is no doubt processed without viewing the physical product. The task, consequently, is to process information from a previous process or feedback from other areas, or to send information with added value (i.e., decisions) to a later process.

From the customer's point of view, it means that the information input to the manufacturer in the form of demanded quality is compared against the output information that is the function of the product (for example, with an automobile, information identified by the human senses, such as "comfortable ride," "accelerates well," "ride feels stable").

The role played by the quality chart should be defined because the quality assurance system is where quality transformation takes place. The quality chart tells, in a systematic and comprehensive way, what kinds of yardsticks are required to measure the needs of the customers contained in the demanded-quality table and what kind of quantitative limits with what range should be set to satisfy these needs. In other words, verbatim data – quality demanded by the customers – is transformed into quantitative information that, in this case, is quality characteristics. As shown in Figure 5.2, the quality chart is placed in the area of information transformation on the main route of the quality assurance system.

Assignment of relative importance to quality factors involves establishment of quality policies, that is, prioritization at the same time information transformation takes place, and determination of objectives, quality targets, and development and product improvements (see Figure 5.2). In the process, quality demanded by the customers is compared with what the company is currently doing, so that strengths and weaknesses are identified. Subsequently, top management contributes ideas and suggestions based on its experience. All of these lead to quality policies and targets that form top management strategic decisions.

The main objective of information transformation in which the quality chart is positioned is to establish and to secure consistency and comprehensiveness; thus, in one sense, the quality chart must possess continuity and equality. In contrast, the formation of strategy includes

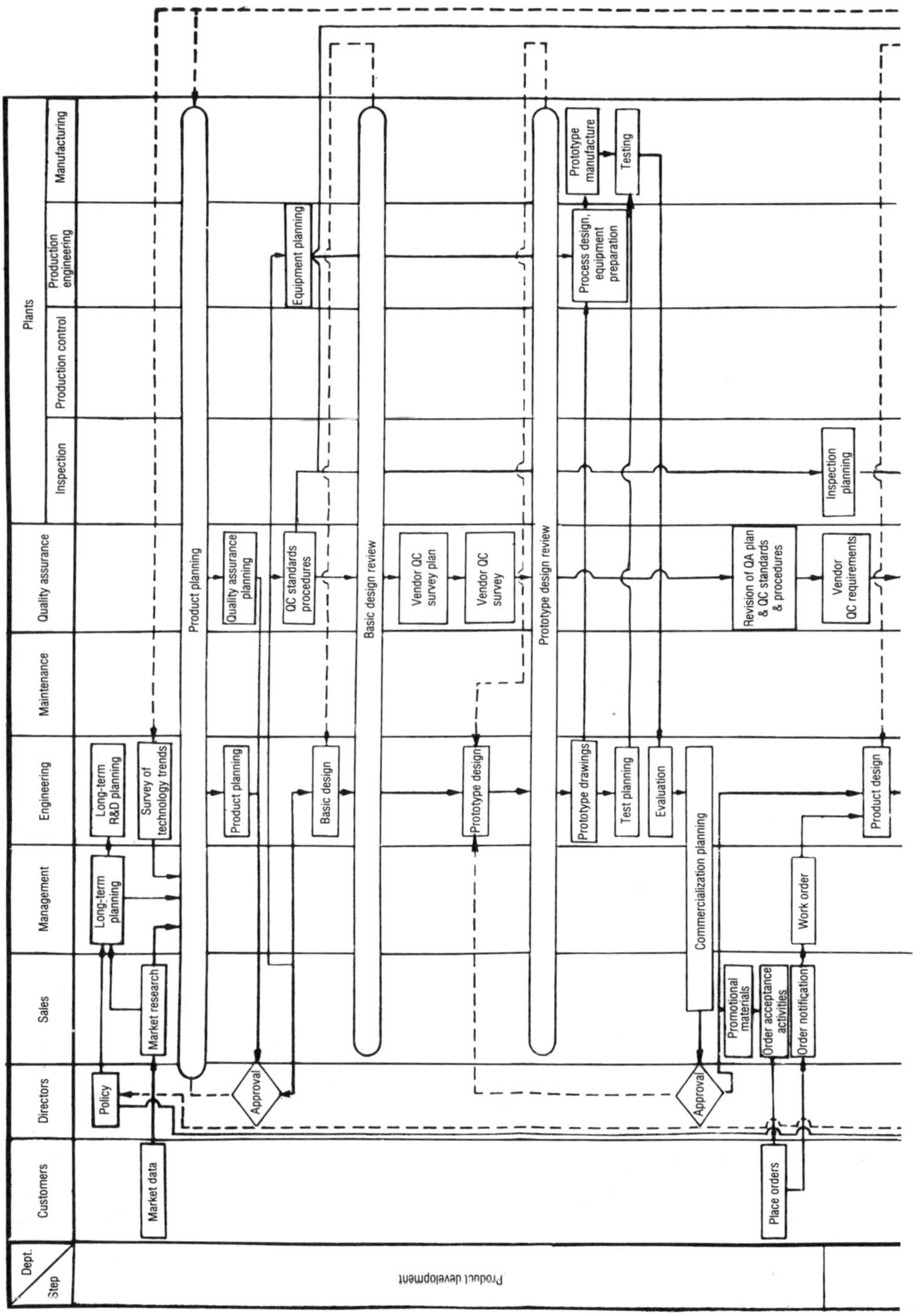

Dept.
Step
Customers
Directors
Sales
Management
Engineering
Maintenance
Quality assurance
Plants
Inspection
Production control
Production engineering
Manufacturing
Market data
Policy
Market research
Long-term planning
Long-term R&D planning
Survey of technology trends
Product planning
Approval
Product planning
Quality assurance planning
Equipment planning
QC standards procedures
Basic design
Basic design review
Vendor QC survey plan
Vendor QC survey
Prototype design
Prototype design review
Prototype drawings
Test planning
Evaluation
Process design, equipment preparation
Prototype manufacture
Testing
Commercialization planning
Approval
Promotional materials
Order acceptance activities
Order notification
Work order
Revision of QA plan & QC standards & procedures
Inspection planning
Vendor QC requirements
Product design
Place orders
Product development

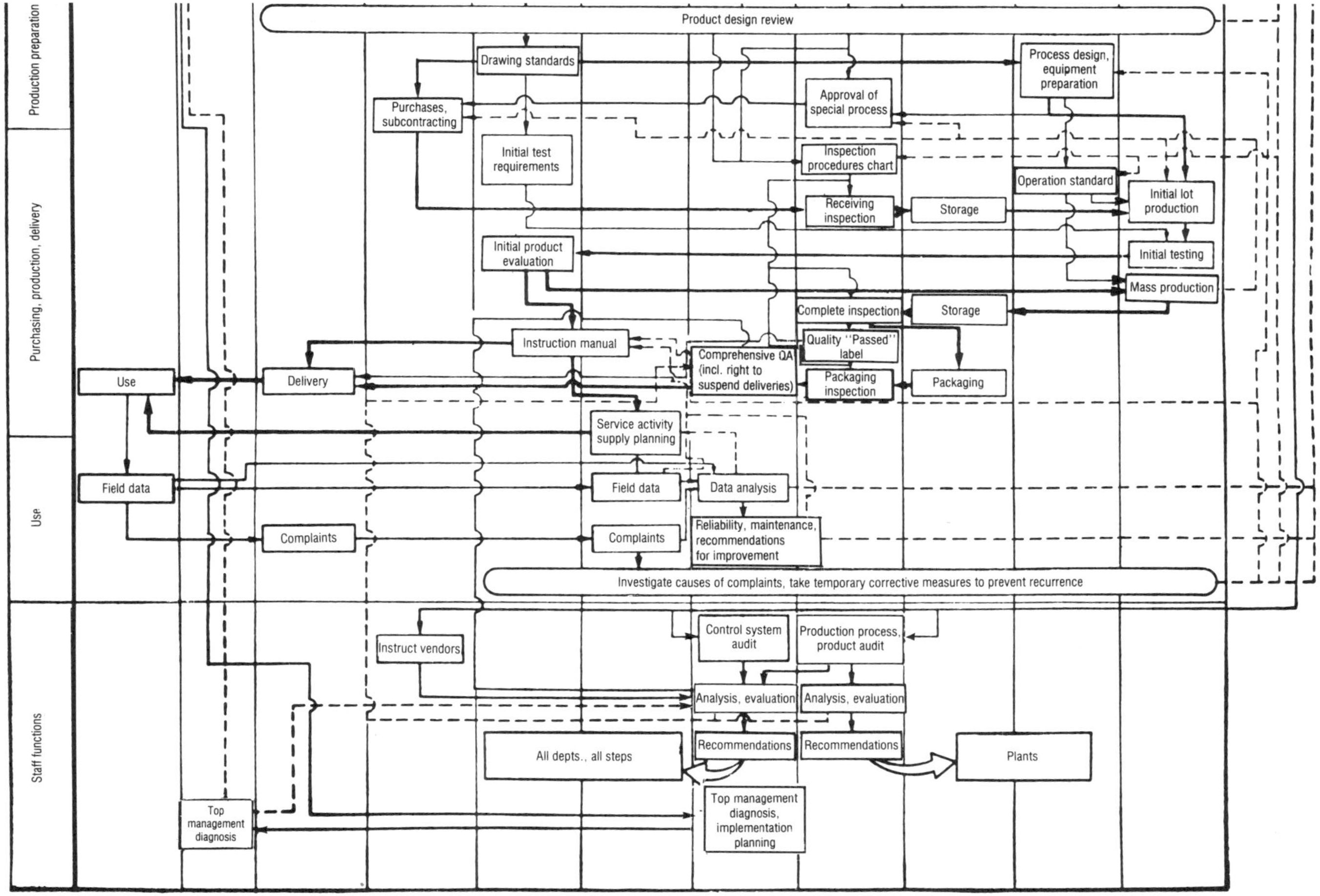

FIGURE 5.1
Sample of a quality assurance system diagram

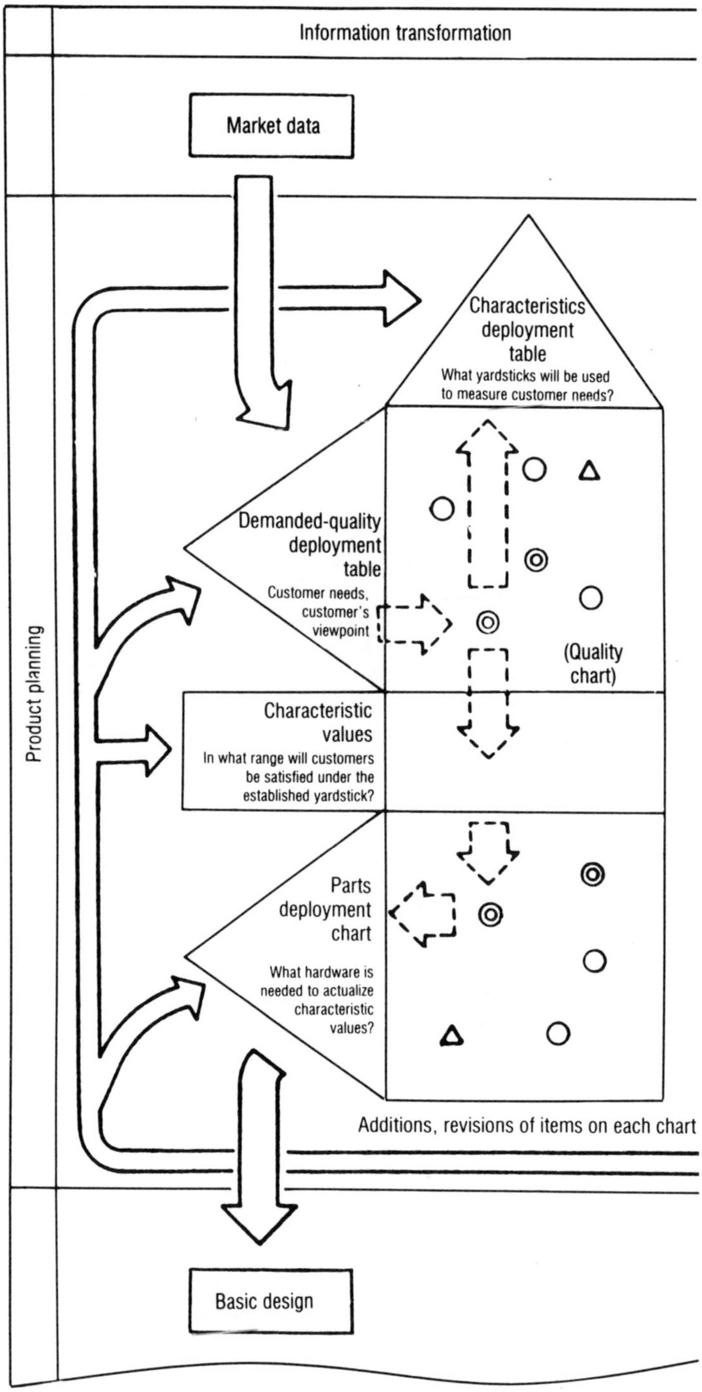

FIGURE 5.2
Quality chart and weighting in the quality assurance system

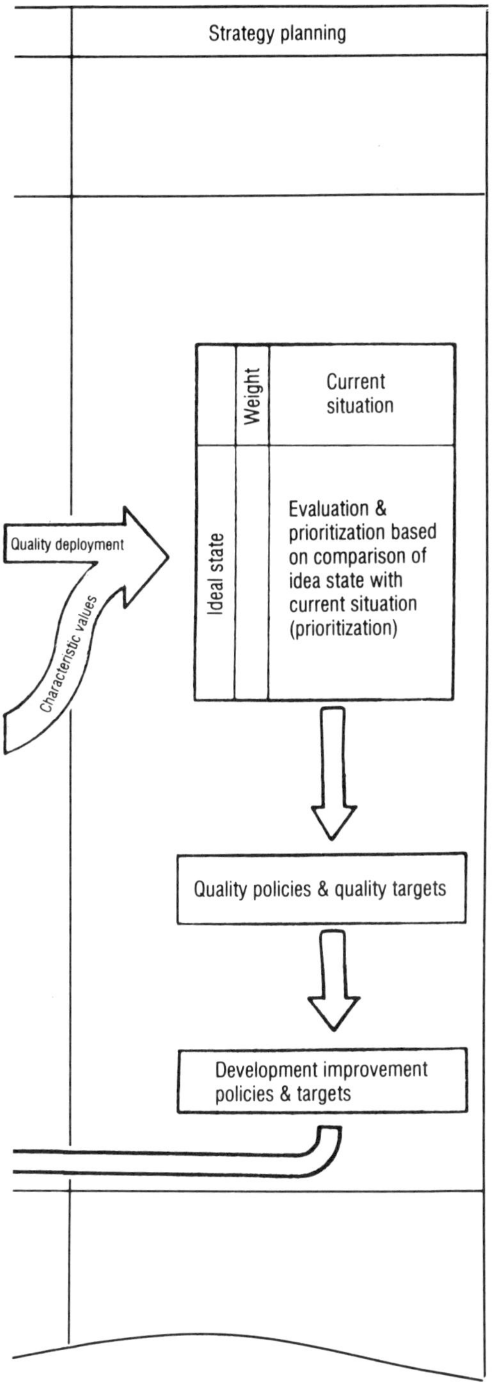
Strategy planning
Weight
Current situation
Ideal state
Evaluation & prioritization based on comparison of idea state with current situation (prioritization)
Quality deployment
Characteristic values
Quality policies & quality targets
Development improvement policies & targets

assignment of relative importance, which adds discontinuity and deformation in the area of quality problems, although it adds continuity to the overall system of management strategy. For example, even if a recommendation were to improve the quality of a product, it could be thrown out for lack of cost effectiveness. For this reason, these two areas must be clearly separated.

This phase of the product cycle, taken as a whole, is called the product planning phase. However, depending on the types of products and the company's organizational structure, the design phase could include relating characteristics deployment to parts deployment. The distinction, therefore, is not always clear, because in many cases the planning and basic design phases overlap. It is important, therefore, to establish clear definitions case by case.

Let us briefly review the methodology. The process of information transformation naturally includes a detailing of information. However, to avoid confusion, it is recommended that in the area of planning illustrated in Figure 5.2, information transformation and strategy be discussed at the same information level.

The demanded quality could be deployed to the most detailed level of individual part functions but, to avoid complexity, it is preferable to deploy no further than four levels. The goal is deployment of quality demanded by the customers, and it is now known that all customer requirements are accounted for when deployment reaches about the fourth level of detail. It is recommended that the detail of information available for current products that will be used to compare characteristics, parts, and priorities correspond to the lowest level of the demanded-quality deployment. With complicated products, it is usually the level of the unit or module. Further deployment occurs in the design phase, if necessary, but here the information transformation and weighting are done at the customer requirements level.

DEMANDED-QUALITY DEPLOYMENT TABLE

Demanded-quality deployment is defined as an arrangement of the customer demands for quality, in the customers' own words, into a system of targets and implementation methods based on functions. From our experience, it is necessary, in order to avoid confusion, to modify the definition as shown below.

The Customers' Viewpoint

1. In order to understand the customers' viewpoint, it is first necessary to identify the customers. For example, in the case of a

machine, the user of the machine and its installer would have different demands for quality, and their weighting of these quality demands would be different.

2. Since it is based on the customers' words, deployment of demanded quality should relate to how customers think. It is easy to let the manufacturer's wishes slip in, even unconsciously, but they must be excluded as much as possible. Inclusion of characteristics and parts in the process of deployment means that the manufacturer's wishes are being reflected.

What Does "Based on Functions" Mean?

"Function" means what the product does, and it is normally considered in a dynamic sense. In actuality, there are a number of functions, some of which are the dynamic functions expressed as verb plus object or modifier (for example, "can drive with stability," "generates electricity," "propels airplane"), the static expressions of a noun plus adjective (such as "easy handling," "good looks," "quiet sound"), those with adverbs, such as "rotate smoothly," and those with limits, such as "does not break from vibration." Though most functions can be expressed in a verb plus object form, too strict an adherence may impede the free flow of information.

Therefore, centering deployment activities around functions means identifying basic functions that can be phrased in a verb plus object form, expressing dynamically and statically what customers say, using simple phrases, and then deploying them.

THE QUALITY CHART

The quality chart, as defined earlier, in a narrow sense relates the demanded-quality deployment table and characteristics deployment table in a two-dimensional matrix. Such a relationship provides a means of measuring customer needs that have been deployed from language data and what performance ranges, expressed numerically, should be established to satisfy customers. Thus language data are transformed into numerical data. It is not a simple task to determine the yardstick for measuring customers' needs and to express the performance range to be established in numerical values. These are determined after examining the relevant circumstances, eight of which are listed below.

1. Cases where the customer's demands are expressed quantitatively
2. Comparison with competing products to determine which is better or worse

3. Does it have sales features making it superior to competitors' products?
4. Does the product fit the market needs?
5. Can design engineering create it?
6. Can the process capability produce it?
7. Can it be produced at an acceptable cost?
8. Can it be put into production by the time it is required?

In brief, this is the stage in which customers' needs, sometimes selfish, are matched for the first time against the manufacturer's desires and capabilities. In many cases, the needs are easily satisfied with conventional technologies and past experience, although it is important that the design manual, the engineering manual, and other items in this area be standardized. If a new product is to be presented to the marketplace, it should offer unique features or possess functions or characteristics that form the theme of the technological development. The right-hand side of Figure 5.2 illustrates the phase containing the strategies for determining the direction of development themes.

MATRIX OF THE PARTS DEPLOYMENT CHART AND CHARACTERISTICS DEPLOYMENT TABLE

At this phase, it is determined how characteristics values established earlier should be expressed in the hardware. This is the first step to actualizing customers' needs.

This, as explained in the eight situations in the preceding section, is determined from several factors. It is impossible for 100% of customer needs to be transformed suddenly into hardware by following the information transformation route shown in Figure 5.2. Sensory needs, for example, cannot be transformed into characteristics. Others, such as overall performance requirements of a machine, even when transformed, cannot be divided into small units and modules.

Consequently, the transformation of such needs should not be forced. Until the relationship between the whole and the parts is identified through research and development, evaluation of prototypes, or market testing, the needs should be defined through the use of high-level functions, characteristics, or system, and tentative targets should be set for lower-level items (perhaps fourth-level characteristics or fourth-level components).

Since it is not uncommon for uncertainties to exist at this stage (the planning phase), it is important to differentiate those needs that are known from those that are not. For those that are unknown, it is important to identify a method (based on who uses the product and when, where, why, and how it is used) to determine them.

The information transformation to this point does not take place smoothly from top to bottom, as seems to be the case in the diagram, but actually is a process of trial and error. This basic concept must be clearly established to avoid loss of consistency and comprehensiveness, which are the greatest advantages of the quality deployment system. For example, the following discussion occurs quite frequently during planning meetings. "It must have a quiet engine." "Maybe so, but a 1000-horsepower unit must be achieved first." "The type of combustion chamber must ________." Discussion like this totally disregard the relationship among levels of information ("upstream," "midstream," and "downstream") and will obstruct the course the project should take.

PRIORITIZATION

The need for consistency and completeness in quality deployment causes the systems to grow very large for products for which the demanded-quality deployment is complex, leading to even greater degrees of complexity and excessively general deployments that lack focus. Yoji Akao provides guidance regarding the need for prioritization methods by which to overcome this crucial problem with demanded-quality deployment. He has concluded that this prioritization is necessary in order to use demanded-quality deployment more assertively for strategic reasons, and is even more important than using prioritization to overcome these problems in demanded-quality deployment.

The method of prioritization, adapted to demanded-quality deployment, is as follows: (1) look at the performance of the company regarding each customer demand set out in the demanded-quality deployment chart; (2) establish themes for improvement that the company should adopt, based on an evaluation of the company's performance. The company establishes its policies and targets for quality, and for development and improvement, based on steps. The concept of bringing together the customer demands and the performance of the company is shown in Figure 5.3.

The customer demands (i.e., the items from the demanded-quality deployment table) are listed down the left-hand side of the chart, along with the weightings that show the strength of the customer demands the company must meet. Next, the performance of the firm is evaluated, and some success in filling these customer demands is achieved. These are listed across the top of the chart. Criteria are set for assigning scores by looking at the combinations of pairs, with high scores

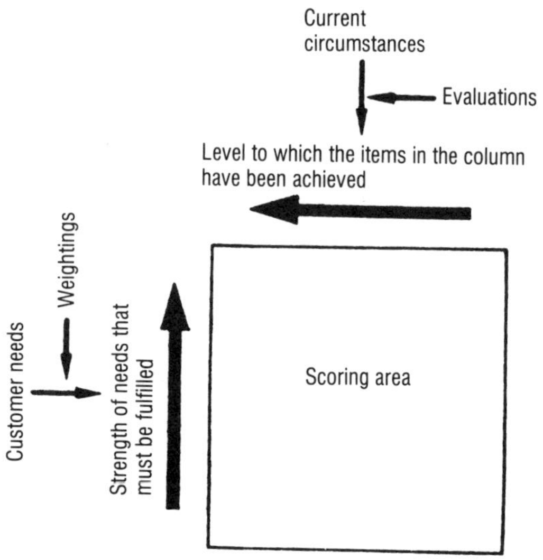

FIGURE 5.3
Method of determining prioritization

assigned to the cases where there is a high level of achievement regarding the stronger demands. High scores imply items that can be regarded as sales points, while low scores imply critical problems.

Example of a Scoring Standards Chart

Because most people are familiar with 100-point scales or the 3- or 5-point scales used for report cards at school, for reporting the results of experiments, and so forth, these scales are useful in gaining consensus on evaluations from group members and do not lead to overly complex calculations when evaluating priorities.

Although various systems are shown in Figure 5.4, the method to be used must be chosen on a case-by-case basis. It is necessary to derive scoring standards according to the purposes for which they will be used, and in any of these methods the absolute scores in any cell are relatively meaningless (despite the fact that these scores are meaningful if the relative relationships between absolute scores are understood). The goal here is to establish a prioritization on relative scores. Another goal is to expand those cases where at first glance it appears that there is little relative difference, focusing especially on problem areas. To do this, one might, for example, expand a three-level evaluation scale to five or seven evaluation levels.

In charts (1) and (2) in Figure 5.4, the areas where the customer demands are important and where the level to which the company fulfills them is high receive particularly high scores. Chart (2) is an extension of chart (1), which was suggested by Assistant Professor Masao Akiba of Tokyo Institute of Technology. Chart (3) focuses by assigning negative scores to those areas where the company is poor in satisfying customer demands. Charts (4) and (5) try to expand the concepts further by using multiplicative methods. In chart (5), 100 importance points are allocated among the various low-level functions in the demanded-quality chart by assigning a certain number of importance points to each according to its relative level of importance; scores are computed by multiplying the importance points by the degree to which the company is fulfilling the customer demands (on a five-point scale ranging from -2 to $+2$). For example, a 15-point customer demand for which the level of satisfaction is a total failure would receive a score of $-2 \times 15 = -30$. (See Figure 5.8.)

(1)

	A	*B*	*C*
a	5	4	3
b	4	3	2
c	3	2	1

(2)

	A	*B*	*C*	*D*	*E*
a	9	8	7	6	5
b	8	7	6	5	4
c	7	6	5	4	3
d	6	5	4	3	2
e	5	4	3	2	1

(3)

	A	*B*	*C*
a	+5	0	−5
b	+3	0	−3
c	+1	0	−1

(4)

		A	*B*	*C*
		5	3	1
a	5	25	15	5
b	3	15	9	3
c	1	5	3	1

(5)

		A	*B*	*C*	*D*	*E*
		+2	+1	0	−1	−2
	15					
	3					
	5					
	10					
Total	100					

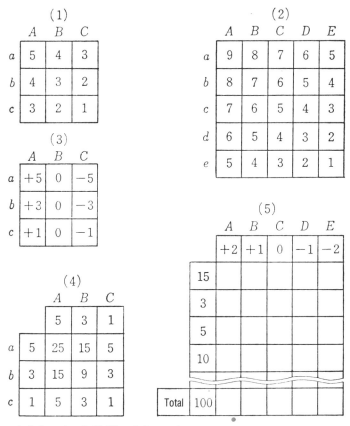

A, B, C . . . Level of fulfillment at present
a, b, c . . . Strength of needs that must be fulfilled

FIGURE 5.4
Examples of scoring standards tables

How to Assign Weightings

When groups first attempt to assign weightings to the customer demands, it is often common to discover that many of the elements are not clearly defined or that there is too little information to assign weightings. Consequently, while it is necessary to make effective use of the information that is available and to obtain the information that is not, it is also important to draw upon the experience of group members and on the knowledge they possess that might not be articulated in a form that would normally be called "data." Below we will discuss several methods by which this might be done.

The Survey Method

Use a customer survey to assign importance ratings to the various functions that have been identified by quality deployment. It is important to derive methods by which to get evaluations that are as frank and honest as possible, and the survey instrument must be simple. Because of this, it is usually not appropriate to try to get the customers to allocate 100 points to the list of functions. A three- or five-point scale is much better. Also, although the level of abstraction chosen for functions that are to be evaluated differs from product to product, it would be meaningless to list hundreds of detailed low-level functions for which the customers have no feel at all. The collected data must be stratified according to user and according to the region in which the user lives.

When there is a great deal of variability—or even outright contradiction—in the surveys returned by the customers, it is necessary to find the reasons for these inconsistences. Rather than compensate for these problems by making decisions based on the Delphi method or on a majority vote, the direct voice of the customer is critical in the survey data.

The Delphi Method

The Delphi method is useful when the information that has accumulated in the minds of the evaluators is not objective. In this method each member of the evaluation team presents opinions through surveys or unstructured discussions, and then each evaluator iteratively and point by point corrects his or her own estimations through looking at the distribution of estimations of all members of the group. In this way all evaluators are eventually brought into consensus. (For a more detailed discussion, see Jiro Kondo, *Systems Engineering* [Tokyo: Maruzen, 1970, and revised edition, 1981].)

Although theoretically all evaluators are functioning from a market-in perspective, differences in point of view and in experience may prevent the group from reaching a consensus when using the Delphi method. When this is the case, the evaluation team might resolve the issue by researching the opinions of the customers, using questionnaire surveys. And when it comes to a lack of consensus resulting from different perspectives, another method that might be used is to derive systems by which to weight the opinions of the various team members. These weightings might be done on the basis of the people with the most experience, the people with the most responsibility, or following the market-in concept.

Whichever method is used, major differences in opinion that arise from differences in perspective, as well as contradictions in the results of market surveys, are certain to appear in the products themselves. These differences should be considered major problems, and it is advisable to trace them back to their root causes.

At Ishikawajima-Harima Heavy Industries Co., Ltd., it appears that it was often the case that when there were major differences in opinions resulting from differences in perspectives, there were biases in the information possessed by the individual evaluators (information that should have been held by all), creating circumstances where not all members were working from the same informational basis.

The Combination Evaluation Method

This method is the one taught by its creator, Masaaki Segawa, in his book *New Product Development Primer* (Tokyo: JUSE Press, 1969). The method begins with the evaluators each assigning preliminary scores to the items to be evaluated. Next, the preliminary standard items (for example, α) are compared with combinations of various items (for example, $\beta + \gamma$ or $\beta + \delta$) and the magnitude of the results is evaluated by a vote of the team members. The final evaluation scores – the weightings – are determined by making corrections when the results of this process contradict the preliminary scores.

This method has the benefit of allowing for more comprehensive decisions through looking at comparisons of combinations of several items rather than merely assigning a single weight to each evaluation item.

The Method for Distributing Points to the Various Functions in Demanded-Quality Deployment

Regardless of what method is used, the fact that the third-level and fourth-level detailed functions usually number in the hundreds invites complexity and confusion in evaluations when assigning weights to the various functions in demanded-quality deployment. Figure 5.5 is an example where 100 points are allocated among the various functions. In this example, scores for the higher-level functions are allocated sequentially to the lower-level functions. First, weightings are assigned to the five level-1 functions, with function 1100 being allocated 30 of the 100 points. Next, the four functions that are beneath function 1100 are allocated points on a 100-point scale, receiving 50, 25, 17, and 8, sequentially. These are used in allocating the 30-point weighting assigned to function no. 1100 to calculate the weightings of the level-2 functions.

No. 1110	$50 \times 30/100 = 15.0$
No. 1120	$25 \times 30/100 = 7.5$
No. 1130	$17 \times 30/100 = 5.1$
No. 1140	$8 \times 30/100 = 2.4$

The same method is used to allocate the scores of the second-level functions to the third-level functions.

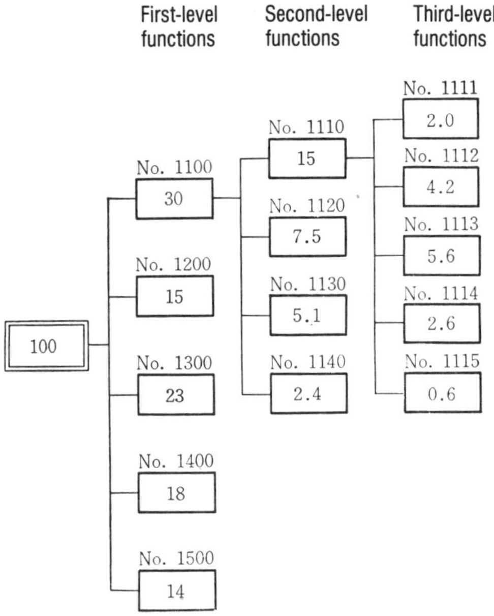

FIGURE 5.5
An example of allocating points to various functions

Evaluating the Current Circumstances

Evaluations of current circumstances focus on the degree to which the products are able to fulfill the needs of the customers, and data surely exist that describe these circumstances. While the items across the top of Figure 5.3 describe the data that must be collected regarding current circumstances, the specific content that should be covered by these data lies within four categories.

1. The level of competitor performance: data from catalogs, trade journals, questionnaires, and so forth
2. Claims from the customers: data from service reports, claim reports, and so forth
3. Technical abilities: data relating to failure analysis, the amount of experience the firm has with given designs, process capabilities, human resources, equipment, and so forth
4. Cost and delivery: data regarding how much the various functions will cost and how many days they will require

Although quantitative data may be used as is, generally it is convenient (and less complicated) to define thresholds and use three-level or 100-point scales. This method is especially useful in comparing characteristics that differ in dimensions, allowing scoring so that comparisons can be made on an "apples-to-apples, oranges-to-oranges" basis.

It is necessary to define clearly the relationships between the facts that are captured in raw data and the scoring or ranking that is performed through establishing threshold levels. For example, confusion will result if, when comparing functions against the competitor's model, there are not clear standards such as "An A ranking implies that X% of the customers believe that the company's model is superior in filling their needs" or "A C ranking is defined as Y% of the customers feel that the company's model is inferior to the competitor's." Figure 5.6 shows an example of definitions that were tried in evaluating outside suppliers. These definitions have two purposes: (1) clear definition of verbal decisions such as "good" or "bad," and of the relationships of these to rankings or facts, and (2) allowing a comprehensive evaluation of qualities, costs, and delivery lead times that have different dimensions.

The formula used to calculate the comprehensive resultant evaluation score was

Rank	Comprehensive results		
	Comprehensive evaluations	Results evaluations	Comprehensive results evaluation points (*a*)
A	Superior company	Results are superior	90–100
B	Good company	Results are good	70–89
C	Normal company	Results are normal	50–69
D	Somewhat poor company	Results are somewhat poor	30–49
E	Poor company	Results are poor	0–29

Rank	Elements								
	Q (Quality)			C (Cost)			D (Delivery)		
	Quality results	Resultant points (*q*)	Defect rates	Cost results	Resultant points (*c*)	Percent cost reduction	Delivery results	Resultant points (*d*)	Delivery delays
A	Very few defects	90–100	0.02–0	Worked extremely hard on cost reductions	90–100	30% cost reduction	Delivery schedules strictly maintained	90–100	0–2 days
B	Few defects	70–89	0.05–0.03	Worked on cost reductions	70–89	10–20% cost reduction	Occasional problems	70–89	2–5 days
C	Average defects	50–69	0.10–0.06	Average	50–69	0–10% cost reduction	We can put up with it	50–69	5–10 days
D	Somewhat high defects	30–49	0.15–0.11	Didn't try very hard	30–49	0–10% cost reduction	Somewhat poor	30–49	10–15 days
E	Many defects	0–29	0–0.16	Hardly tried at all	0–29	10% + cost increase	Severe problems	0–29	15 + days

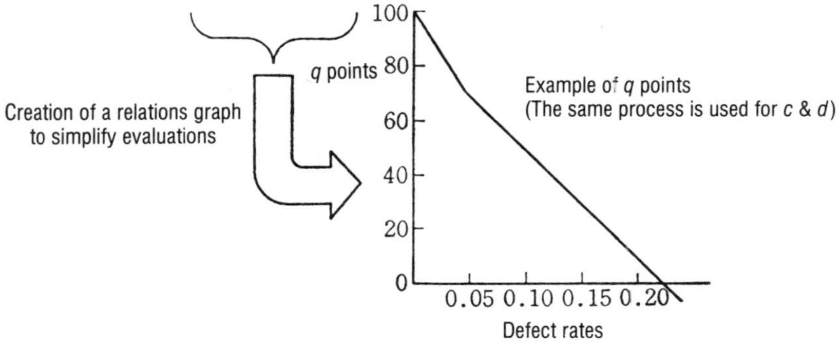

FIGURE 5.6
Definitions regarding evaluations

$$\alpha = 100 - \sqrt{\frac{(100 - q)^2 + (100 - c)^2 + (100 - d)^2}{3}} - 30\ \text{(critical) or } 20\ \text{(major)}$$

where

α = comprehensive resultant evaluation score
q = resultant score on quality
c = resultant score on cost
d = resultant score on delivery
−30 (critical) or 20 (major) = quality assurance prioritization; when defects appear in critical characteristics, this score is lowered by an average of one or two ranks, and when defects appear in major characteristics, the score is reduced by one rank.

General Cautions Regarding Prioritization

The field of operations research has developed sophisticated methodologies for establishing prioritization through weighting schemes. However, when it comes to their practical application in extracting critical problems as part of demanded-quality deployment, such applications were limited at Ishikawajima-Harima. From this narrow experience several general cautions can be made.

First, when attempting to create prioritization, it is easy to become confused if one simply prepares a matrix at random (hoping that something could be gleaned from it), without clearly defining its objectives in advance. Through tracing back and having direction and objectives, one is able to decide just what information should be combined with the demanded-quality deployment chart in a matrix. For example, comparisons between the products of one's company and those of one's competitors focus on the strengths and weaknesses in the qualities of the competitors' companies. Matrices with technical capabilities can be used to determine prioritization for technical development in the future.

Second, it is necessary to specify the evaluation members in advance. If members are selected without due thought, a bias in the individuals may result in incorrect evaluations. Naturally, appropriate members will vary according to the objectives. In this case, perhaps because of inexperience, original results were not obtained. However, even though all results were of the "commonsense" variety, through combining the knowledge and wisdom of many evaluators, it was possible to gain a consensus regarding critical areas, thus allowing avoidance of major discrepancies in the findings.

Third, it is necessary to define evaluation standards in advance, and to design evaluation methods and items that are in line with the objectives of the exercise. It is recommended that the evaluation members discuss the items to be used and the methods to be employed (such as survey methods, the Delphi method, and so forth). Because the evaluation methods used should vary according to the circumstances of the firm, the types of products, and the purpose of the evaluation, it is necessary to standardize the basic evaluation methods to be used under the various circumstances.

Fourth, although the prioritization in the demanded-quality deployment chart will, in the end, relate to quality, many other evaluations and prioritization analyses should be performed during the planning and design stages. For example, there are many marketing problems, profitability problems, productivity problems, equipment investment issues, and so forth; these are data that must be analyzed. Multidimensional evaluations of these multiple factors must be performed from the perspective of business strategy. The prioritization based on demanded-quality deployment is only a part of this process. Although the need for multidimensional evaluations from all angles is obvious, the results of any of the evaluations are not decisions in themselves – they are merely means to making higher-level decisions more precise.

CASE STUDIES

Based on the philosophy discussed above, Ishikawajima-Harima experimented with prioritization based on demanded-quality deployments in various fields. However, a wholly systemic level has not yet been reached, nor has prioritization been totally accepted into the quality assurance system. The activities performed were incomplete. Because of this, the case studies presented here have many problems.

Example 1

This example focuses on strengths and weaknesses of the quality of the company's products through comparative evaluations against the products of competing firms (see Figure 5.7). The example is based on the demanded-quality deployment table and includes six competitors (company U–company Z).

The importance of the various third-level functions in the demanded-quality deployment table were weighted, using a three-level (*a*, *b*, and *c*) method based on the importance of the customer needs. Using catalogs and salespersons' knowledge regarding the level of success the company and its competitors have had in fulfilling these needs, evaluations were performed on a three-level system (*A*, *B*, and *C*) at a joint meeting of the sales department and the engineering department. The standards by which evaluations points were assigned are specified in part (3) of Figure 5.4.

The result of the analysis was that Ishikawajima-Harima was near the bottom, with a score of +8 points (see the bottom line of Figure 5.7). Moreover, various problematic quality functions that have great effects surfaced during the evaluation. Some of these are shown in the example. It was discovered that there was a 16-point difference between Ishikawajima-Harima's performance and the performance of the top manufacturers (companies V and U) when it came to problems dealing with internal leaks, rotational clearances, and lubrication. Including other qualities, a target quality score was set at +34. As is shown in the detail function deployments columns, a detail function deployment was performed for critical qualities, and corresponding characteristic values and critical development themes were determined.

Example 2

This is an example pertaining to a motive device for power generation equipment (see Figure 5.8). The purpose of this case was the same as that in example 1: a comparative analysis of Ishikawajima-Harima's products versus those of competitors.

Because this example deals with production materials and because there are few customers, there was much debate on the range of values for characteristics the customers demanded. Therefore, a matrix was created using conversions of the characteristic values from the quality deployment chart as the customer needs in the left-hand column.

Because the characteristic values were compared with each other, the evaluation was relatively easy. The existing product was first compared with two products (model X and model Y) of the competitor. In this evaluation, if the product was entirely superior to the competitor's product, the score would be +2 points; if superior, +1 point; if the same, 0 points; if inferior, −1 point; if greatly inferior, −2 points.

Next the relative importance of the customer needs was researched through application-specific questionnaires. The results permit the allocation of 100 points among the various quality characteristics. Customer needs regarding identical quality characteristics varied according to the application.

Multiplying the weight and the evaluation points, we were able to evaluate Ishikawajima-Harima's product performance in each application against that of our competitor's products. In this method, the more negative the score, the weaker our product's performance. The result of our analysis, as can be seen in the totals on the bottom row,

Demanded-quality deployment					Company U		Company V		Company W		Company X		Company Y		Company Z		Ishikawajima-Harima Heavy Industries Co., Ltd.			
Category	Primary	Secondary	Tertiary	Degree of importance	Evaluation	Points	Evaluation	Points	Evaluation	Points	Evaluation	Points	Evaluation	Points	Evaluation	Points	Evaluation	Points	Quality targets	Detailed function deployment
Basic functions	Generates pressure energy	Expels oil	Intakes oil	*a*	*A*	+5	*A*	+5	*A*	+5	*A*	+5	*B*	0	*A*	+5	*A*	+5		
			Outputs oil	*a*	*A*	+5	*A*	+5	*A*	+5	*A*	+5	*A*	+5	*A*	+5	*A*	+5		Reduce gaps
		Produces pressure	Creates oil pressure	*a*	*A*	+5	*A*	+5	*A*	+5	*A*	+5	*B*	0	*B*	0	*A*	+5		Create oil film
			Has no external leaks	*a*	*A*	+5	*A*	+5	*A*	+5	*A*	+5	*A*	+5	*A*	+5	*A*	+5		Does not deform under pressure
			Has no internal leaks	*b*	*B*	0	*B*	0	*B*	0	*B*	0	*B*	0	*B*	0	*C*	−3	0	Does not deform with temperature changes
	Does not heat up	Friction is minimal	Rotating parts do not rub	*b*	*B*	0	*B*	0	*B*	0	*B*	0	*B*	0	*B*	0	*C*	−3	0	Does not warp
			Good lubrication	*a*	*A*	+5	*A*	+5	*A*	+5	*A*	+5	*A*	+5	*B*	0	*C*	−5	+5	Create oil film; Maintain oil film; Renew oil film; Protect against contamination

Hazard free	Is safe	People are not exposed		a	B	0	B	0	B	0	B	0	B	0	B	0	B	0	
		Does not spurt oil		a	B	0	A	+5	B	0	B	0	B	0	B	0	B	0	
		Does not break		a	A	+5	B	0	A	+5	A	+5	A	+5	B	0	A	+5	
	Is quiet	No pressure surges	No fluctuations in oil flow	a	B	0	B	0	B	0	B	0	B	0	B	0	B	0	
			No capping	a	B	0	B	0	B	0	B	0	B	0	B	0	B	0	
		Does not vibrate	No binding	a	B	0	B	0	B	0	B	0	B	0	B	0	B	0	
			Turns smoothly	a	B	0	B	0	B	0	B	0	B	0	B	0	B	0	
Maintainability	Handles easily	Transports easily	Small, compact	b	B	0	C	−1	C	−1	C	−1	C	−1	B	0	B	0	
			Lightweight	b	B	0	B	0	C	−1	C	−1	B	0	B	0	B	0	
		Fasteners remove easily	Accessory equipment is not necessary	c	C	−1	C	−1	C	−1	C	−1	C	−1	C	−1	C	−1	
			Specialty tools are not necessary	c	C	−1	C	−1	C	−1	C	−1	C	−1	C	−1	C	−1	
			Procedures are simple	c	B	0	B	0	B	0	B	0	B	0	B	0	B	0	
Grand total						+26		+27		+19		+22		+6		+14		+8	+34

FIGURE 5.7
Example 1

No.	Characteristic	Evaluation of existing product: Against model X	Evaluation of existing product: Against model Y	Application I: Degree of importance	Application I: Evaluation: Against model X	Application I: Evaluation: Against model Y	Application II: Degree of importance	Application II: Evaluation: Against model X	Application II: Evaluation: Against model Y	Qualities of existing product: Characteristic values	Qualities of existing product: Evaluation against model X	Quality targets: Characteristic values	Quality targets: Evaluation against model X	Critical items
1	Output	−1	0	1	−1	0	2	−2	0		−1		0	Improve by 1 point
2	Rotational frequency fluctuations	0	−1	3	0	−3	5	0	−5		0		0	
3	Fuel efficiency	−2	+1	1	−2	+1	1	−2	+1		−2		−2	
4	Startup time	−1	+1	5	−5	+5	5	−5	+5		−5		0	Improve by 5 points
5	Weight	+2	+1	1	+2	+1	2	+4	+2		+2		+2	
6	Space	+2	0	3	+6	0	3	+6	0		+6		+6	
7	Laws and regulations	−1	0	2	−2	0	1	−1	0		−2		−2	
8	Noise	+1	0	2	+2	0	2	+2	0	Omitted	+2	Omitted	+2	
9	Vibration	+1	0	2	+2	0	2	+2	0		+2		+2	
10	NOx	+1	0	2	+2	0	3	+3	0		+2		+2	
11	Smoke	+1	0	3	+3	0	4	+4	0		+3		+3	
12	Fuel in use	−1	0	1	−1	0	1	−1	0		−1		−1	
13	Starting reliability	+2	+1	5	+10	+5	5	+10	+5		+10		+10	
27	Time to equip	−2	0	5	−10	0	4	−8	0		−10		0	Improve by 10 points
28	Serviceability of parts	0	+1	5	0	+5	5	0	+5		0		0	
29	Foolproof	0	0	3	0	0	3	0	0		0		0	
30	Fire retardants	−1	0	1	−1	0	2	−2	0		−1		−1	
31	Fire resistance	−1	0	2	−2	0	2	−2	0		−2		−2	
32	Human safety	0	0	3	0	0	4	0	0		0		0	
	Total			100	−32	0	100	−3	+6		−32		+18	

Performed poorly against model X in application I → The critical points to remedy this are as follows.

FIGURE 5.8
Example 2

was that Ishikawajima-Harima's product was about the same as model X or model Y in application II, and about the same as product Y in application I. However, our product performed poorly in its evaluation against model X in application I, with a score of −32. Thus, improvement activities began after realizing that our product's quality needed to be raised to a level higher than that of model X (in its use in application I). A goal of achieving a score of +18 points in an evaluation against model X, and appropriate quality targets for critical items, were established.

Example 3

This example comes from the development of aviation gas turbines and engine turbines (see Figure 5.9). It has to do with establishing the critical themes for technical development. By creating a matrix of the demanded-quality deployment chart that related aviation gas turbines and complete engine systems to a characteristic deployment table that focused on the turbine part itself, a prioritization based on the weighting system and evaluation standards shown below was derived.

1. A 100-point system for weighting the various functions in the demanded-quality deployment chart was used.
2. The ease with which the various characteristic target values could be achieved was evaluated on a three-level scale.

Technology available	1 point
Technology can be made available with slight improvements	5 points
Very difficult to accomplish	10 points

3. The relationship between the demanded qualities and the characteristics also were evaluated on a three-level scale.

Strong relationship	◎ 5 points
Average relationship	○ 3 points
Weak relationship	Δ 1 point

The overall evaluation, based on the above, was performed using the formula given below.

Comprehensive evaluation = (weight of demanded quality
+ ease of achieving characteristic target value)
× strength of relationship.

However, it is preferable to use

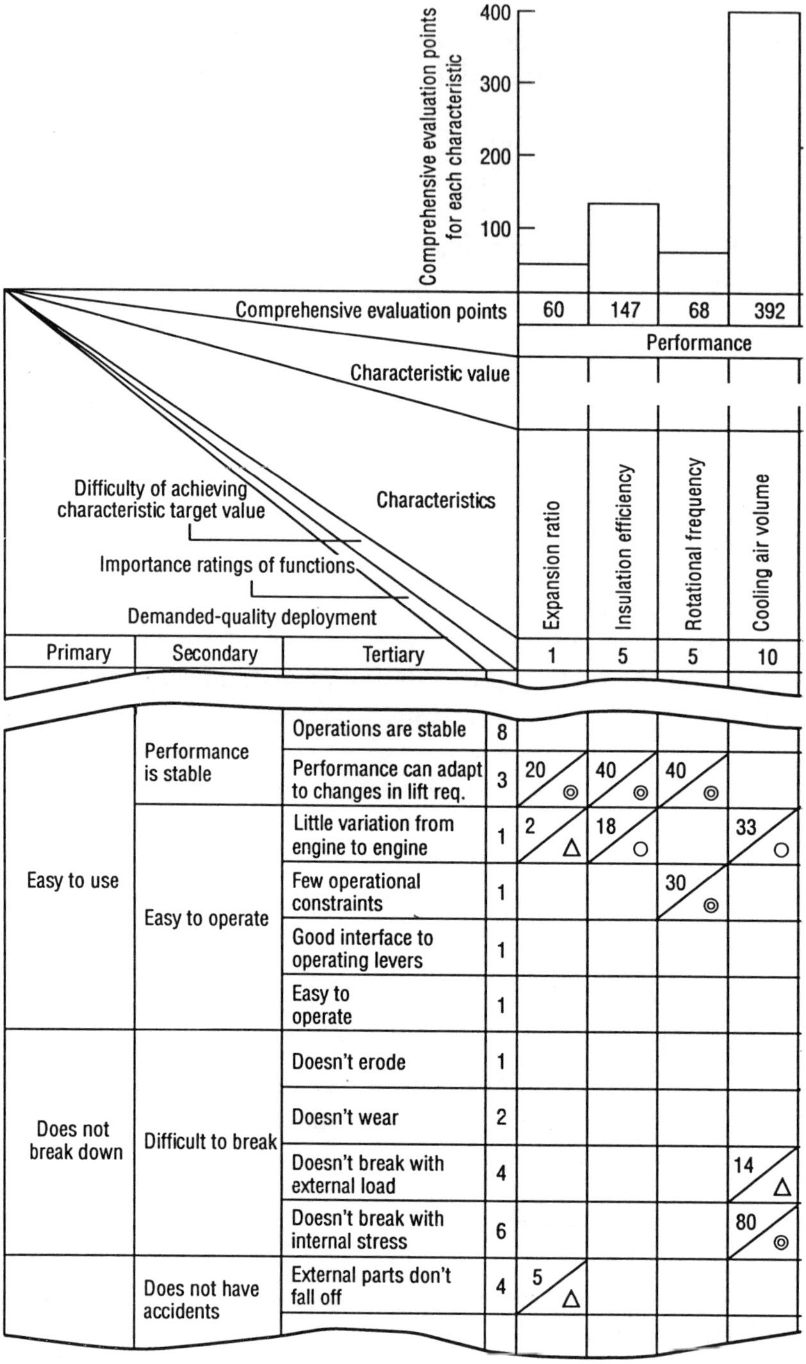
Comprehensive evaluation points for each characteristic
400
300
200
100
Comprehensive evaluation points
60
147
68
392
Performance
Characteristic value
Difficulty of achieving characteristic target value
Importance ratings of functions
Demanded-quality deployment
Characteristics
Expansion ratio
Insulation efficiency
Rotational frequency
Cooling air volume
Primary
Secondary
Tertiary
1
5
5
10
Easy to use
Performance is stable
Operations are stable
8
Performance can adapt to changes in lift req.
3
20
40
40
Easy to operate
Little variation from engine to engine
1
2
18
33
Few operational constraints
1
30
Good interface to operating levers
1
Easy to operate
1
Does not break down
Difficult to break
Doesn't erode
1
Doesn't wear
2
Doesn't break with external load
4
14
Doesn't break with internal stress
6
80
Does not have accidents
External parts don't fall off
4
5

FIGURE 5.9
Example 3

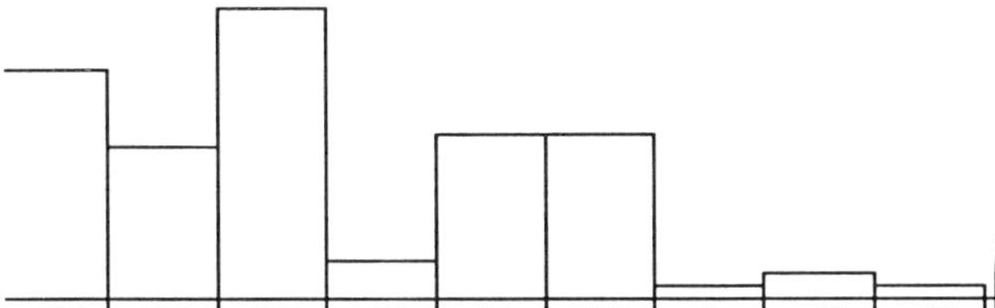

221	171	242	39	174	174	9	15	10
Strength						Dimensions		
		(Omitted)						
Average temperature at turbine intake	Maximum temperature at turbine intake	Rotational acceleration	Maximum pressure at turbine intake	Lifetime	Number of cycles	Maximum diameter	Maximum length	Maximum width
5	5	5	1	5	5	1	1	1
24 ○								
	30 ◎							
	30 ◎	30 ◎						
30 ◎	30 ◎			30 ◎	30 ◎			
	55 ◎	55 ◎	35 ◎	55 ◎	55 ◎			
		45 ◎	5 △					

Comprehensive evaluation = (weight of demanded quality)
× (ease of achieving characteristic target value)
× (strength of relationship).

For example, the intersection of the demanded-quality "few operating constraints" and the characteristic "rotational frequency" is evaluated at 30 points.

Comprehensive evaluation {30} = (weight of demanded quality {1}
+ ease of achieving characteristic target value
{5}) × strength of relationship {5}

The results of the calculations are shown in the comprehensive evaluation scores and the bar graph at the top of the diagram. High evaluation scores indicate that the customers have strong needs and the characteristics have strong relationships to those needs, combined with the fact that there are many technical problems to be overcome in fulfilling those needs. Consequently, the value shown in the characteristic target value column for the turbine coolant air flow (the actual numeric values were omitted) was adopted as a quality target; it was clear that in order to achieve this target, it was necessary to establish some form of critical technical development program.

CONCLUSION

Prioritization performed by using the demanded-quality deployment table was the focus of active experimentation in Ishikawajima-Harima Heavy Industries Co., Ltd., during the planning and design stages. However, because the procedures were not conceptually or methodologically mature, they could not be used systematically. The firm has been experimenting with using what has been explained above to gain insights into future developments in their field. From this experience, it was clear that when language data are transformed into quantitative data in the planning and design stages, it is often difficult to secure a common understanding and interpretation among the evaluators, resulting in diverse opinions that are far from providing the key to prioritization. Many problems remained unsettled after being argued at great length.

Because of this, the most critical area of focus in the future is that of defining concepts, and designing systematic activities based on those concepts, activities that must be operationalized. If this is done, it is expected that it will be possible to implement and use operations research and other superior control technologies to reach an even higher level of customer satisfaction.

6

Roles of the Quality Chart in the Design Stage and Its Application to Simultaneous Multidimensional Design

Yoichi Negoro and Yasuhiro Tanaka

BACKGROUND OF PRODUCT DEVELOPMENT

The types of farm implements seen in Japan today have a relatively short history; the period since World War II has seen great improvements. The developmental objectives for agricultural implements during this period focused on mechanizing farm labor previously performed by oxen, horses, and people. Consequently, the quality demands of the farmers were simple and straightforward. User satisfaction could be obtained by emphasizing the design of operation functions. Compatibility of new products to market needs could be assured through on-site test runs of prototype equipment.

With the increased use of agricultural machines and intensification of competition among manufacturers, however, it became very difficult to survive with only a conventional understanding of market quality demands that emphasized operation efficiency. It became necessary to build maneuverability, sensory functions, and even fashion-related functions into the product.

Further complicating Japanese farming are the many traditional methods peculiar to each locality and practiced for long periods. Farm equipment should, therefore, preserve traditional methods of farming; be as accurate as oxen, horses, and humans; and be highly efficient. User needs are becoming increasingly diverse as a result of the wide variety of topography, soil quality, and crops.

To satisfy this wide range of quality demands in new products, and thereby satisfy as large a consumer group as possible, it has become necessary to investigate what quality is and how this quality should be built into the product. Figure 6.1 summarizes the system of farming, especially rice farming; the machinery features required for it; and the

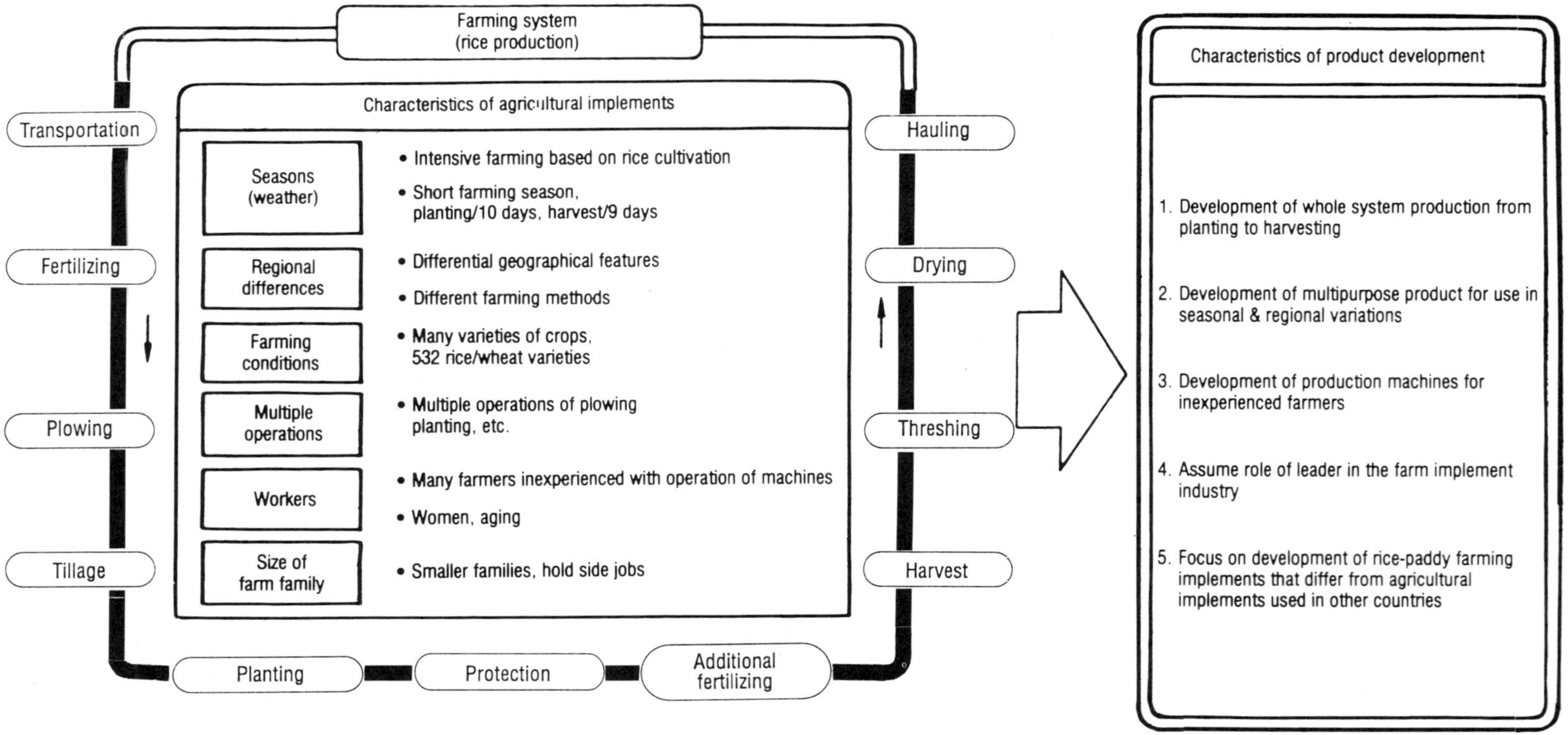

FIGURE 6.1
Features of agricultural machinery and required characteristics for product development

corresponding special characteristics that should be considered in new product development.

PROBLEMS IN ESTABLISHING DESIGN QUALITY

Although faced with the growing trends of the farm equipment market previously described, design quality and its communication were established in the following manner.

1. Personnel responsible for development used their past experiences with similar products and information, plus requests for development supplied by the sales department, to formulate the demanded quality.
2. On the basis of experience, this demanded quality was deployed into design quality from the viewpoint of the designers, and the new product was designed. Verification relied on prototype testing.
3. Quality was communicated to the production group with drawings and a request for assembly form.

Handling procedures created many problems for development activities, particularly with the demanded quality, the setting of design quality, and communication of quality into the later phases of design, prototype and testing, and transfer to production. There were four reasons for this.

1. In setting design quality, communications are often limited by individual abilities and, as a result, variation is excessive.
   a. Often quality is based on personal opinions and some vital quality aspects are overlooked.
   b. Generally, development engineers do not easily accept the successes of others, and therefore good features in the existing products occasionally are not retained in new products.
2. Developers of later products do not "understand quality" at the same level, thus obscuring established development objectives.
   a. Some items are not tested and the checking is inadequate.
   b. Unnecessary tests are conducted.
   c. Compromises are made too easily.
3. Comparisons with existing technologies are not adequate.
   a. Technical expertise accumulates with the individual and may not be available for broad implementation.

   b. In the process of development, an unexpected technological barrier can cause a loss of time and missed opportunities.
4. Evaluation and use of the results from development activities are not assured.
   a. Sound evaluations cannot be produced because the comparison against demanded quality is not clear.
   b. Communication of critical quality items to the production group is not adequate and results in frequent market complaints.

The overall picture of the quality assurance system to solve this series of problems is described in Chapter 11. For now let us concentrate on the quality chart as the heart of such a system.

PURPOSE OF THE QUALITY CHART

The internal combustion equipment division of Kubota used the quality chart for four reasons.

1. To identify quality demanded by the market and to establish exact design quality to realize it
2. To make certain that technological capabilities are applied to the fullest extent in each step of new product development
3. To evaluate the results of development activities against the demanded quality
4. To deploy critical quality items into the QA chart and to link them to control items when designing the manufacturing process.

Having achieved these, targeted quality is now reflected in Kubota's products. In addition, Kubota can take two more steps.

5. Use the quality chart as quality checking standards in cost reduction activities like value analysis and value engineering
6. Accumulate technologies from development activities and production engineering, and use them to upgrade the Kubota engineering standards.

At Kubota the quality chart has been defined as something in which "demanded quality is deployed and systematized and its relationship to technologies needed to materialize it is clarified." It is used as a management tool and for horizontal deployment of technologies to engineers with lower skill levels.

USING QUALITY DEPLOYMENT IN THE DEVELOPMENT PHASE

Basic Quality Deployment

At Kubota, quality deployment, shown in Figure 6.2, is performed from demanded quality all the way to parts and parts characteristics. Since demanded quality is the objective, the means to realize it are classified as primary functions; and with the primary functions as the objectives, the means to attain them are classified as secondary functions. Likewise, quality is deployed as a system of targets and the means to attain them, down to the level of deployment into items directly related to the actual manufacture of products, such as dimensions of the parts, shape, material, and so on.

Figure 6.2 is a basic quality deployment. Depending on the product type, the purpose of the quality chart and the nature of the demanded

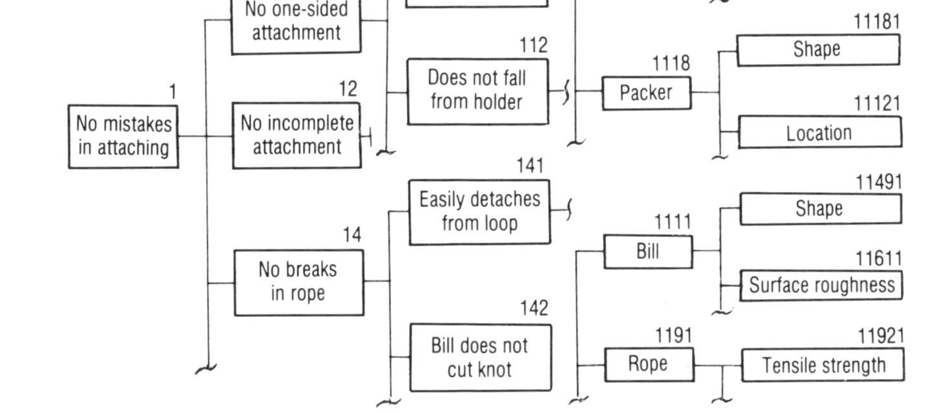

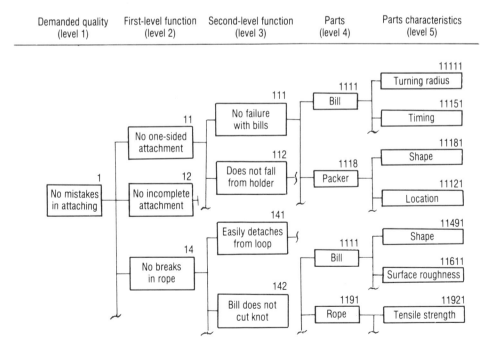

FIGURE 6.2
Sample quality chart

quality (whether for control or for horizontal deployment of technologies), the actual method of deployment and its scope vary.

1. If it is used to achieve a certain level of quality for new products, it is
   a. A management tool for department and section managers (types A_1, A_2, B in Figure 6.3)
   b. A horizontal deployment of advanced technologies (type C in Figure 6.3).
2. If it is used for design engineering, it is
   a. An identification tool of advanced research areas and control (type A_1 in Figure 6.3, a quality chart that "dead ends")
   b. A maximization of cost performance under a limited time for development (types A_2 and B in Figure 6.3)
   c. An establishment of a range of applications when used in simultaneous multidimensional design (type A_2 in Figure 6.3).

Types of Quality Charts

In the Kubota division, there are several modified versions of the quality chart, depending on the purpose of use; a standard format does not exist. Currently, they can be organized as in Figure 6.3, as types of quality charts customized and used by various engineering groups for specific products. Figure 6.3 shows general classifications of quality charts, who uses them, and in which step they are used. The research department prepares quality charts A_1 through C, while the central research and production groups work together to prepare QA charts types I and II. The production group handles the design process master table and everything that follows.

Figure 6.4 depicts the relationships in the total deployment that covers demanded quality all the way to components and their characteristics (shown in Figure 6.2). Figure 6.3 shows these classifications. However, the quality chart is not divided into types A_1, A_2, B, and C. Rather, combinations of A and B or B and C or A, B, and C are frequent. Generally, it can be said that items toward the left of Figure 6.4 are for control by management, and those toward the right, for control by personnel at the operating level.

Identification of Market-Demanded Quality

In the product planning phase, market needs and demanded quality must be identified and deployed into planned quality. The market re-

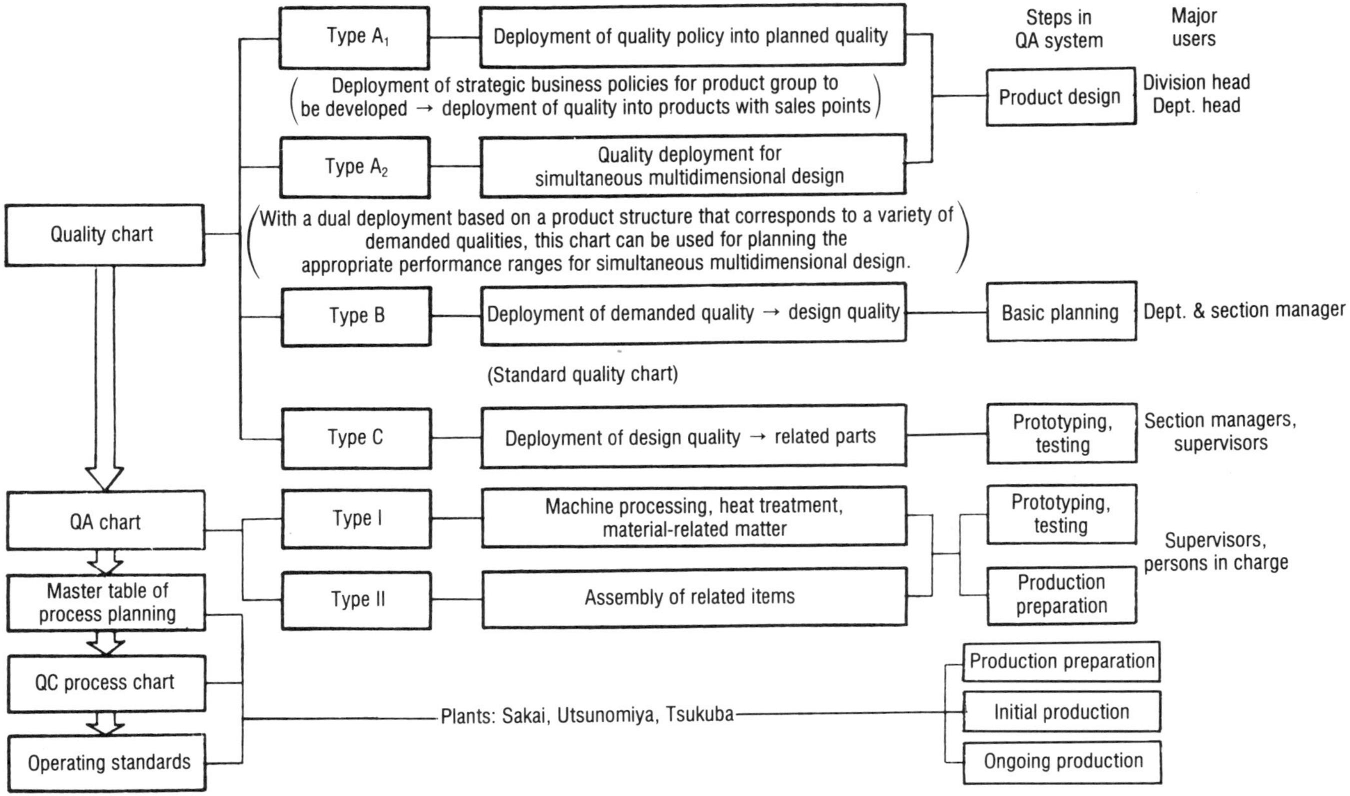

FIGURE 6.3
Quality deployment for a business division

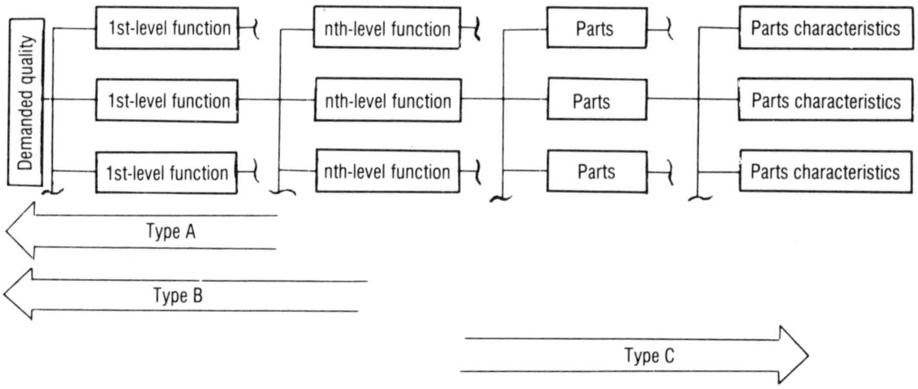

FIGURE 6.4
Total deployment system and its relationship to each type of chart

search group should provide data on market-demanded quality, including sales information, service data, information on complaints, information from questionnaires, and so on. The development group must also obtain data on deployed quality through its own activities, however, without relying solely on information supplied by other groups.

Market-demanded quality includes known and hidden needs. Known needs can be obtained easily, but identification of hidden needs is difficult. The Kubota division has been in contact with product users at product test locations and has talked with them in order to obtain firsthand information on the hidden needs of the farmers.

Classification of Quality

Hidden needs are not necessarily discovered from informal conversations with farmers. Their identification requires keen insight and awareness. First there must be classification of quality and evaluation of each individual item. In other words, this is the first-level deployment of demanded quality. If this first-level deployment is not comprehensive, good products cannot be developed even when the succeeding deployment is precise. Therefore, efforts must be exerted to develop a quality chart most appropriate for the product.

Classification of agricultural implement quality is based on its (1) basic functions, (2) auxiliary functions, (3) peripheral functions, (4) functions to support other functions, (5) functions to adapt to the environment, and (6) fashion-related functions. The structure of such functions is two-dimensional. When the value of the product is considered, cost factors must be added to make the structure given in Figure 6.5.

Demanded-Quality Deployment

Market demands for quality come from the salespeople and service technicians, who are relatively familiar with technical matters; but experience reveals that such information often has pitfalls. These personnel occasionally translate true customer needs into technical issues from their own point of view, thus causing customer needs to be communicated improperly. Consequently, true demanded quality must be obtained in the most direct form and at an even higher level for pursuit of the real requirements.

Types of Quality Charts

Quality Chart Type A_1

Type A_1 is linked to the quality policies and targets of the corporate strategies for the product under development. The division manager often uses it during discussions of strategies to determine the sales points of the new product.

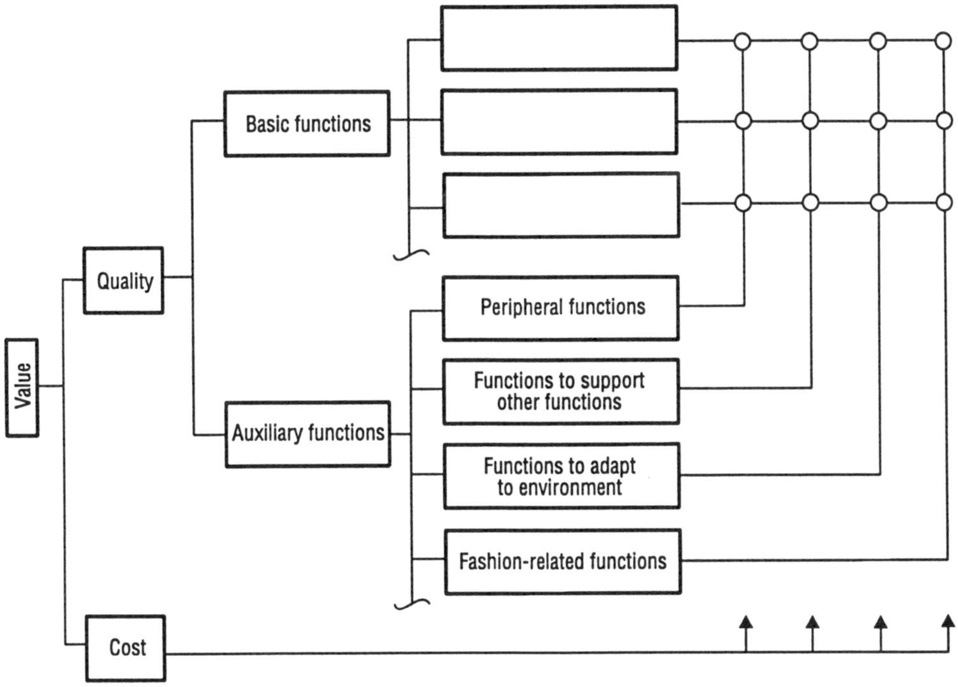

FIGURE 6.5
Structure of functions as related to quality

In Figure 6.6, sometimes the right section of the chart is a product group (in many cases, a product line) that satisfies sales points or rankings by importance based on the market forecast of nth-level functions. Department managers use the latter to identify and to manage advanced research. It is easy to understand from this example that the quality chart used at Kubota is modified with some formats to accommodate different purposes.

Quality Chart Type A_2

Quality chart type A_2 outlines the demanded qualities peculiar to farm equipment and its cost structure. It is used for the selection of component structures to achieve the maximum cost/performance ratio in as short a time as possible, and to establish product ranges for simultaneous multidimensional design. It is basically for high-level management personnel. Simultaneous multidimensional design is a design activity for series of products in a product line that starts in the planning phase. With a range of as few types of products as possible, and using many standard parts, cumulative production volume of products or their parts is as high as possible, resulting in cost reduction through the establishment of a learning curve.

The quality chart for these activities in Figure 6.7 has product system structures and parts structures, and demanded quality, ar-

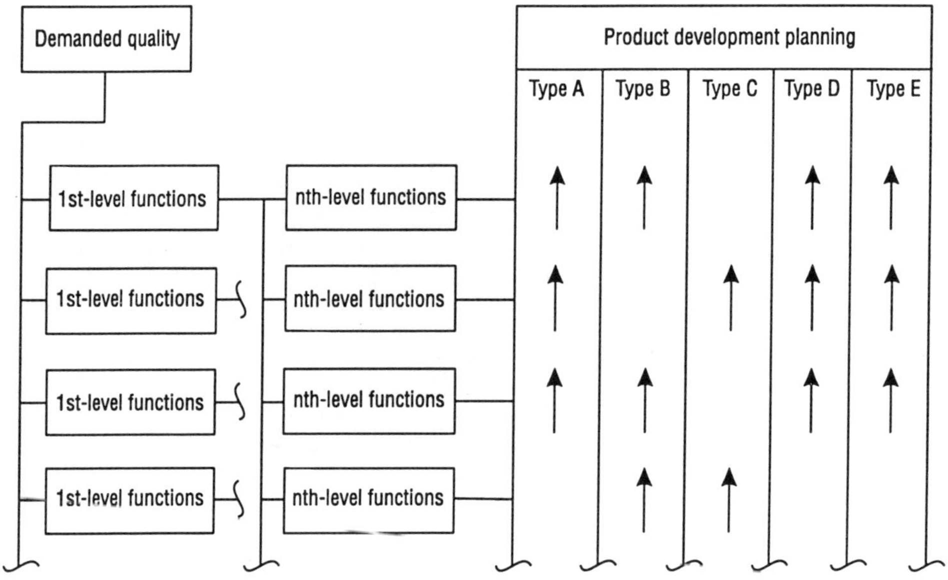

FIGURE 6.6
Quality chart type A_1

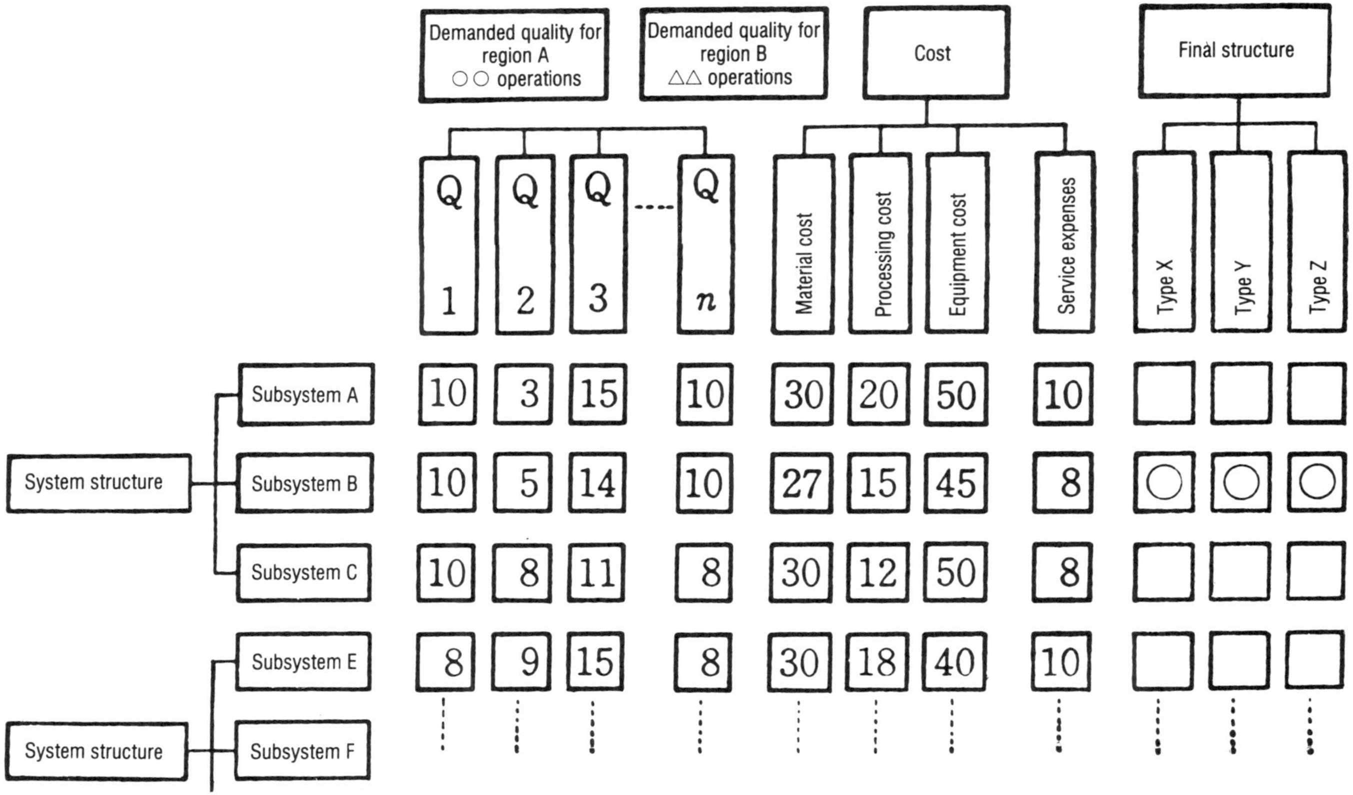

FIGURE 6.7
Quality chart type A_2

ranged as a two-dimensional matrix. This permits evaluation and determination of the subsystems of each system structure based on the overall concept. Personnel with the expertise on the product to make these technical judgments assign the evaluation points of Figure 6.7. Finally, they are multiplied by coefficients reflecting the degree of difficulty of achieving them, resulting in the final overall points for each system structure on the right side of the chart. These final points determine the structure for each product.

Quality Chart Type B

The purpose of quality chart type B is to deploy demanded quality and to set the exact design quality. It is used for (a) selection of critical quality items from demanded quality and (b) determining the degree of difficulty to realize such quality and to discern the necessity of advanced research or acquisition of technologies. It usually looks like Figure 6.8. For example, a department manager would control the program directly, in order to materialize a quality item that has been assigned an importance rating of A and a degree of difficulty of "difficult."

Quality Chart Type C

Type C, used for relatively low levels of deployment, deploys quality in detail to such items as part shape, dimensions, and material and component characteristics for use in the detailed design and the process design. The acquisition of previous engineering experience and results of analyses are reflected on quality chart type C (Figure 6.9); by its use even engineers with a lower skill level have ready access to the top-level technologies accumulated in the company. It also serves as the first step in communication of quality to the manufacturing group.

Type C is extremely useful to section managers because they can see the degree of difficulty in attaining design quality and which items must be given high priority for test and verification. They can prepare alternatives, test programs beforehand, and avoid omission of necessary tests. This quality chart is the one most widely used at the Kubota division. It has been observed that an increasing number of test reports issued within the division follow quality chart type C. People have submitted reports to their supervisors following its format, along with their recommendations, on the design standards or engineering standards to be established and added to the far right of the form.

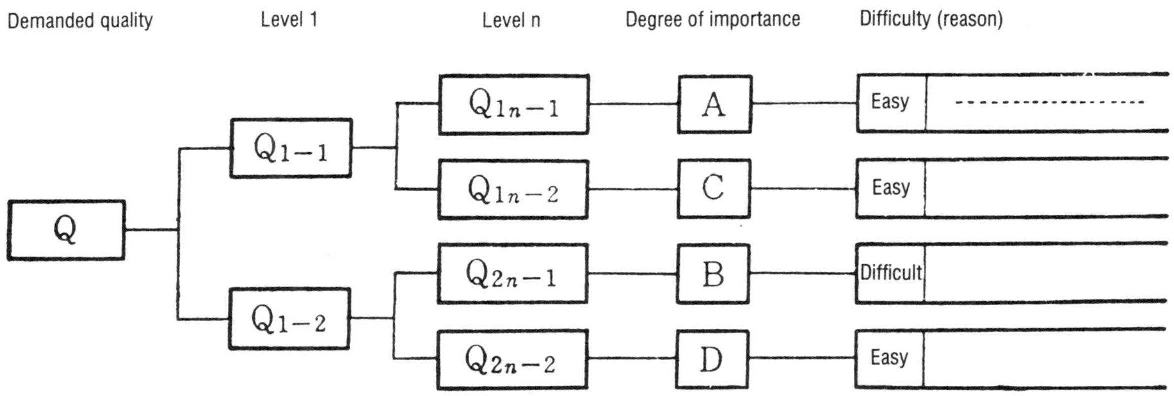

FIGURE 6.8
Quality chart type B

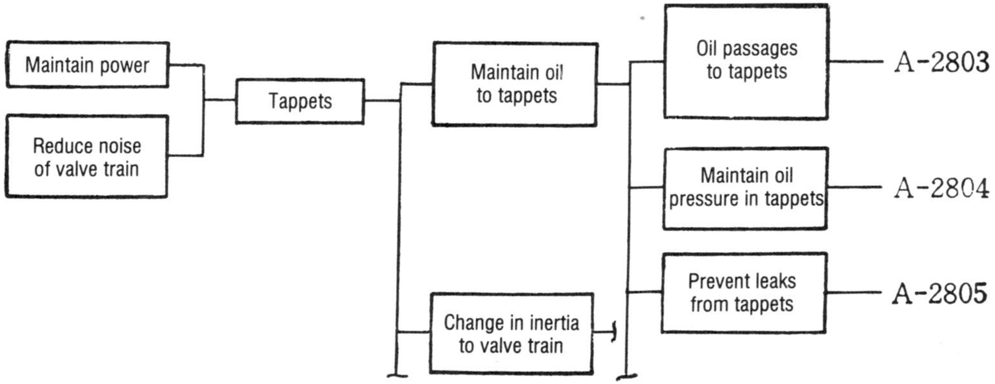

FIGURE 6.9
Quality chart type C

SIMULTANEOUS MULTIDIMENSIONAL DESIGN

The wide variation in market needs for agricultural implements reflects the regional differences of farming and the types of farm products. Performance requirements of farm machinery vary depending on the scale of operations, even for the same operation. For example, machine capability required by a farmer who owns less than one acre differs from that of a farmer who owns over 10 acres. In order to respond to such varied requirements and to meet every demand, a wide variety of products is needed.

The production of a wide variety of items inevitably increases cost, since the production volume of individual product types decreases. It also creates many problems for quality assurance.

Cost-Related Problems

Efforts are continuously made to reduce cost in the product development and production phases by concentrating on design, including the pursuit of functions and cost, using value engineering and value analysis to increase productivity. However, it has been rather difficult to make significant progress because of the wide-variety, small-lot production system.

As James C. Abegglen of the Boston Consulting Group points out, products from many industries have proven that "cost per unit decreases at the rate of 20%–30% every time the cumulative production volume of a product doubles" (see Figures 6.10 and 6.11).

This type of wide-variety, small-lot production not only decreases the profitability of the manufacturer but also increases the cost to the user because of higher initial cost. To solve these cost problems, it is necessary to satisfy a wide variety of market needs and at the same time to increase the cumulative production volume.

Quality Assurance Problems

Normally, development specialists refine the product into its individual types. When the types of products to be developed increase, it is necessary to add experienced engineers to the staff. Also, development of many types of products causes a nonuniform configuration between products that belong to the same group and can create variations in the design quality level. Further, this type of production generates problems in production. Since production volume of individual

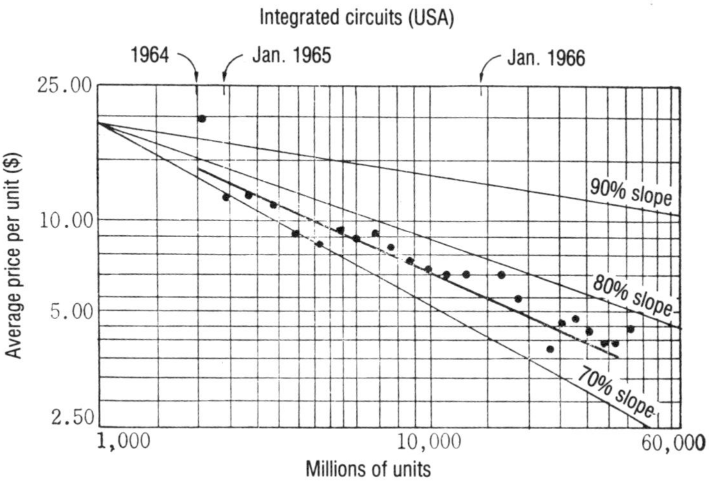

FIGURE 6.10
Cumulative production volume of the entire industry

items is low, investment in production facilities is limited. This means production with general-purpose machines, and the inevitable frequent machine setups can cause uneven quality. Workers will have difficulty improving their skills, too. In sales and service, knowledge the sales personnel must have increases, inventory requirements for service parts increase, and the need for immediate delivery of parts to the customers rises.

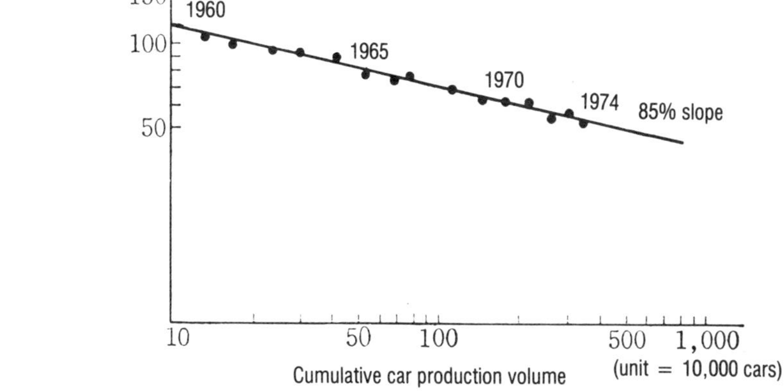

FIGURE 6.11
Cumulative production curve for passenger car (Japan)

The cumulative production volume must increase in order to solve the problems of quality assurance.

Aims of Simultaneous Multidimensional Design

Simultaneous multidimensional design occurs as follows: when new products are developed, starting with the product planning phase, many market requirements faced by these products are identified by product groups. The range one product line encompasses is based on the choice of standardized components used to maintain the demanded level of quality and to minimize cost. This is also done from a strategic standpoint. This description differs from normal standardization, commonization, and unitization because the components being standardized, commonized, or unitized are derived from the overall product grouping concepts. To solve the problems with cost and quality assurance inherent in wide-variety, small-lot production, trial and error has been used to devise and to perfect a method of simultaneous multidimensional design as a means to increase cumulative production volume and to bring it as close to mass production of a small number of products as possible.

At the Kubota division the definition of the simultaneous multidimensional design is a "method to plan and to design simultaneously various types of products with different demanded quality (conditions of use, types of operation and functions, capacity, etc.) as a series of types and models of products to be manufactured, with a high degree of part standardization, by the manufacturing process with high efficiency." The purposes of simultaneous multidimensional design are described below. They play an important role in the process of deploying demanded quality into design quality.

Assurance of Critical Quality

By concentrating development activities on the reduction in number of basic models, increase of standard parts, use of highly experienced engineers in design research for critical parts, and so on, quality is upgraded and stabilized.

Satisfaction of Diversified Customer Needs

Diversified customer needs for product capability (output) and usefulness are stratified and analyzed, and are reflected in the products within the series at the time of planning product grouping to satisfy a wide variety of consumers.

Stabilization of Product Quality

Stabilization of quality achieves low cost and reduces development time in four ways. First, through commonization of parts with proven quality, product quality is assured and development time is reduced. Second, production dies and tooling are standardized, productivity is increased by reducing setups, and worker skills are upgraded, all of which contribute to increased product quality. Third, adding high-performance equipment such as transfer presses brings substantial increases in productivity that assure quality and improve profitability. Fourth, the number of part types is reduced, making inventory control easy and the financial burdens lighter.

Increase of Sales and Service Efficiency

By standardizing the mechanical structure of products within the same group, the range of product knowledge among sales personnel is increased and they acquire broader knowledge with the same effort. Types of service parts are fewer, with a reduction of inventory and easier supply support; the prompt delivery of parts to customers is thereby improved.

Classifications for Simultaneous Multidimensional Design

The simultaneous multidimensional design brings wide-variety, small-lot production to mass production for a small number of products that are more adaptable to the market. However, its implementation varies according to the products. At the Kubota division, Table 6.1 classified it into type [S], type [M], and type [SM], depending on the purpose, contents, and product application for which simultaneous multidimensional design is used. In Table 6.1, type [S] is applied to

TABLE 6.1
Classification of Simultaneous Multidimensional Design

Type	*S*	*M*	*SM*
Purpose	Series design	Multiple-use design	Series, multiple-use design
Content	Series deployment of performance output	Multiple-use deployment	Performance, multiple-use deployment
Major product	Engine	Combine	Tractor, bulldozer tractor

planning and designing of products in a family that has different output capabilities, such as engines with 10 horsepower, 15 horsepower, 20 horsepower, and so on. Type [M] designates parts used for purposes other than originally intended, such as a tractor engine anticipated for use as a combine, electrical generator, or marine use. Adaptation of such a product to other possible uses occurs in the planning phase.

The [SM] type is for a group of products requiring evaluation as a series and meant for multipurpose usage, such as tractors for use in rice paddies, in dry fields, and for mowing lawns. It must be designed to satisfy all the demanded qualities and at the same time must cover the entire range of required usage, such as engines of 10, 15, and 20 horsepower.

Extent of Application of Simultaneous Multidimensional Design

The success of the simultaneous multidimensional design depends on the appropriate range to be covered by the product series. Let us suppose that market demands exist for product capabilities (output) as given in Figure 6.12. Let us find out how many product series should be created to cover the entire range of demands.

In the figure, graph (a) is an attempted solution to the development of individual products according to required capability. For example, when the entire market demand for capacity can be classified into six categories, from low capacity (for small-scale operations) to high capacity (for large-scale operations), this method requires development of six types of products, from type (1) to type (6), according to individual output requirements. In this case, rigidity of strength requirements in design is in accordance with the capability demanded by the market; therefore, the solution to durability is easy. However, various levels of output capability are not the only market requirement, because they change for different uses. If products are developed for each of these requirements, the trend to wide-variety, small-lot production goods is compromised, since problems inherent in wide-variety, small-lot production, especially that of high cost, will never be solved.

The method shown in graph (c) of Figure 6.12 attempts to cover the entire range of capability requirements with one group of products. Since type (4) is the basis for models (1) through (6), special measures are needed to achieve greater durability for types (5) and (6), which are positioned in the higher capability zone. With type (4) as the basis, too many cases were reported where type (6), two levels higher, could not be covered in terms of strength. As a result, the basic type deployment had to be changed to type (5). This raised the cost of the entire product

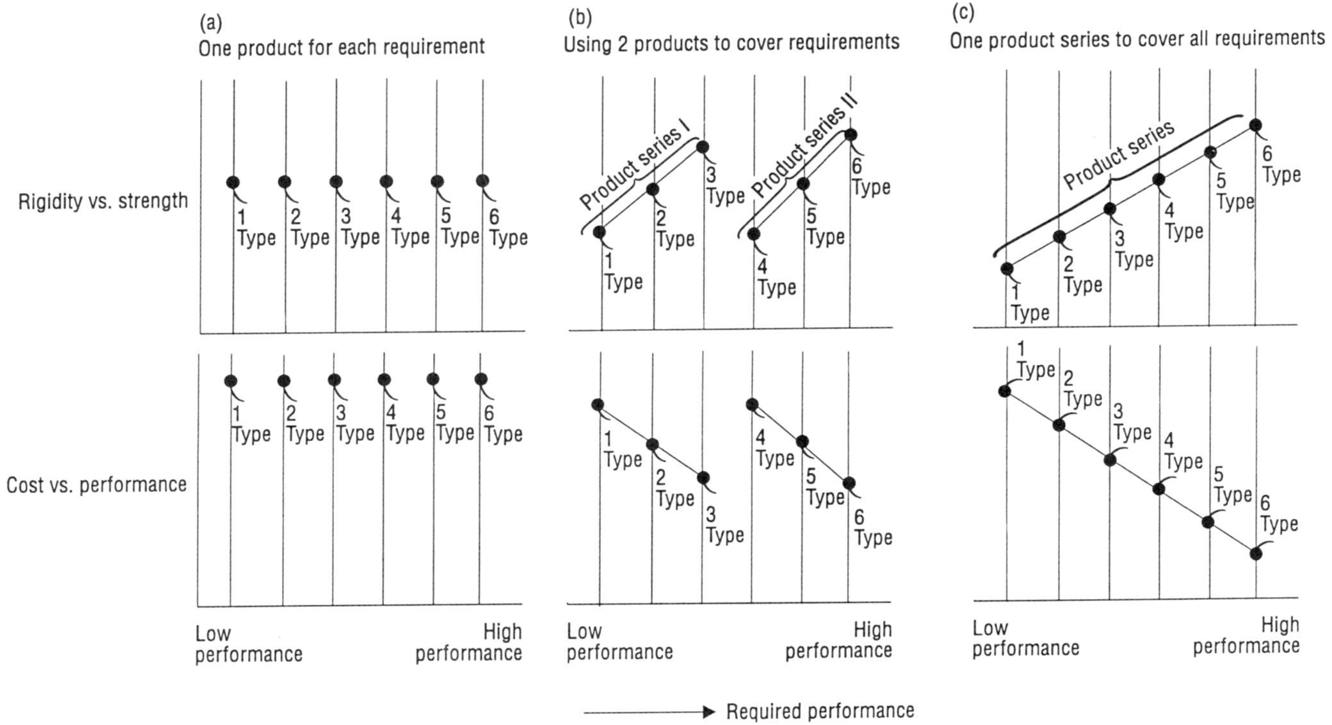

FIGURE 6.12
Application range of simultaneous multidimensional design

TABLE 6.2
Major Evaluation Points of Simultaneous Multidimensional Design

Series S deployment	High-performance (high-ouptut) range	Strength, durability	• Precise stress measurements based on engineering calculations • Strength forecasting • Confirmation by quality analysis, reliability testing
	Low-performance (low-output) range	Weight, cost	Prevention of negative impact of excessive weight or dimensions such as diminished functionality or increased cost
Multiple-use deployment M	Diminished functionality		Prevent structural complications & diminished intended-functionality resulting from adding too many features; offer options instead

group and increased the product weight. Special consideration must be given to the low-capability range of operation, where the requirement is not low capability but weight reduction of the product, even at the expense of capability.

In summary, when the entire market range is to be covered by one product line, the machinery designed for the high-capability range presents problems of cost and weight in the low-capability range, and machinery designed for the low-capability range lacks capability and durability in the high-capability range. In both cases, the products have a tendency not to satisfy the demanded quality.

When graph (b) in Figure 6.12 is divided into, say, two product lines, with product line I having two basic types and product line II having five basic types, capability versatility between the high-capability side and low-capability side is smaller than shown in graph (c), and adjustments between the two in the same series are straightforward. In other words, having both capability and durability on the high-capability side and low cost and weight on the low-capability side in the same product group is easier when there are more product lines. At the same time, however, the advantages of simultaneous multidimensional design decreases.

The number of product lines needed to cover the entire demand range is determined by the coverage range of the basic types. Evaluation of the coverage range for the basic types must be made not for the entire product line but for individual functional systems and parts.

Evaluation of the simultaneous multidimensional design varies, depending on what type is at issue; Table 6.2 presents major items.

USE OF THE QUALITY CHART IN SIMULTANEOUS MULTIDIMENSIONAL DESIGN

In a simultaneous multidimensional design, the quality demanded by the market determines the limits of the range to be covered by one product line. For functions that were deployed from demanded quality in a quality chart, one must study the range of requirements to which the planned products or parts structures can adapt. Therefore, the quality chart is essential and serves a critical role in simultaneous multidimensional design.

Many of the quality charts that are used for simultaneous multidimensional design are type A_2. However, its format is not necessarily the same as the one shown in Figure 6.7; therefore, how the charts are applied will be explained.

Application of the Quality Chart to Type [S] Simultaneous Multidimensional Design

The quality chart of Figure 6.13 is used to create a series of products, such as engines designated by different performance outputs; it is a combination of type A_2 and type B.

This quality chart has demanded quality deployed to the nth functions. The types of parts structures considered, and product types (1) through (6) within the demand range, are like a two-dimensional matrix. Its purposes are to select the product line that achieves the demanded quality while being the most economical, and to select the

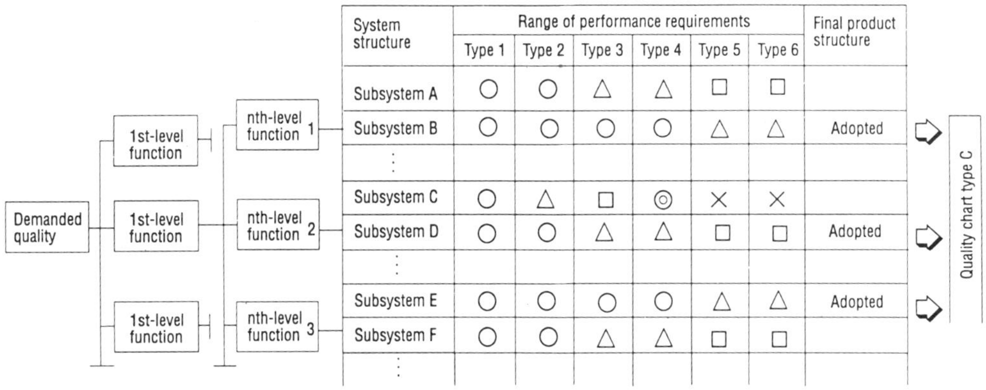

FIGURE 6.13
Application sample of quality chart in type [S] simultaneous design

method of parts construction. From the examples in the figure, by adoption of subsystem B, two product lines can cover nth-level function 1, while three product lines are needed for nth-level function 2. This type of contradiction happens often. To solve this problem, other related components must be adjusted separately; then the number of product lines can be determined.

Application of the Quality Chart in Type [SM] Simultaneous Multidimensional Design

The quality chart shown in Figure 6.14 delineates the range of the product line for the combined requirements of range (such as for performance [output]) and of use (as for rice paddies and dry fields).

The format of this quality chart is almost identical to type [S] (Figure 6.13). However, conflicts caused by variance in the range that must be covered by each component are far more frequent than for type [S]. Problems that can be solved by adjusting other components are significantly fewer. The key to success in widening coverage of simultaneous multidimensional design of this type of product is to include different parts structures α_1, α_2, α_3, α_4 in product line I in the example.

QUALITY ASSURANCE IN SIMULTANEOUS MULTIDIMENSIONAL DESIGN

To bring wide-variety, small-lot production as close to limited-variety mass production as possible, the simultaneous multidimensional design divides the range of product requirements into product lines and covers each product line with one basic style. Consequently, quality assurance of products developed from this method is not for each individual product but for the entire line. In other words, effects of performance and durability on the high-performance types and of low cost and weight on the low-performance types within the same product line are critical quality assurance items. Thus low cost and low weight for the high-performance side, and performance and durability for the low-performance side, can mostly be ignored. Figure 6.15 summarizes the quality assurance activities in the simultaneous multidimensional design.

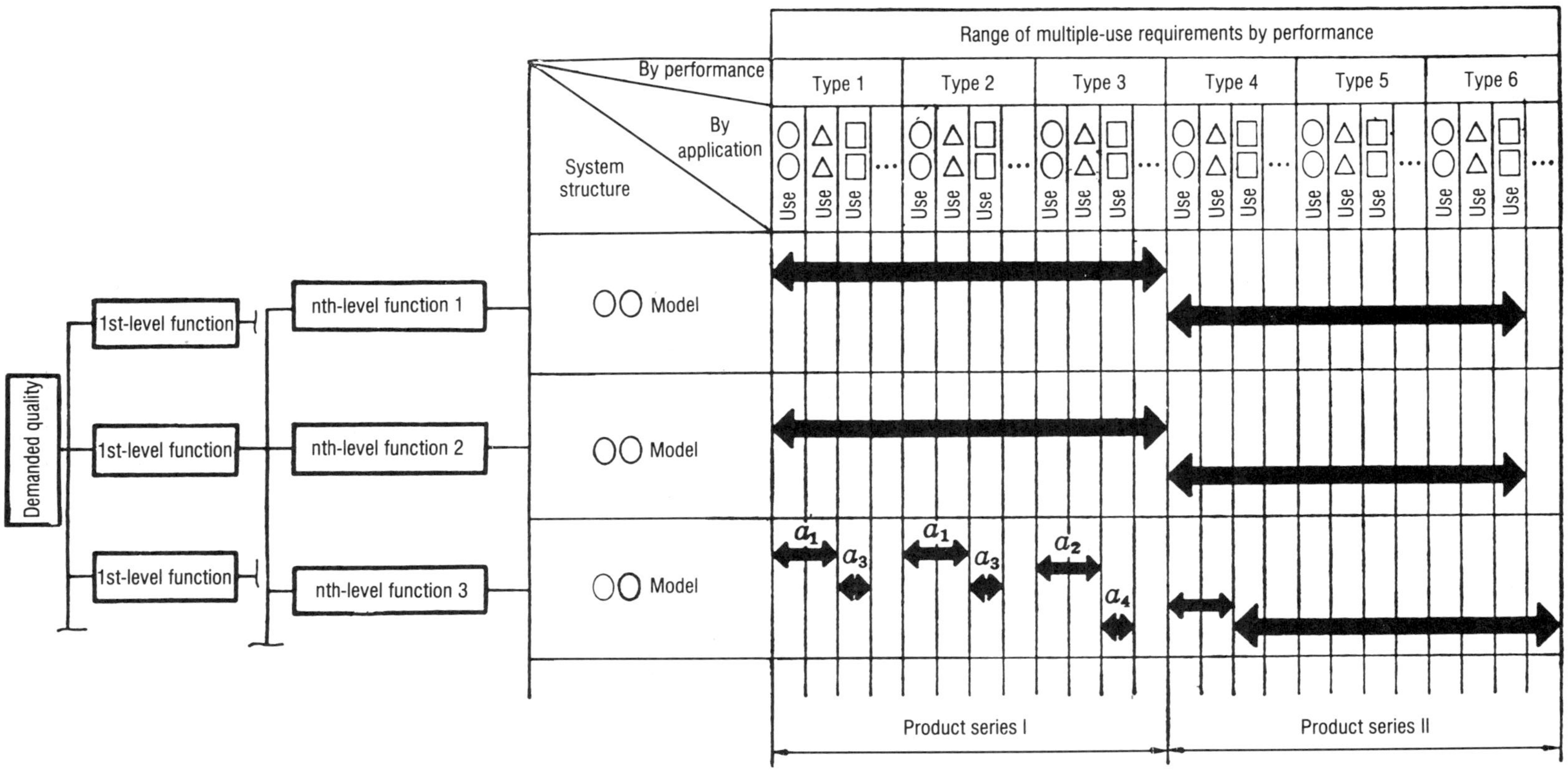

FIGURE 6.14
Application sample of quality chart in type SM simultaneous multidimensional design

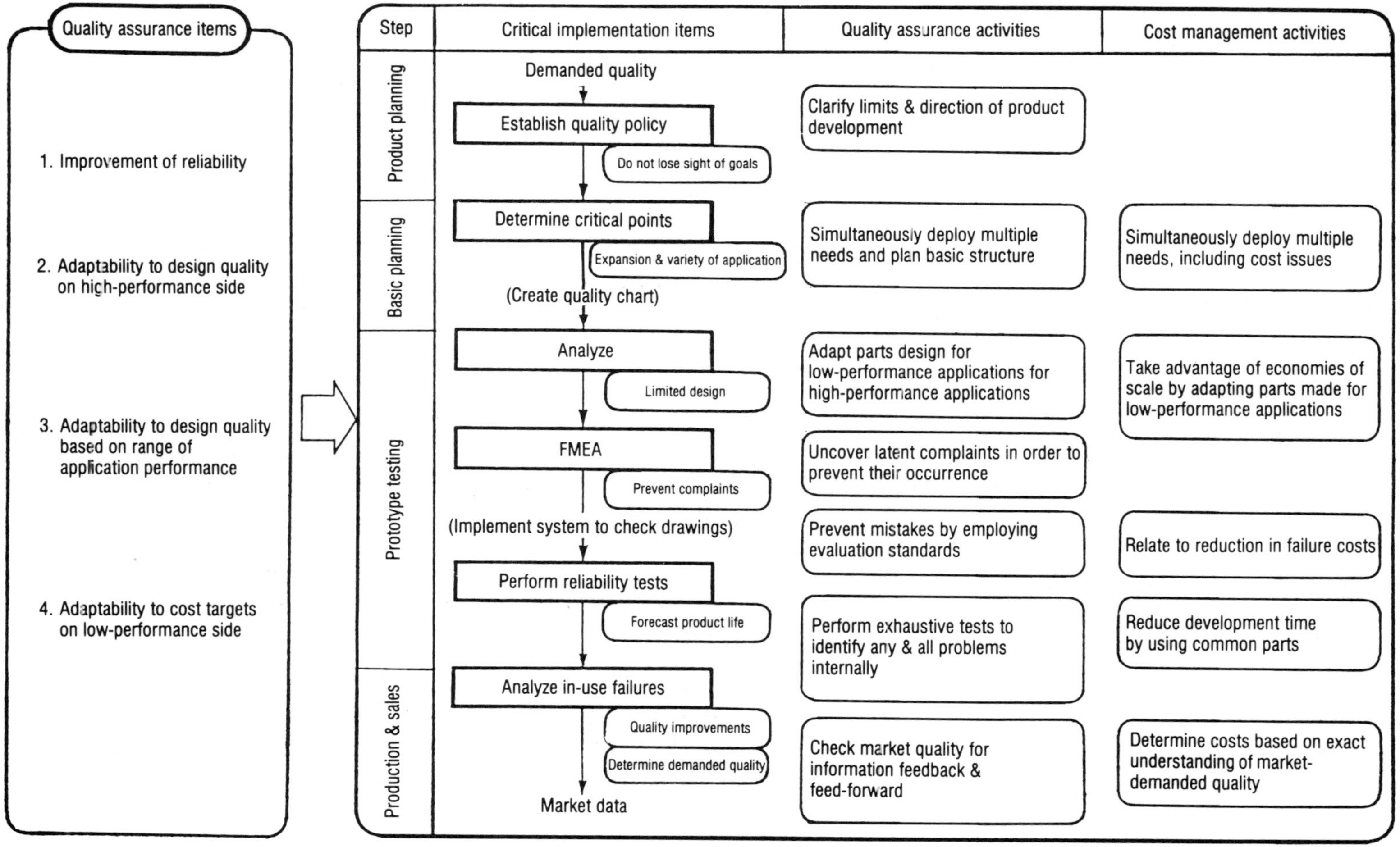

FIGURE 6.15
Simultaneous multidimensional design and quality assurance

USEFULNESS OF THE QUALITY CHART IN THE DESIGN PHASE

As described, from the promotion of quality function deployment and the resulting communication benefits centered on the quality chart, the latter plays an important role in the product development stage, especially in design and initial production runs. Kubota experienced nine advantages.

1. Demanded quality is identified without any omissions. By encompassing everything in design quality, the degree of market satisfaction with the products increased.
2. The critical control items in the development phase became clear in relation to the demanded quality, and there were fewer omissions of necessary test items.
3. Accumulated technologies are now identified clearly, and easier accessibility to them has led to development of the most advanced technologies available. This has contributed to upgrading Kubota's engineering capabilities.
4. Problems reported from past complaints are more clearly understood, and measures are taken to prevent recurrence.
5. Items for transfer to the production group are now clear. Product quality is stable from the initial production run and also has improved because of implementing simultaneous multidimensional design.
6. Standardization of parts has increased, and sharing of parts with proven quality has stabilized the quality level.
7. Unevenness of quality among different products has decreased.
8. Development time has been reduced substantially.
9. Use of high-performance production has been realized.

The quality chart and the simultaneous multidimensional design based on the quality chart have produced numerous benefits. The Kubota division invested in a new plant equipped with the most advanced production equipment, costing tens of billions of yen. Kubota believes that the combination of all these has resulted in the profitable operation of the new plant from the startup, even with the depreciation factor included.

PART III
Quality Deployment in Production Engineering and Manufacturing

7

Process Design and Quality Deployment

Mitsuo Tsurusawa

INTRODUCTION

One of the high priorities at the internal combustion division of Kubota for upgrading quality assurance is quality deployment. To set up quality control items through the quality assurance system steps, a comprehensive system of quality deployment activities, including the quality chart, QA chart, process planning master table, and operating standards, was created. (Chapter 11 contains the details; Chapter 6, the details of the quality chart.) This part contains examples of how the QA chart and process planning master table at a Kubota plant link the quality chart to the QC process chart so that quality, as communicated from the development department, can be realized in the preproduction and manufacturing phases.

COMMUNICATING QUALITY TO THE MANUFACTURING PHASE (QA CHART)

At the internal combustion division of Kubota, in order to communicate the target quality defined in the product development phase to manufacturing and achieve this quality in products, the QA chart is prepared and submitted with production drawings to the manufacturing department. The QA chart identifies control items for process design so that the quality characteristics that have been deployed in the quality chart can be achieved. It is prepared by the engineering department, in cooperation with the manufacturing group, to cover critical characteristics of parts and components. The type I QA chart summarizes items relating to machining, heat treatment, materials, and so on; type II summarizes the items relating to assembly. Both are extensively used.

Figures 7.1 and 7.2 show two forms of the QA chart as actually used at the internal combustion division of Kubota. Based on the philosophy that values serving as standards for control should be a joint decision between design and manufacturing, the activities began with the format of Figure 7.1. The format of Figure 7.2 has wider use because it offers better control when the anticipated effect of unattained design quality is also communicated. This format is more suitable for control of the critical-to-safety and critical-to-function parts to be explained later.

Formerly, drawings and assembly manuals communicated quality from the development department to the production department. Three steps were taken to upgrade the quality of the quality control activities.

1. The development department determines deployment of demanded quality, using the quality chart.
2. The manufacturing department prepares the process planning master table, upon which the process design is based.
3. The manufacturing department prepares the QC process chart, which identifies the control items for individual processes.

Based on the sequence of activity mentioned, the manufacturing department builds quality into the product. These activities had three shortcomings.

1. Critical quality characteristics associated directly with the deployed quality were not clearly communicated to the manufacturing department.

Parts		Quality item		Design	
	Parts/ elements	Level 4	Level 5		Production
Camshaft	Cam	No variation in performance	Intake & exhaust timing to be correct	Phase drift ±15′	Gap with key groove Key slot dislocation +8′
			⋮	⋮	⋮
	Journal	Loss from friction should be minimal	Maintain oil flow	Clearance to shaft hole 0.05–1.10	e6 (shaft hole H7)

FIGURE 7.1
QA chart type I

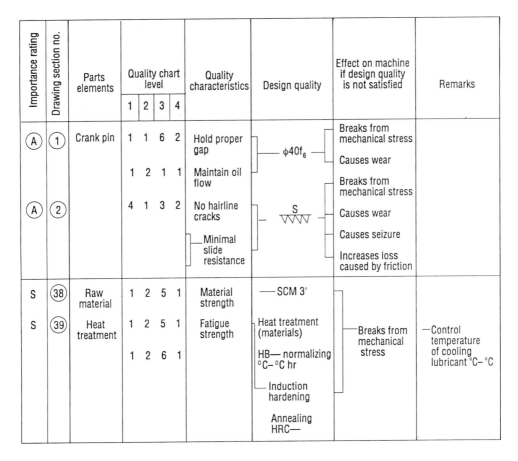

Importance rating	Drawing section no.	Parts elements	Quality chart level 1	2	3	4	Quality characteristics	Design quality	Effect on machine if design quality is not satisfied	Remarks
Ⓐ	①	Crank pin	1	1	6	2	Hold proper gap	$\phi 40f_6$	Breaks from mechanical stress Causes wear	
			1	2	1	1	Maintain oil flow		Breaks from mechanical stress	
Ⓐ	②		4	1	3	2	No hairline cracks	S ∇∇∇∇	Causes wear	
							Minimal slide resistance		Causes seizure Increases loss caused by friction	
S	㊳	Raw material	1	2	5	1	Material strength	SCM 3′	Breaks from mechanical stress	Control temperature of cooling lubricant °C–°C
S	㊴	Heat treatment	1	2	5	1	Fatigue strength	Heat treatment (materials)		
			1	2	6	1		HB— normalizing °C–°C hr		
								Induction hardening		
								Annealing HRC—		

FIGURE 7.2
QA chart type II

2. The activities did not provide the basis for stratification of areas the manufacturing department must control closely.
3. Deployment of the quality chart is according to each product function. This chart is also useful to design. The manufacturing department, however, sometimes finds it difficult to use because its production processes are based on parts.

To solve these problems that have slowly come to attention, the QA chart was created as a tool to communicate critical quality from the development department to the manufacturing department. It is being used at the internal combustion division of Kubota.

Main data & forms

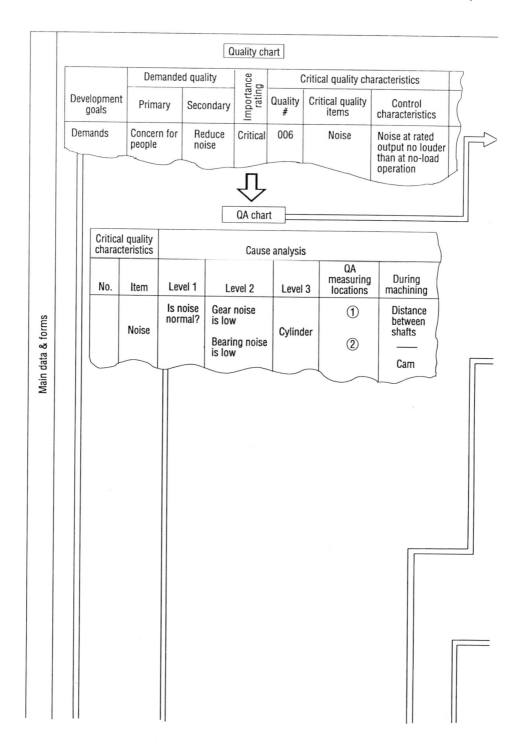

Quality chart

Development goals	Demanded quality		Importance rating	Critical quality characteristics		
	Primary	Secondary		Quality #	Critical quality items	Control characteristics
Demands	Concern for people	Reduce noise	Critical	006	Noise	Noise at rated output no louder than at no-load operation

QA chart

Critical quality characteristics		Cause analysis				
No.	Item	Level 1	Level 2	Level 3	QA measuring locations	During machining
	Noise	Is noise normal?	Gear noise is low Bearing noise is low	Cylinder	① ②	Distance between shafts —— Cam

Process planning master table [A]							
Model	Part no.	Material	Production plan	Line name		Line capacity	Machine man-hours
Engine	13621	ADC12T	Units/month	Manufacturing section 6		Units/month	0.123H
			Machine/equipment			Set die	
Process	Machining standard	Equipment name	Process capability	Man-hours			
BO	Base	7ST Index (customized)	Crank hole $C_p \geq 1.33$	0.017H			

⇩

Process detailed planning table [A]							
Part no.	13621	Part name	Cylinder	Control item	Standard	Measuring instrument	Estimated C_p
Process no.	0 – 5	Process	BO	Crank hole diameter [A]	———	0.001mm cylinder gauge	
Machine	7st Index (customized)	Model		Cam hole diameter	———	0.001mm cylinder gauge	
Die no.	———	Die	———	Crank hole depth	———	0.001mm depth gauge	
Machining conditions							

⇩

QC process chart

Product type	Engine	Classification	Process
Part no.	13621	Material	ADC12T
Part	Cylinder	Quantity	1

Process step	Process			Control points	
	Process name	Process detail	Machine/die	Control item	Standard value
2	Crank hole	Crank hole	RP-366	Crank hole diameter	———
	Cam hole	Cam hole	7st	Crank hole depth	———
	Knocking hole	Knocking hole	Index	Crank cam hole pitch	———
		Rough finishing	Custom machine		———

(*Figure 7.3 continues*)

(continued)

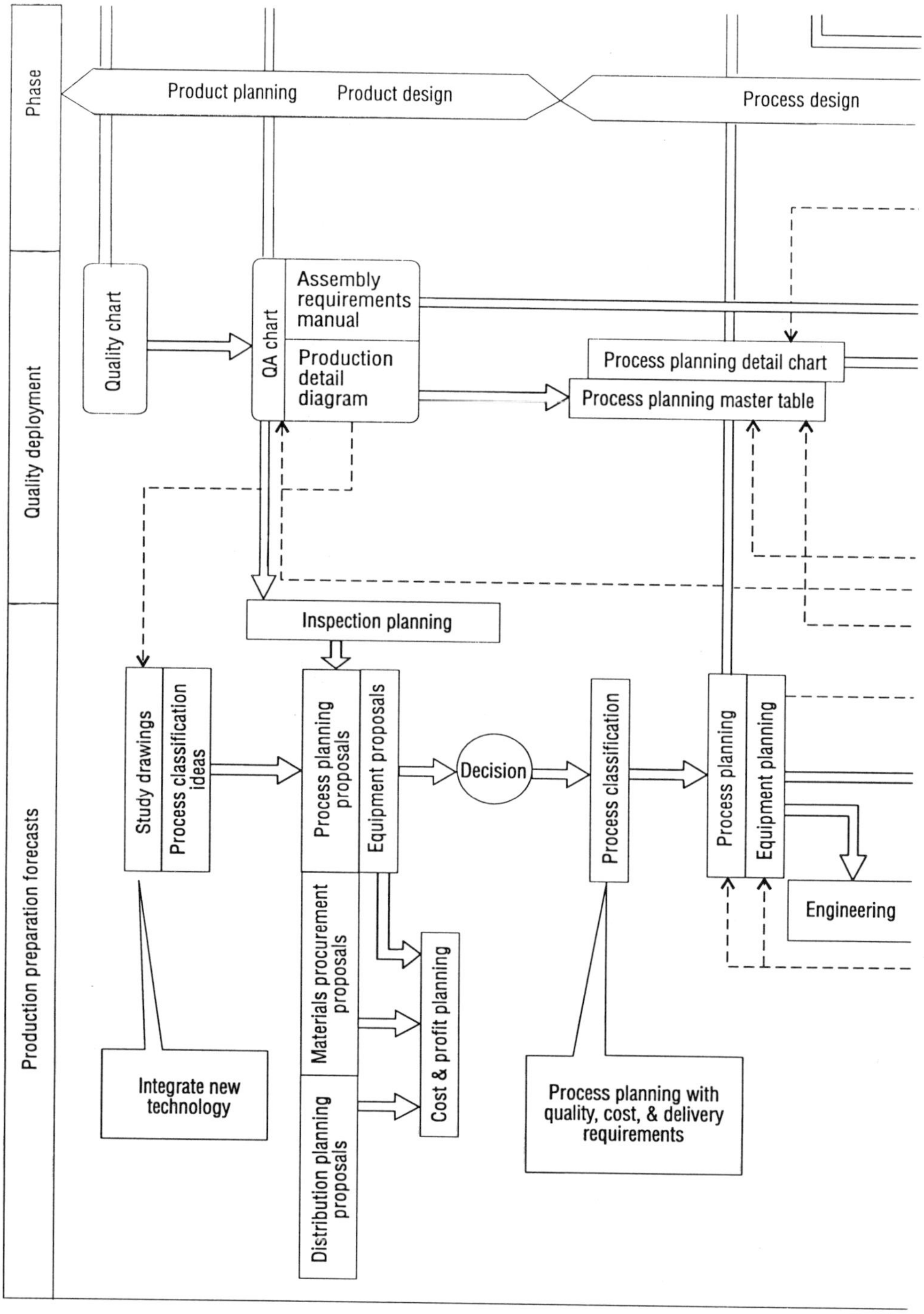

FIGURE 7.3.
Process planning in a quality assurance system

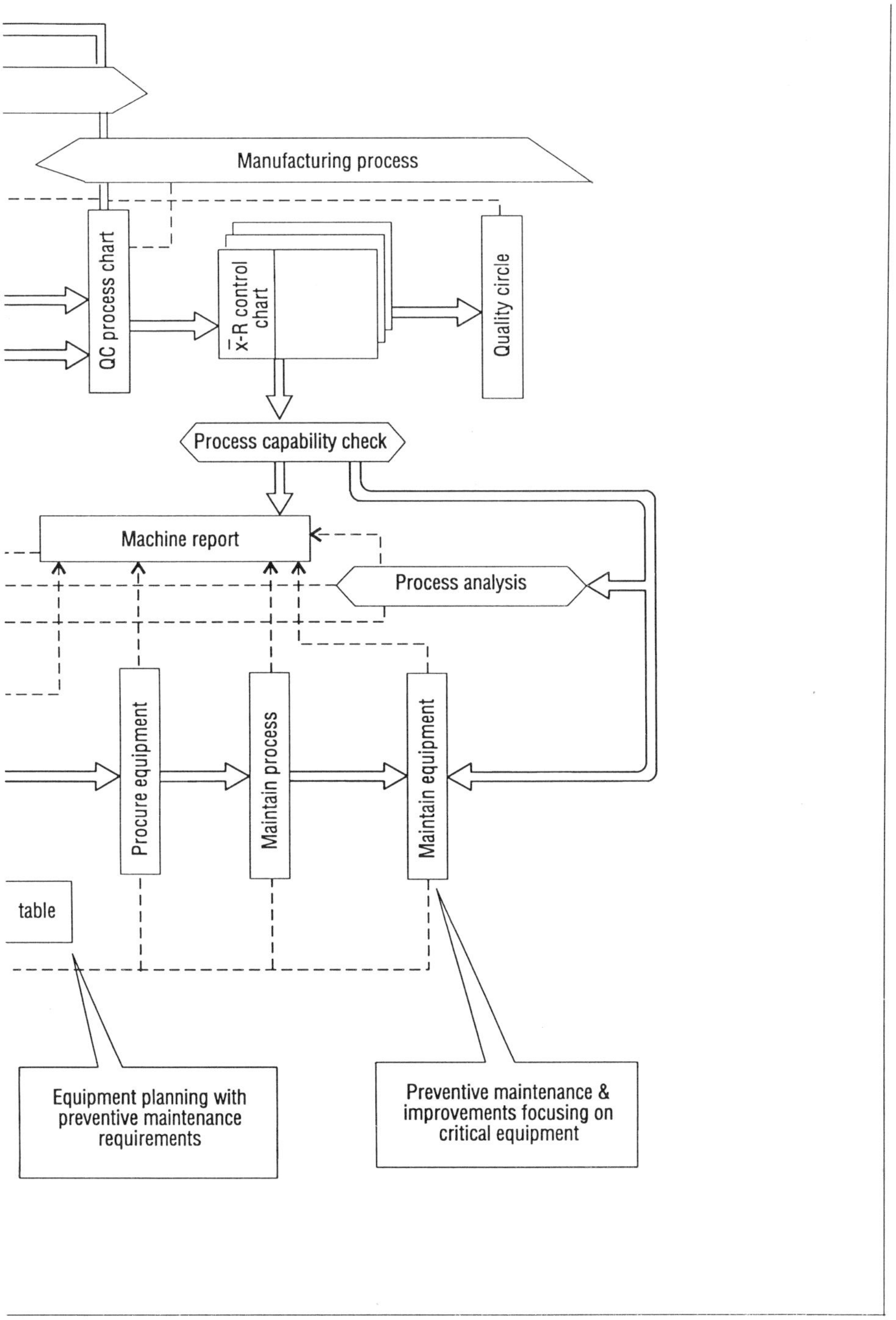
Manufacturing process
QC process chart
x̄-R control chart
Quality circle
Process capability check
Machine report
Process analysis
Procure equipment
Maintain process
Maintain equipment
table
Equipment planning with preventive maintenance requirements
Preventive maintenance & improvements focusing on critical equipment

QUALITY DEPLOYMENT IN PROCESS DESIGN

In the quality assurance system at the internal combustion division of Kubota, the major activities of the manufacturing department in the preproduction stage include broad production planning in which the departments cooperate in the procurement of materials, material handling, inspection planning, and so on, and in the process design, which is the prime responsibility of the production engineering department. Quality deployment by the manufacturing department is promoted by close cooperation with the research department, which is responsible for product development.

Figure 7.3 illustrates the production preparation activities corresponding to quality deployment by the division, with focus on the process design. Use of the process planning master table and process planning detail chart links the QA chart with the QC process chart, and brings together the quality assurance activities of the development and production departments. Statistical analysis improves the quality assurance system of the process quality deployment and the solution of quality problems to produce a more rational process design.

Process Planning Master Table and Process Planning Detail Chart

Figure 7.4 focuses on process planning and details how process planning and market-demanded quality are built into the product during manufacturing. The chart explains how market-demanded quality is summarized in the QA chart through quality analysis, and by process planning is pulled through to the QC process chart for manufacturing processes.

Prior to the implementation of TQM, process planning was little more than setting the sequence of machining operations and listing the dies and tooling. It had minimal connection to the other departments, with resulting trouble in the initial production because of poor process planning. This sequencing was not technical information of value and did not contribute to accumulation of production technologies. It also caused a recurrence of similar problems. TQM was introduced to solve these problems with process planning, and to promote accumulation of production technologies for use in other departments. The process planning master table was created for use in equipment planning and cost calculations. However, it was found to be inadequate for deploying design quality to the control items for production. To upgrade the process capability of each manufacturing process, critical-to-safety and critical-to-function processes were established through the QA chart, and the process planning detail chart was added to include information needed for process control. Figure 7.3 shows the data for machining operating conditions for each process control item and the standards (manufacturing specifications, measuring instruments, etc.).

This chart has an area for entry of actual results for comparison against target data established in the planning process. It simplifies the buildup of production technologies and the deployment to successive similar processes. It has upgraded the capability of handling the increasingly diversified agricultural equipment in manufacturing, with shorter delivery time.

The result of this activity is a smooth quality deployment, from the QA chart to the process planning master table and the QC process chart.

Upgrading of Process Design by Improving the Machine Record

In equipment planning, the "machine record" has been used to record the history of individual machine critical factors such as design, manufacture, and installation. It is an effective means to feed back important information for new planning, but most of the data in the record address the functions of individual machines, with little information concerning quality. Therefore, it could not be used to provide information to process planning.

The development department created the QA chart, which improved the communication of critical control items that permit each process to perform at full capacity. Because of inadequate equipment planning, certain processes were not given enough capacity. The reason was that the machine records did not have the data on the process capability available for equipment planning. It led to the need to accumulate data for all production lines. For equipment used in the critical processes contained in the QA chart, a data bank was created to record the history of each machine from time of installation to scrapping. The machine records were improved and became useful for future equipment planning.

Table 7.1 contains the items included in the machine records. It is evident that many items of information are entered in the machine records as the equipment passes through the stages of useful life: design, fabrication, installation, and improvement of processes. The records then proceed through the initial control phase for the first six months of installation or the first three production lots, reach the equipment maintenance and manufacturing departments by way of the process completion release notice, and from there go to the process control and preventive maintenance departments.

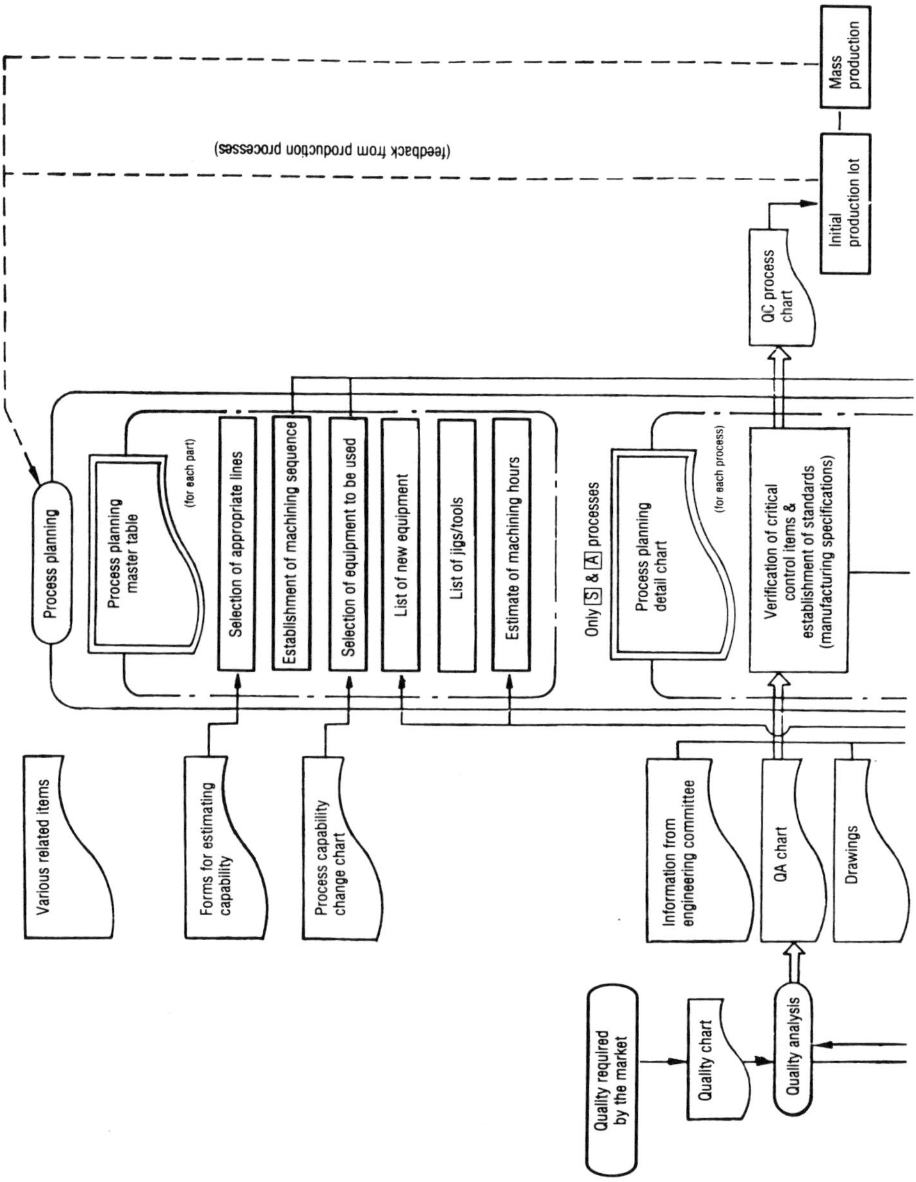
Process planning
Process planning master table
(for each part)
Selection of appropriate lines
Establishment of machining sequence
Selection of equipment to be used
List of new equipment
List of jigs/tools
Estimate of machining hours
Various related items
Forms for estimating capability
Process capability change chart
Only [S] & [A] processes
Process planning detail chart
(for each process)
Verification of critical control items & establishment of standards (manufacturing specifications)
QC process chart
Initial production lot
Mass production
(feedback from production processes)
Information from engineering committee
QA chart
Drawings
Quality required by the market
Quality chart
Quality analysis

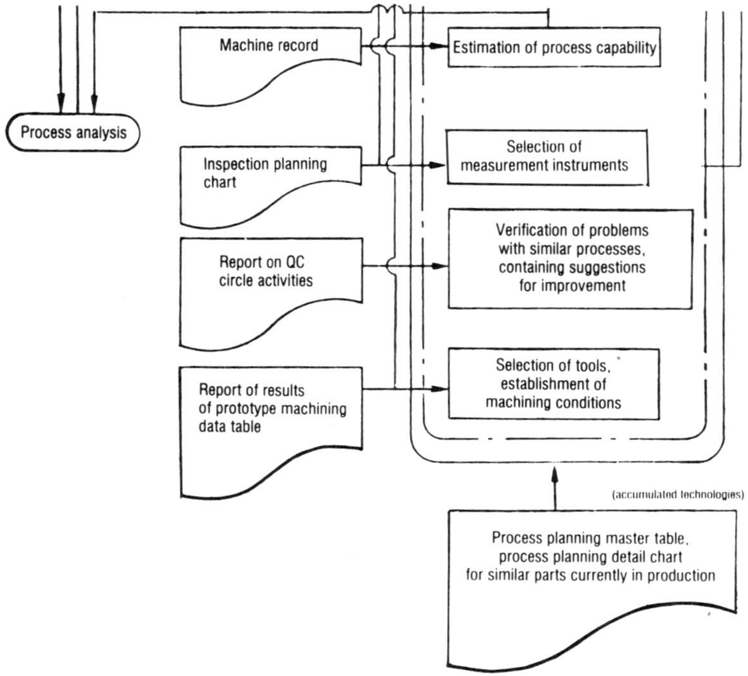

FIGURE 7.4
Details of plan to build quality into the manufacturing process

Machine type		Classification		QC process chart	Dept. manager
Product no.		Material			
Product		Qty.			

Process	Process				Control points			Control manager				
	Process code	Process name	Description of operation	Machine die	Control item	Standards value	Production standard	Section manager	Staff leader	Foreman	Unit leader	Team leader
Enter sequence no. of process	Enter code for workflow	Enter name of the process referred to at right	Description of each process Indicate on margins drawings when necessary	Enter name, model, control no., etc., of equipment, machines, & fixtures for each process	Enter items that must be controlled in the process	Enter standards on drawings & assembly guidelines for control items	Enter standards for those requiring special attention due to the following process or drawing specification guidelines		Individual responsible for control items for each process		Circle title of appropriate manager	
1	(Example) ○	Machine balance O.D.	Machine balance O.D.	Kubota custom machine	Balance O.D.	$\phi\,110^{\pm 0.1}$	$\phi\,110^{\pm 0.1}$				○	
2	○	Machine center area	Machine center area	Ohkuma Ikegai NC lathe	Center O.D.	$\phi\,44^{-0.060}_{-0.079}$	$\phi\,44.4^{\pm 0.1}_{-0}$				○	
3	○ A	Machine pin	Machine pin	Heller pin milling machine	Pin O.D.	$\phi\,37^{0}_{-0.025}$	$\phi\,37.9^{\pm 0.1}_{-0}$				○	
		〃	〃	〃	Radius	$3R^{\pm 0.02}$	$3R^{\pm 0.02}$				○	

Code	Date	Revision contents & reason	Person responsible	Checked by	Visual	Date

FIGURE 7.5
Guidelines for preparing a QC process table

Production Dept., no. 2 section					Est. date	Document no.
Senior leader	Section manager	Staff leader	Person responsible	Foreman	Effective date	
						Page ____ of ____

Check items				Measuring instrument	Record	Problem handling		Related standards
At lot startup		Daily				In charge	Method	
Sample qty. & frequency	Person responsible	Sample qty. & frequency	Person responsible					
Enter sample qty. & person in charge of sampling, for each change in process equipment, fixtures (operator, team leader, QC supervisor)		Enter sample qty. & person in charge of sampling performed daily (operator, team leader, supervisor)		Enter name of instruments used for measuring control items	Enter type of documents used for control (control chart, checksheet)	Enter name of person responsible & corrective measures for problems		Enter types & no. of related standards for process
2 after sampling	Person responsible for QC	n = 5/Day	Operator	Caliper (150mm)	Checksheet	Unit leader	Unit leader implements corrective measures	F35-1-2
″	″	n = 5/Day	″	Micrometer	$\bar{x}$-R control chart	″	″ ″	F35-1-3
″	″	n = 5/Day	″	″	″	″	″ ″	″ 1-4
″	″	n = 2/Day	″	Radius gauge	Checksheet	″	″ ″	″ 1-5

Revision contents & reason	Person responsible	Checked by	Remarks	

TABLE 7.1
Machine Record Items

Form	*Machine Record Main Contents*	
Planning forms	Process planning master table	Process planning detail chart
	Current process capability survey	Analysis data sheet
	Machine basic plan	Engineering table
Specification sheet	General specifications	Individual machine specifications
Precision inspection chart	Data on cutting conditions	Static precision chart
Equipment inspection form	Process capability inspection chart	Static precision chart
Process equipment report	Improvement data Analysis data sheet	Process capability inspection chart
Machine initial use control chart	Failure status 6 months after initial use	Process capability change
Maintenance records	Failure analysis report Process capability maintenance & improvement measures report Process capability index history Precision index history	

Improvement of machine records has made possible (a) good feedback to future projects and (b) good feed-forward for improved maintenance. The deployment to manufacturing of critical-to-quality characteristics, as fed down from the development department, is truly possible, and it has proven effective for rapid stabilization of processes, reduction of machine breakdowns, and so on.

QUALITY DEPLOYMENT TO MANUFACTURING PROCESSES

QC Process Chart and Operating Standards

The QC process chart at the internal combustion division of Kubota is the control standard for the manufacturing processes in which con-

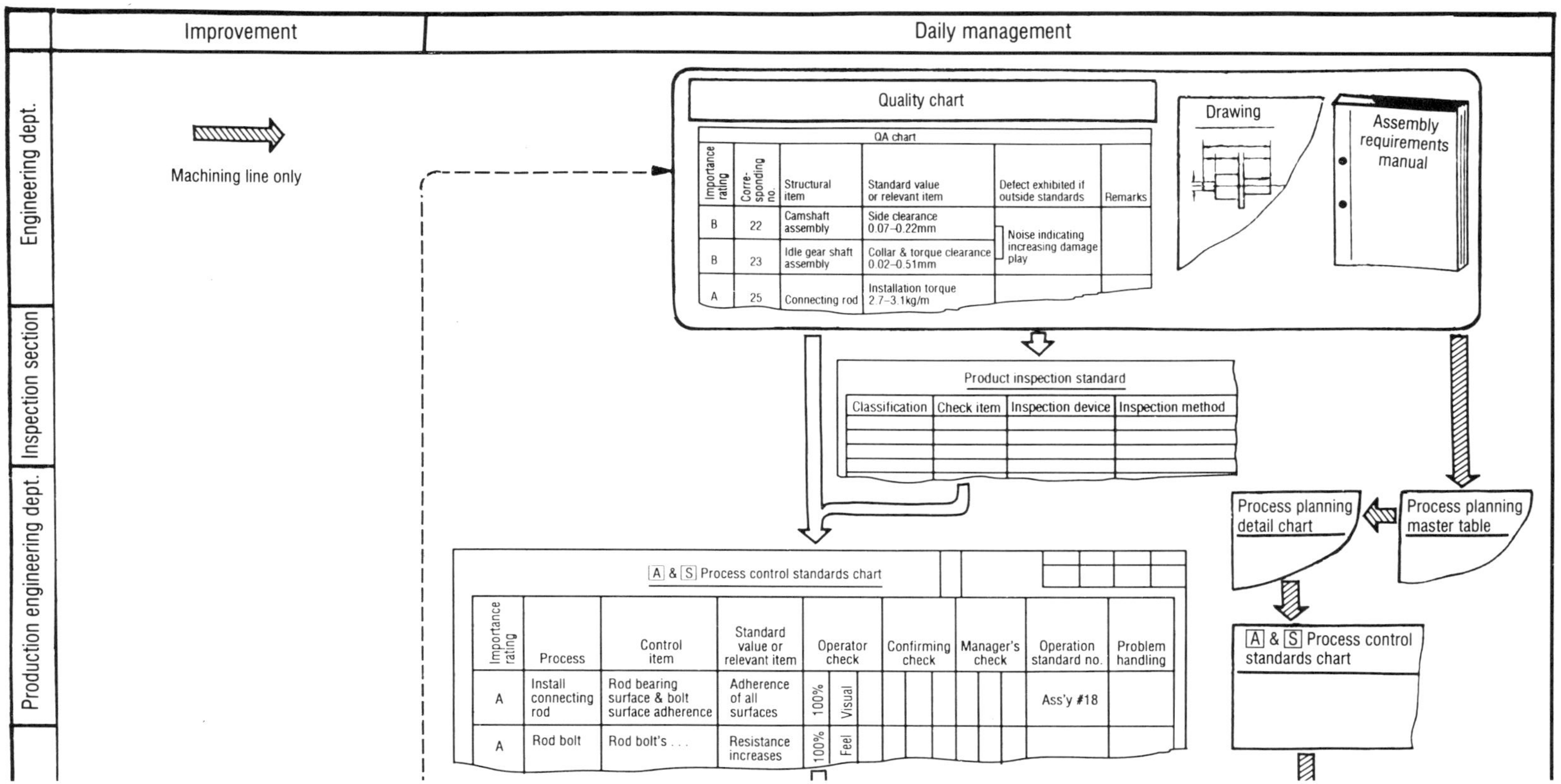

(*Figure 7.6 continues*)

(*continued*)

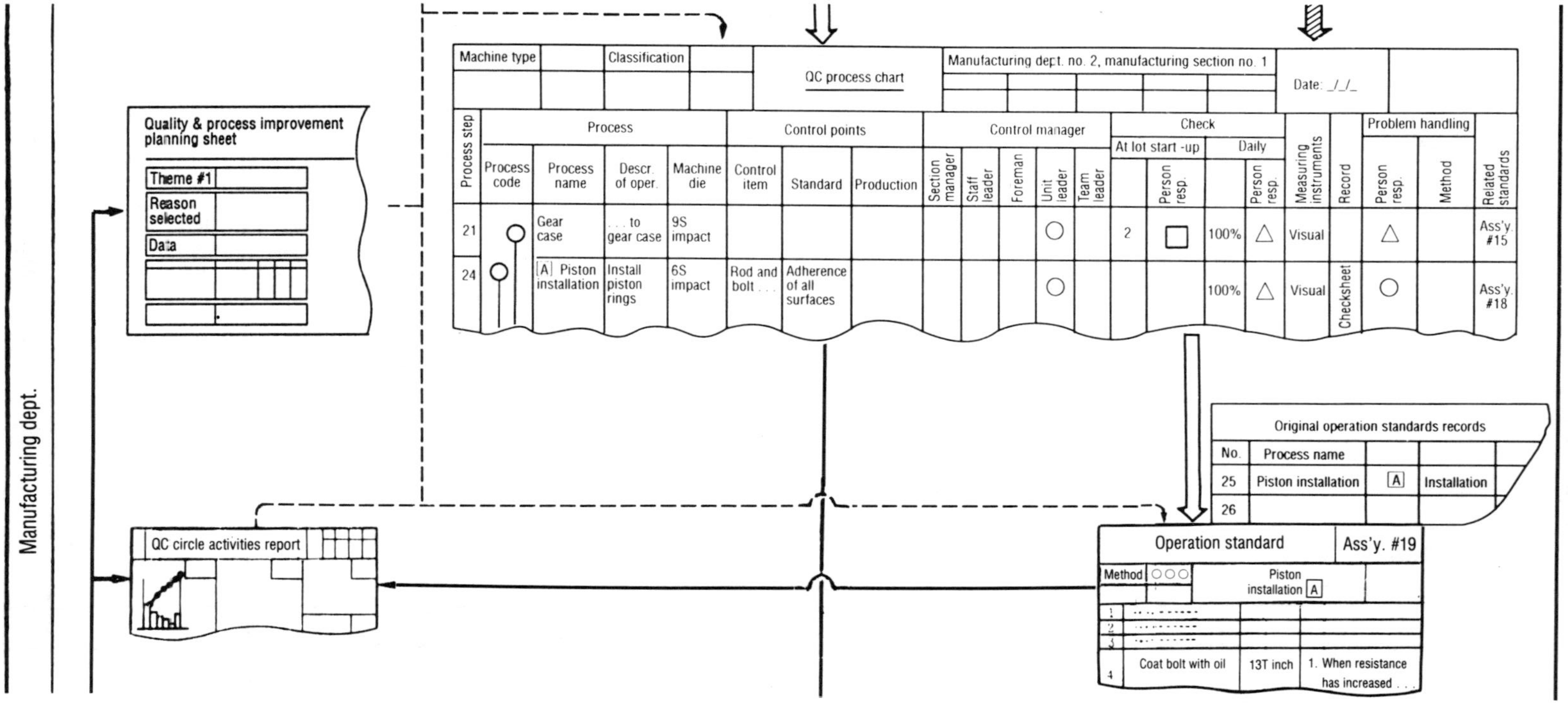

Manufacturing dept.
Quality & process improvement planning sheet
Theme #1
Reason selected
Data
Machine type
Classification
QC process chart
Manufacturing dept. no. 2, manufacturing section no. 1
Date: _/_/_
Process step
Process
Process code
Process name
Descr. of oper.
Machine die
Control points
Control item
Standard
Production
Control manager
Section manager
Staff leader
Foreman
Unit leader
Team leader
Check
At lot start -up
Person resp.
Daily
Person resp.
Measuring instruments
Record
Problem handling
Person resp.
Method
Related standards
21
Gear case
. . . to gear case
9S impact
2
100%
Visual
Ass'y. #15
24
[A] Piston installation
Install piston rings
6S impact
Rod and bolt . . .
Adherence of all surfaces
100%
Visual
Checksheet
Ass'y. #18
Original operation standards records
No.
Process name
25
Piston installation
[A]
Installation
26
Operation standard
Ass'y. #19
Method
Piston installation [A]
1
2
3
4
Coat bolt with oil
13T inch
1. When resistance has increased . . .
QC circle activities report

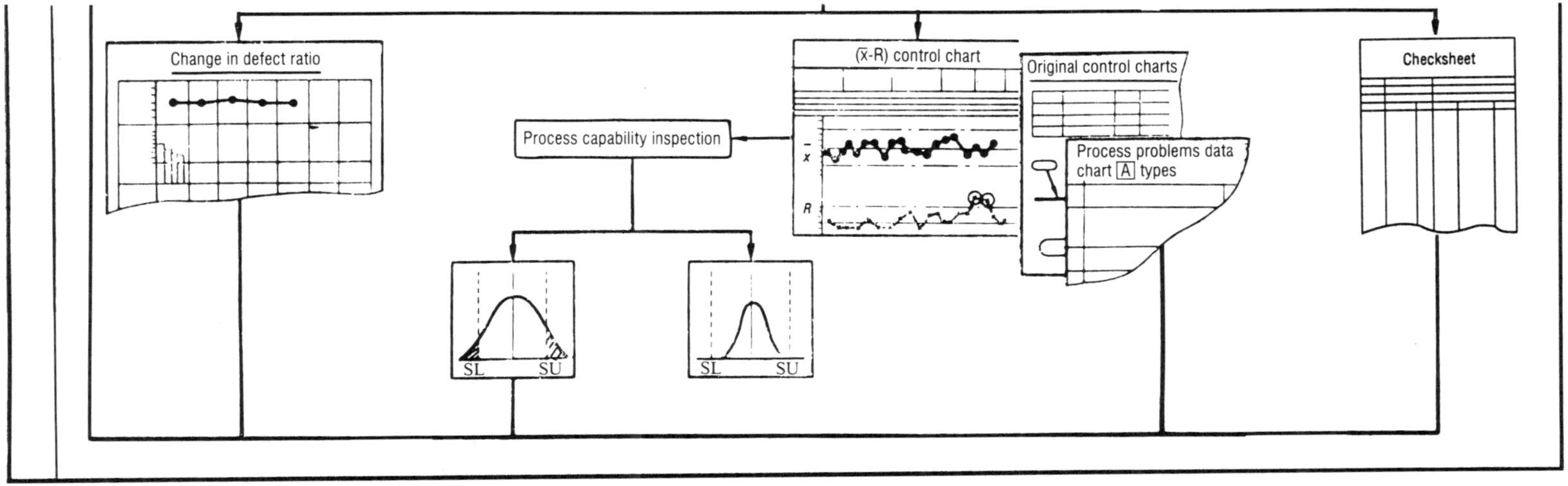

FIGURE 7.6
Document flow in the manufacturing process

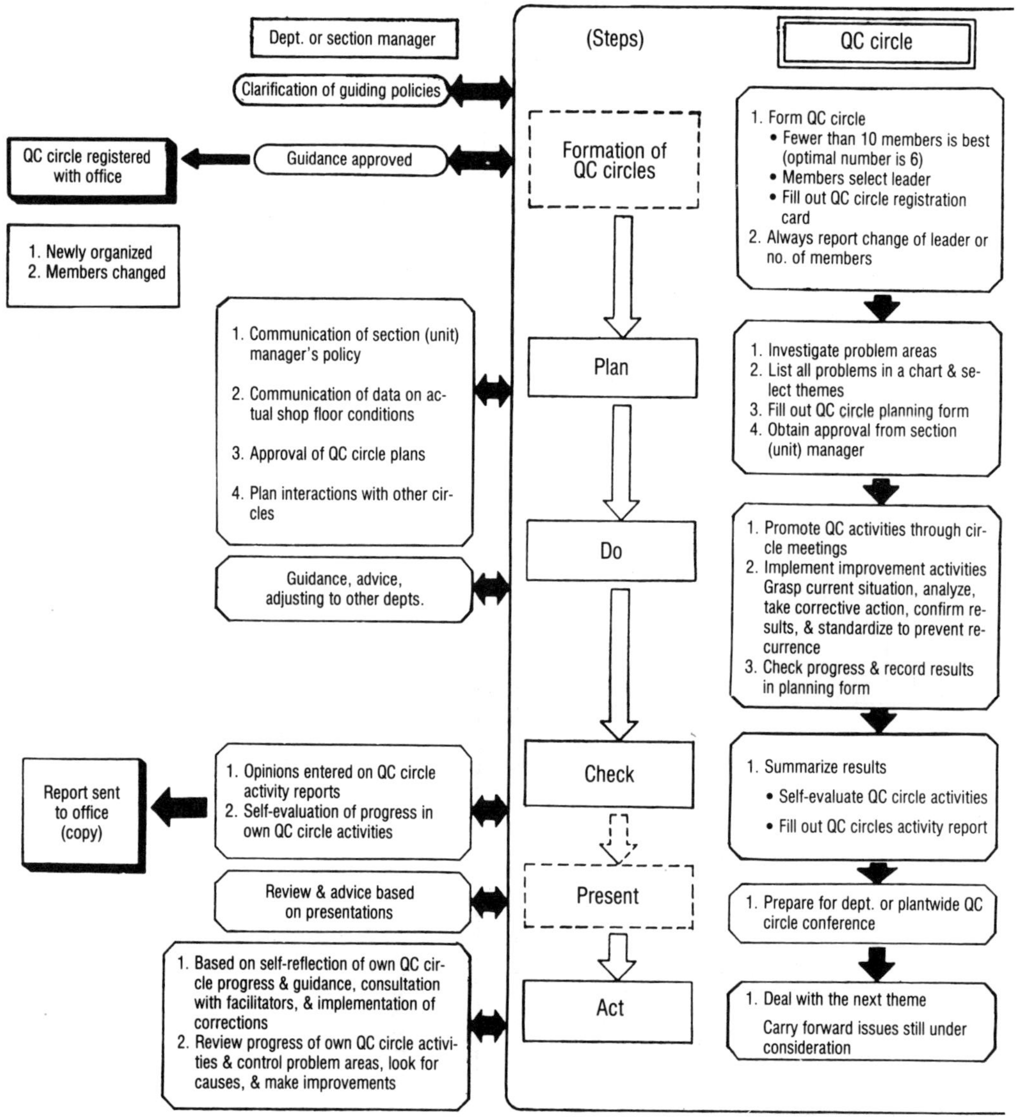

FIGURE 7.7
Guidelines for quality (QC) circles

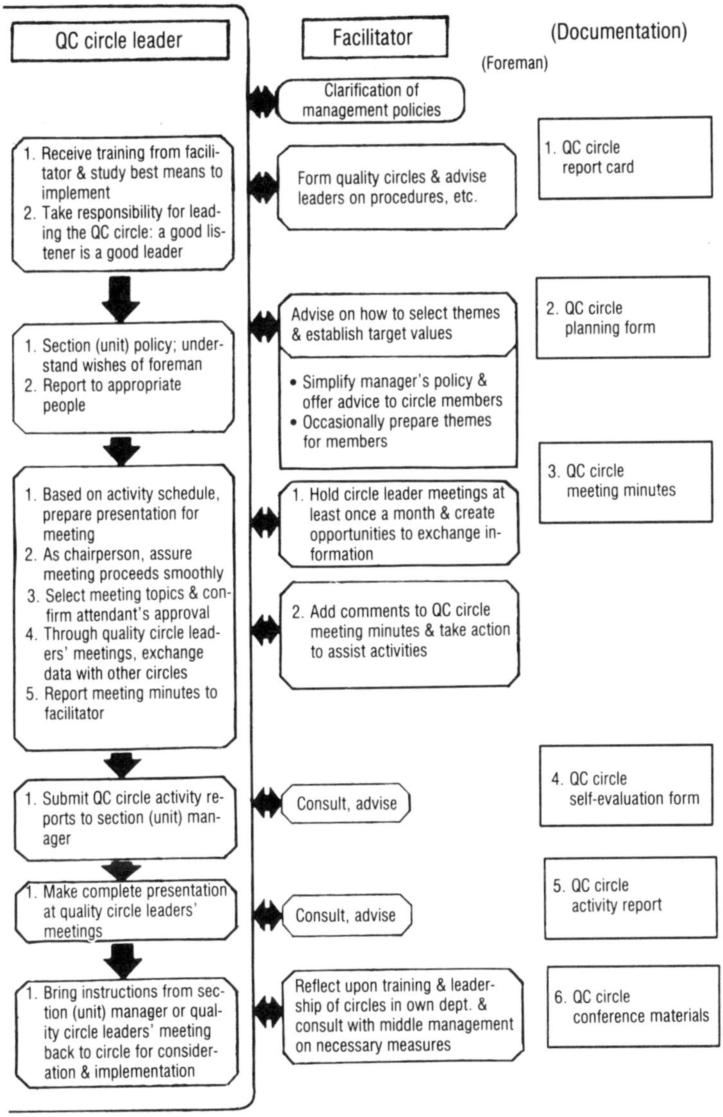
QC circle leader
Facilitator
(Foreman)
(Documentation)
Clarification of management policies
1. Receive training from facilitator & study best means to implement
2. Take responsibility for leading the QC circle: a good listener is a good leader
Form quality circles & advise leaders on procedures, etc.
1. QC circle report card
1. Section (unit) policy; understand wishes of foreman
2. Report to appropriate people
Advise on how to select themes & establish target values
• Simplify manager's policy & offer advice to circle members
• Occasionally prepare themes for members
2. QC circle planning form
1. Based on activity schedule, prepare presentation for meeting
2. As chairperson, assure meeting proceeds smoothly
3. Select meeting topics & confirm attendant's approval
4. Through quality circle leaders' meetings, exchange data with other circles
5. Report meeting minutes to facilitator
1. Hold circle leader meetings at least once a month & create opportunities to exchange information
2. Add comments to QC circle meeting minutes & take action to assist activities
3. QC circle meeting minutes
1. Submit QC circle activity reports to section (unit) manager
Consult, advise
4. QC circle self-evaluation form
1. Make complete presentation at quality circle leaders' meetings
Consult, advise
5. QC circle activity report
1. Bring instructions from section (unit) manager or quality circle leaders' meeting back to circle for consideration & implementation
Reflect upon training & leadership of circles in own dept. & consult with middle management on necessary measures
6. QC circle conference materials

trol items, names of responsible individuals, method of control, measuring instruments employed to assure quality in manufacturing, and the method of handling unusual circumstances, along with related documentation, are all summarized and grouped according to types of operation and the manufacturing sequence.

In the past, operating standards were set up as operating instructions for the production department according to the engineering technology, and did not adequately identify control items or control standards. The QC process chart clarified the relationship among the processes, standardized the specifications, and established a method for handling abnormal situations. However, standards that still existed only for the manufacturing department did not adequately reflect design quality, a situation that caused difficulties even after the beginning of commercial production.

The most important role of the QC process chart, it has been said, is the study and identification, from product planning to service in the marketplace, of control characteristics and control methods based upon an appropriate control plan. In the past an effective mode for communicating design quality did not exist, and problems occurred. To remedy the situation, the QA chart, along with the process planning master table for the production engineering department, was upgraded to improve the deployment of design quality into the QC process chart. Concurrently, there was a revision of the operating standards manual and QC process chart, which involved process improvement activities. From these improvements production engineering technologies were accumulated, and there were upgrades of the quality chart in the development department and of the system control for critical processes. These activities contributed to implementation of the QC process chart as part of the quality deployment system of the internal combustion division of Kubota.

Figure 7.5 shows the construction of the QC process chart. Figure 7.6 is quality deployment to production with the QC process chart at the center, illustrated by the flow of the forms.

Quality Control Circle Activities

The important issue in quality deployment for manufacturing operations is that everyone in the organization, even the plant workers, participates in quality deployment. It is not easy for every worker to be conscious of quality when each individual is assigned to a single task that later produces a complete product. Kubota successfully established the system by improving the QA chart and the QC process chart, in which market-demanded quality was fully deployed down to

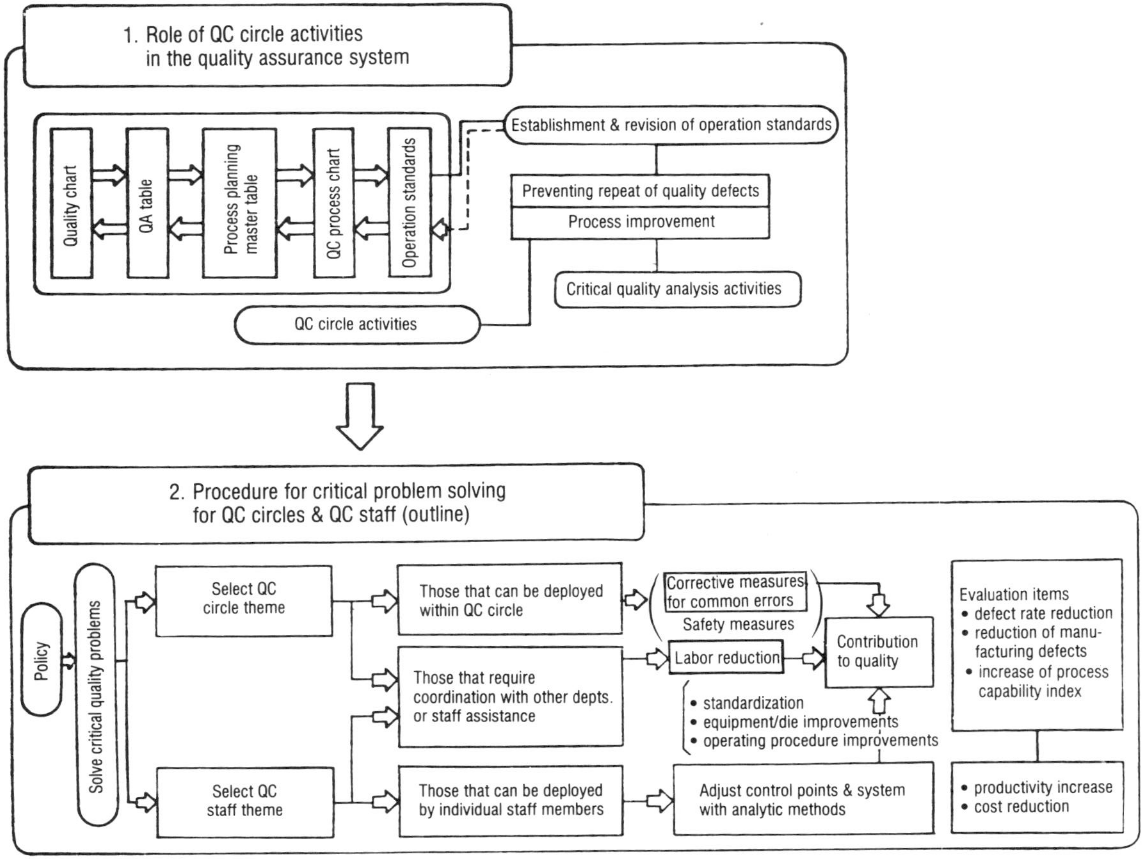

FIGURE 7.8
Quality assurance based on the QC circle activities

the operating standards manual. These activities focused on the critical processes and occasional simple mistakes in the general processes that led to complaints from customers. The effective solution to this problem was the implementation of quality control (QC) circle activities at the division.

The QC circle activities were fully realigned to correct the discrepancies revealed by implementation of TQM. They have significantly contributed to the realization of Kubota's three mottoes.

1. Unlimited prosperity
2. Enthusiasm on the job
3. Trust our fellow workers.

Figure 7.7 summarizes how the QC circle is conducted. Only when the effects of QC circle activity and the activity of the earlier quality deployment were united did deployment of quality in its true sense begin at the Kubota division. Figure 7.8 shows the position and outline of the QC circle in the quality control system. It should give the reader a good picture of quality deployment for the entire organization, down to the shop floor.

CONCLUSION

This chapter has described Kubota's experience with implementation of quality deployment for production engineering and manufacturing, with concentration on the relationship between the QA chart and process planning in process design, followed by communication to the QC process chart. Kubota believes that the QA chart not only should be used to communicate design quality but also, in order for deployment of quality to be fully effective, must include information to permit the manufacturing department to handle the newly added functions and corresponding process capability in new products, and to conduct reliability activities. The later relationship chart is one example, but at this point it is not perfected and is one of the major objectives to be accomplished. It requires further accumulation of production engineering technology through the machine records and QC process charts.

QC circle activities have become daily events, and the operating standards are well established. With a stronger communication of quality, it is expected that true quality deployment will spread through the entire organization, down to the shop floor.

8

Selection of Critical-to-Safety Parts and Critical-to-Function Parts, and Control by Prioritization

Mitsuo Tsurusawa

INTRODUCTION

Kubota's program to improve the quality assurance system has focused on the solution of problems associated with the traditional quality assurance systems and on improvements for coping with the changing climate of the industry. Specifically, it includes problems of inadequacy of the system to respond to the rising trend of product liability. To strengthen this area, parts and processes critical to safety were identified and followed with tight control. At the same time, parts and processes critical to product function were differentiated from noncritical ones so that additional attention could be paid to their control. The results of these efforts are reflected in noncritical parts and processes as well, and so are actively promoted with attention to all the activities in the process design and quality deployment already explained.

This chapter outlines control by prioritization of the critical-to-safety and critical-to-function parts and processes as activities associated with quality deployment in preproduction and production phases at Kubota's internal combustion products division. Since the critical activities in the preproduction phase have been explained in connection with process design and quality deployment, duplication will be avoided by describing the critical purchasing and manufacturing process activities here.

CONTROL OUTLINE FOR CRITICAL-TO-SAFETY PARTS AND PROCESSES

At the Kubota division, from product planning to sales and service, closer control was applied to critical-to-safety parts and processes more closely than to noncritical or general ones, in order to prevent occurrence and recurrence of accidents resulting in personal injuries or fire resulting from use of Kubota's products.

Fundamentally, each department must prioritize parts (differentiate noncritical parts), so that critical-to-safety part and process control manuals, and critical-to-safety part control standards, can be established for each step. Figure 8.1 shows how the control systems and quality deployment related.

Critical-to-safety parts (called [S] parts) are those that, if defective from machining or from the assembly process, could cause injuries or fire; and the critical-to-safety processes are designated [S] processes. Parts and processes are reviewed on the quality chart from past records, claims information, predicted frequency of occurrence, applicable laws and regulations, and so on. [S] parts and processes are chosen on the basis of discussions in the engineering, inspection, production engineering, and manufacturing departments. They are then included in drawings, QA charts, assembly instruction manuals, and so on; marked with an [S] and fed forward to the succeeding steps.

CONTROL SYSTEM FOR CRITICAL-TO-FUNCTION PARTS AND PROCESSES

Critical-to-function parts and processes are those that, if defective, can cause the final product to lose its functional characteristics. They are called [A] parts and [A] processes, respectively. Control of these parts and processes is similar to the control of the [S] parts and [S] processes, in accordance with the critical-to-function parts and processes control standards.

The mode of control, basis of selection, and mode of communication of [A] and [S] parts are identical. However, unlike the [S] parts, which are controlled by strict standards from the product liability standpoint, changes in [A] parts are frequently based on quality and process analyses. Failure mode and effect analysis is applied, and special activities in the manufacturing processes, to be described later, are an important upgrade for the quality assurance system.

CONTROL BY PRIORITIZATION FOR PURCHASING ACTIVITIES

In the past there was no special control for differentiating other parts and processes from [S] and [A] parts in regard to selection of

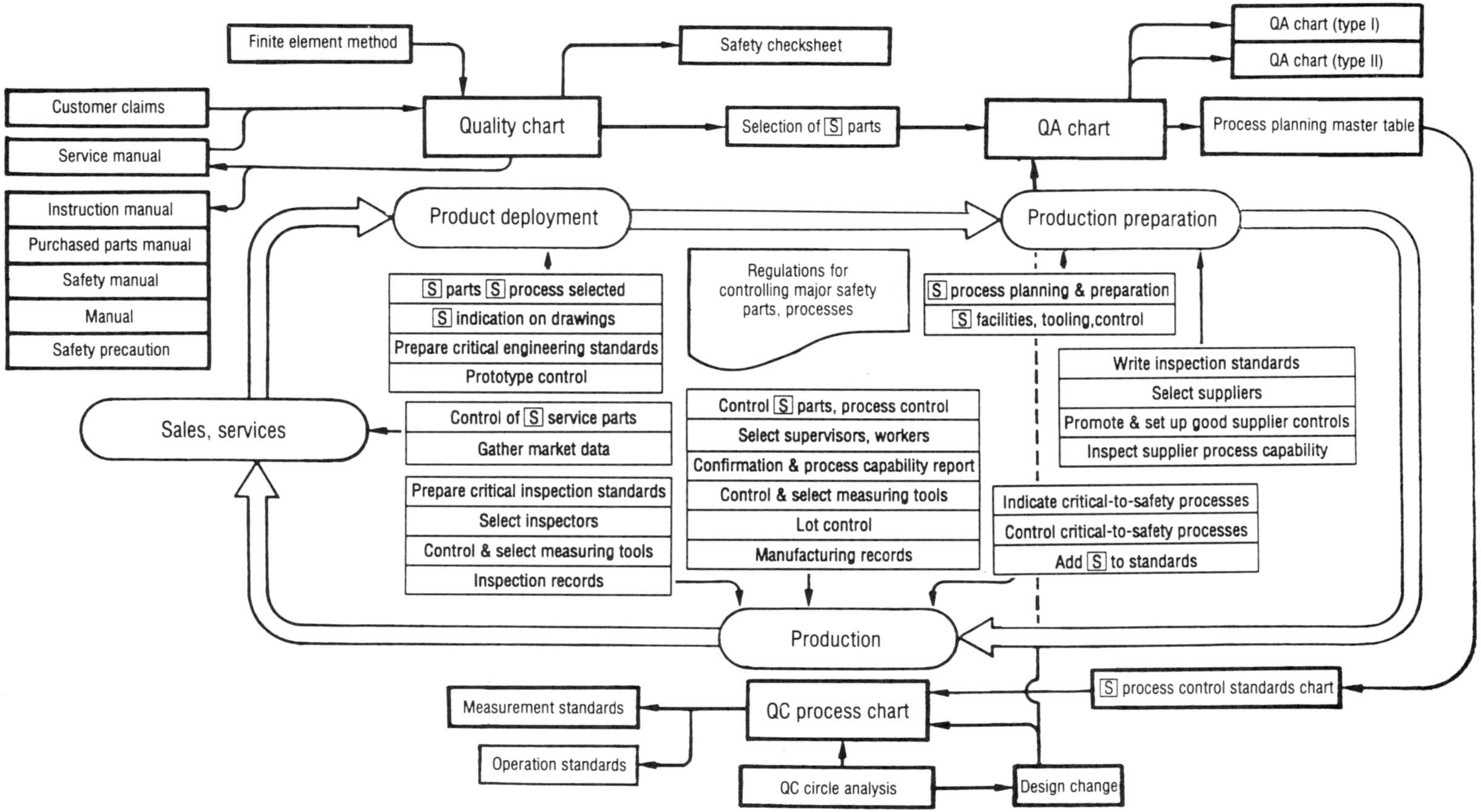

FIGURE 8.1
Control of critical-to-safety parts and processes

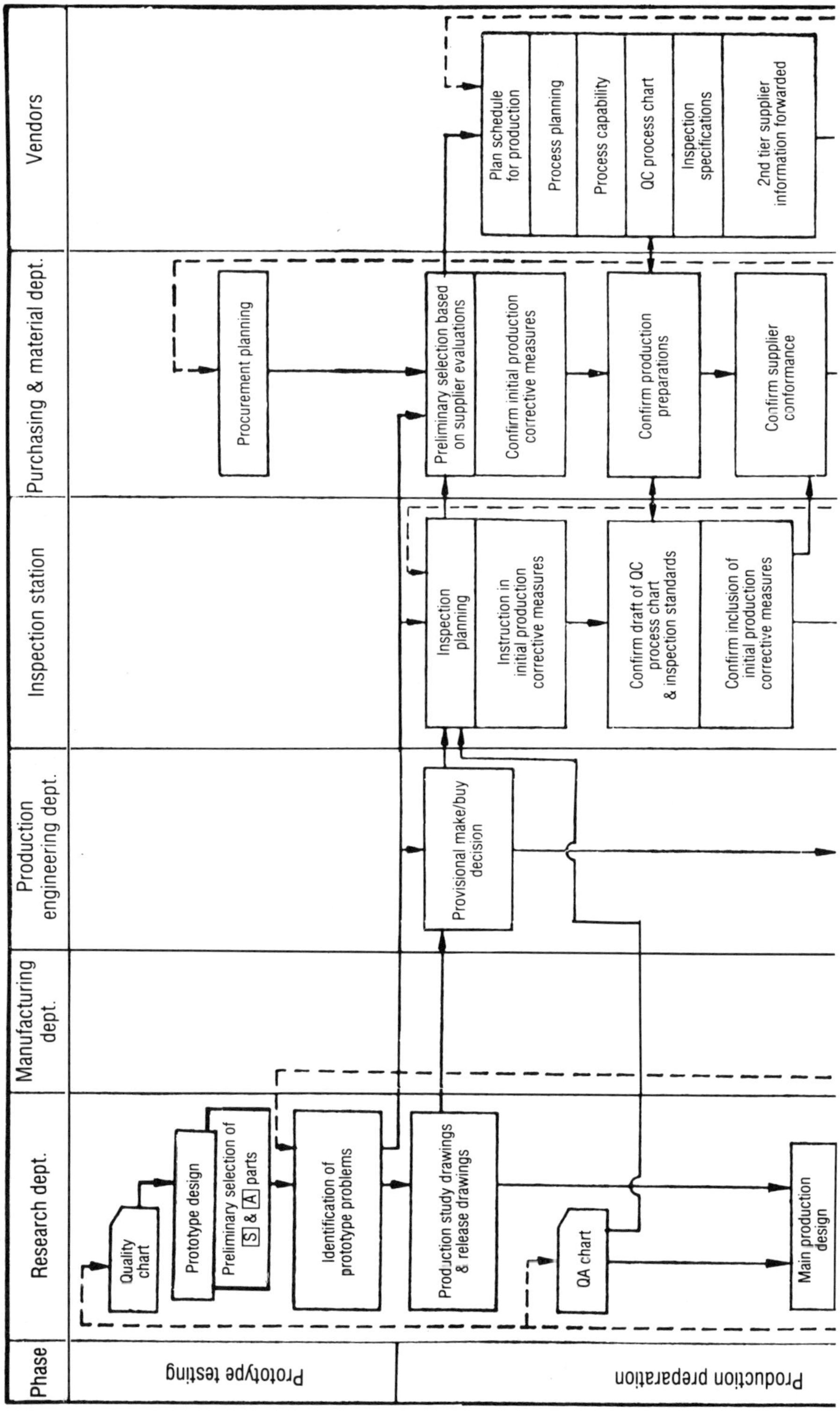
Phase
Prototype testing
Production preparation
Research dept.
Manufacturing dept.
Production engineering dept.
Inspection station
Purchasing & material dept.
Vendors
Quality chart
Prototype design
Preliminary selection of S & A parts
Identification of prototype problems
Production study drawings & release drawings
QA chart
Main production design
Provisional make/buy decision
Inspection planning
Instruction in initial production corrective measures
Confirm draft of QC process chart & inspection standards
Confirm inclusion of initial production corrective measures
Procurement planning
Preliminary selection based on supplier evaluations
Confirm initial production corrective measures
Confirm production preparations
Confirm supplier conformance
Plan schedule for production
Process planning
Process capability
QC process chart
Inspection specifications
2nd tier supplier information forwarded

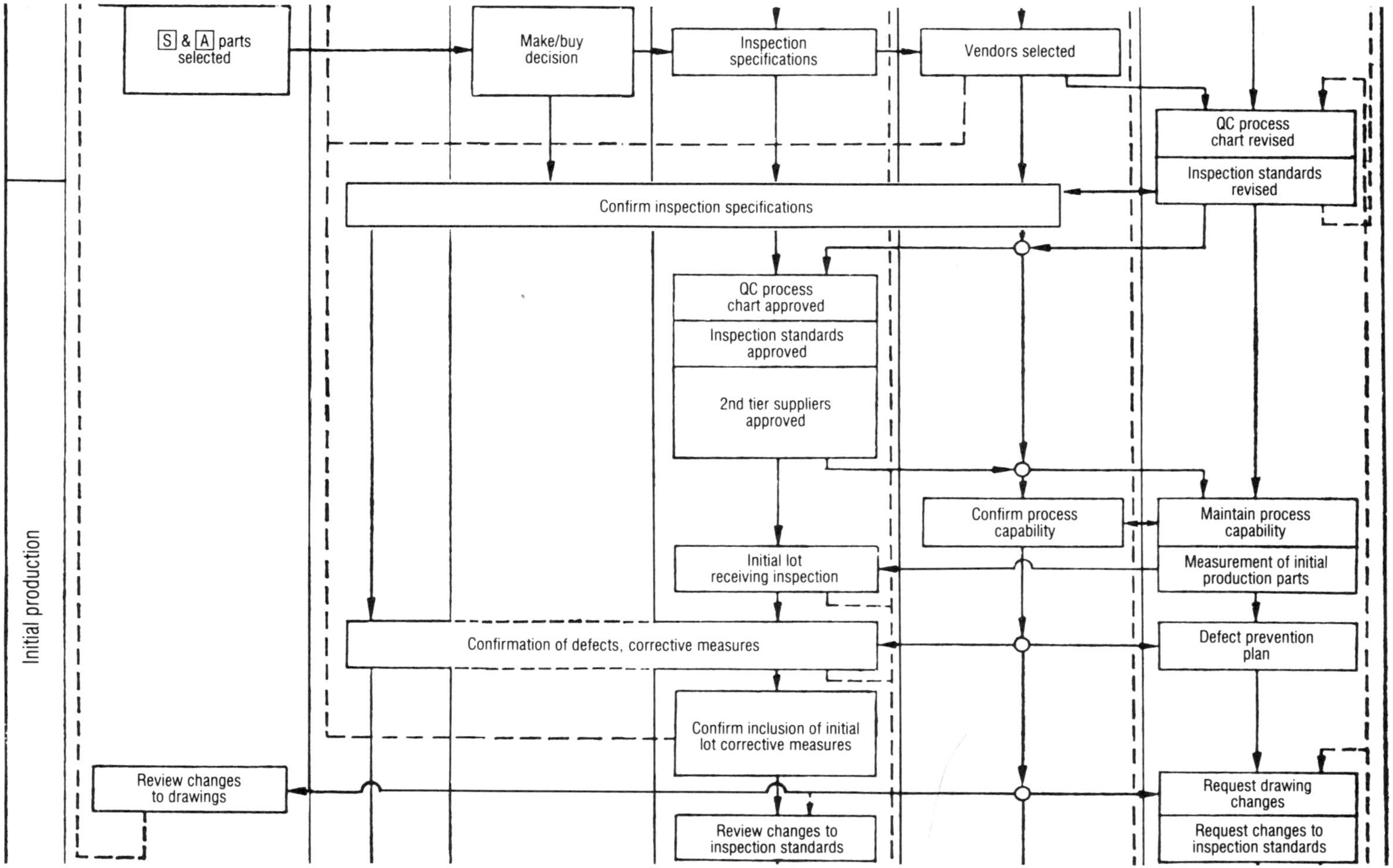

(*Figure 8.2 continues*)

(continued)

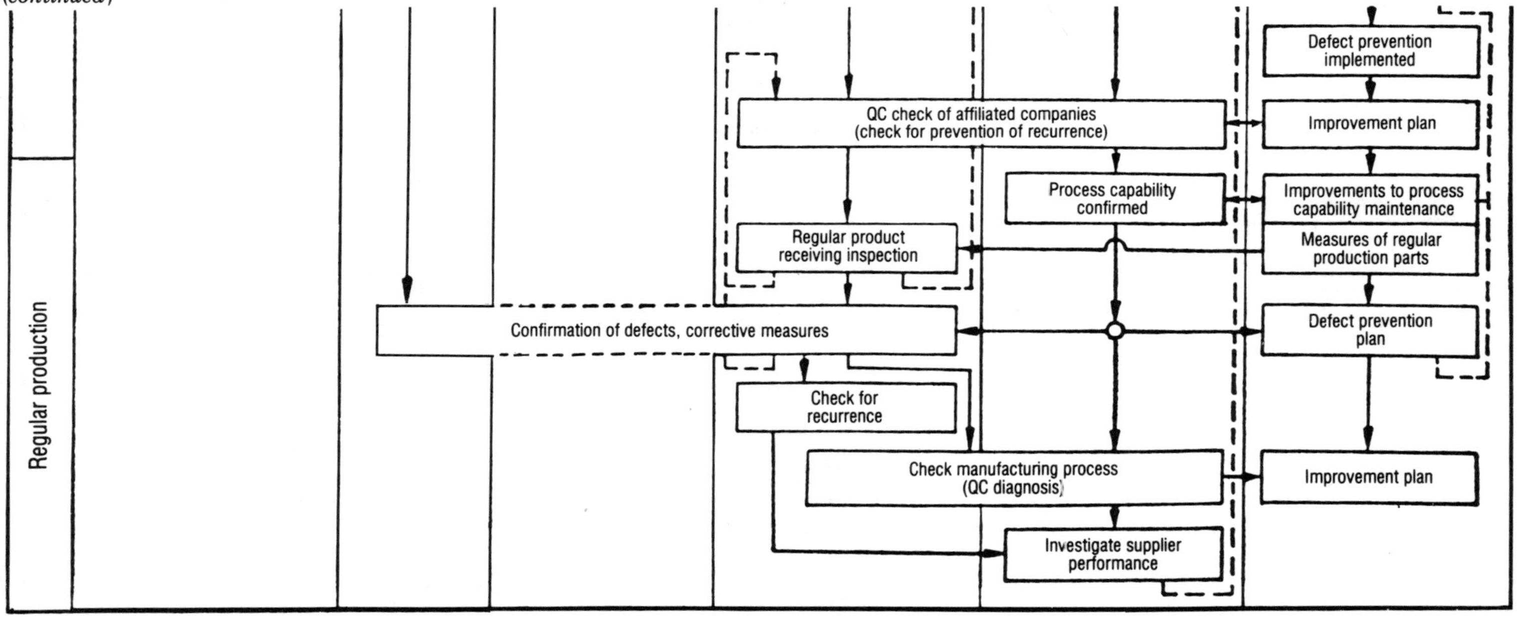

FIGURE 8.2
Control by prioritization of critical-to-safety parts and critical-to-function parts

suppliers and process control at subcontractors. When control by prioritization for the [S] and [A] parts was established, control standards for critical-to-safety and critical-to-functional parts were established for the purchasing department. They were subjected to special control from the production preparation stage in four areas.

1. Supplier certification according to ordering standards that place a priority on quality assurance
2. Limits on second- and third-tier suppliers
3. Verification of supplier inspection standards and QC process charts that were deployed from the Kubota QA chart, and assistance to suppliers to improve process control
4. Investigation of process capability, maintenance, and improvement of processes.

A high level of process capability has been achieved by building quality into the product during the manufacturing process at the suppliers' plants rather than the use of stricter inspections.

Figure 8.2 illustrates the system of control for [S] and [A] parts for the purchasing department. It has three major objectives.

1. Vendor certification in the preproduction stage
2. Maintenance and improvement of process capability
3. Prevention of recurring quality problems with [S] and [A] parts.

As a result of the implementation of these prioritization activities, the rejection rate at receiving inspection decreased significantly. The current methods of control for [S] and [A] parts are identical. Kubota plans gradually to develop a different control system for [A] parts as the system gains more use.

CONTROL ACTIVITIES IN THE MANUFACTURING PROCESS

Prior to the full development of quality deployment, it took a long time for new product quality to become stabilized, and chronic production defects resulted in serious market complaints. To improve the situation, the [S] and [A] processes received top priority, in an effort to stabilize new product quality at an earlier phase. Through analysis and refinement of the QC process chart by deployment from the QA chart, process capability, technical training, and education of plant workers (with more QC circles activities) were improved. The time for stabilizing new product quality was greatly reduced, and the quality deployment system was upgraded to include operating standards.

Figure 8.3 is an example of a quality analysis of critical quality areas (maximum output, amount of oil consumed) for the initial production run of engines. Frequently occurring causes were identified, and processes were improved to stabilize quality. In this example, the QA chart and QC process chart reflect the improvements in the early stabilization of initial production quality of a new product. Figure 8.4 illustrates the quality deployment system leading through the QA chart, QC process chart, and operating standards manuals. Its purpose is the early stabilization of product quality.

Figure 8.5 shows that the [S] and [A] processes are controlled separately from other processes. Assignment to these processes is limited to well-trained, highly skilled workers, and a special training program exists for each step of the production process. It sets worker selection criteria for the [S] and [A] processes, evaluates the individuals selected, specifies training and education, assigns in accordance with skill level, and follows up with additional training and education to upgrade skills. Figure 8.6 explains this process. Figure 8.7 is a chart for evaluating the skill of those assigned to the [S] and [A] machining processes. The evaluation chart permits evaluation prior to assignment, planning and implementation of training, and confirming evaluation after training. In Figure 8.8 the workers are assigned to new jobs on the basis of skill level created by the training.

EVALUATION AND IMPROVEMENT OF PROCESS CAPABILITY

For the evaluation and improvement of process capability of the [S] and [A] processes, medium-term quality policy has two parts.

1. Placing top priority on customer safety and hazard-free products
2. Consistently achieving the planned capability of functions vital to agricultural machinery and diesel engines.

In addition, for critical-to-safety parts there must be a review of control conditions for all parts and a process capability index of 1.33 or above. For critical-to-function parts there must be identification of critical functions and a review of control conditions of critical-to-function parts.

A review of the actual capability of the manufacturing processes to establish measures against chronic defects was initiated for stabiliza-

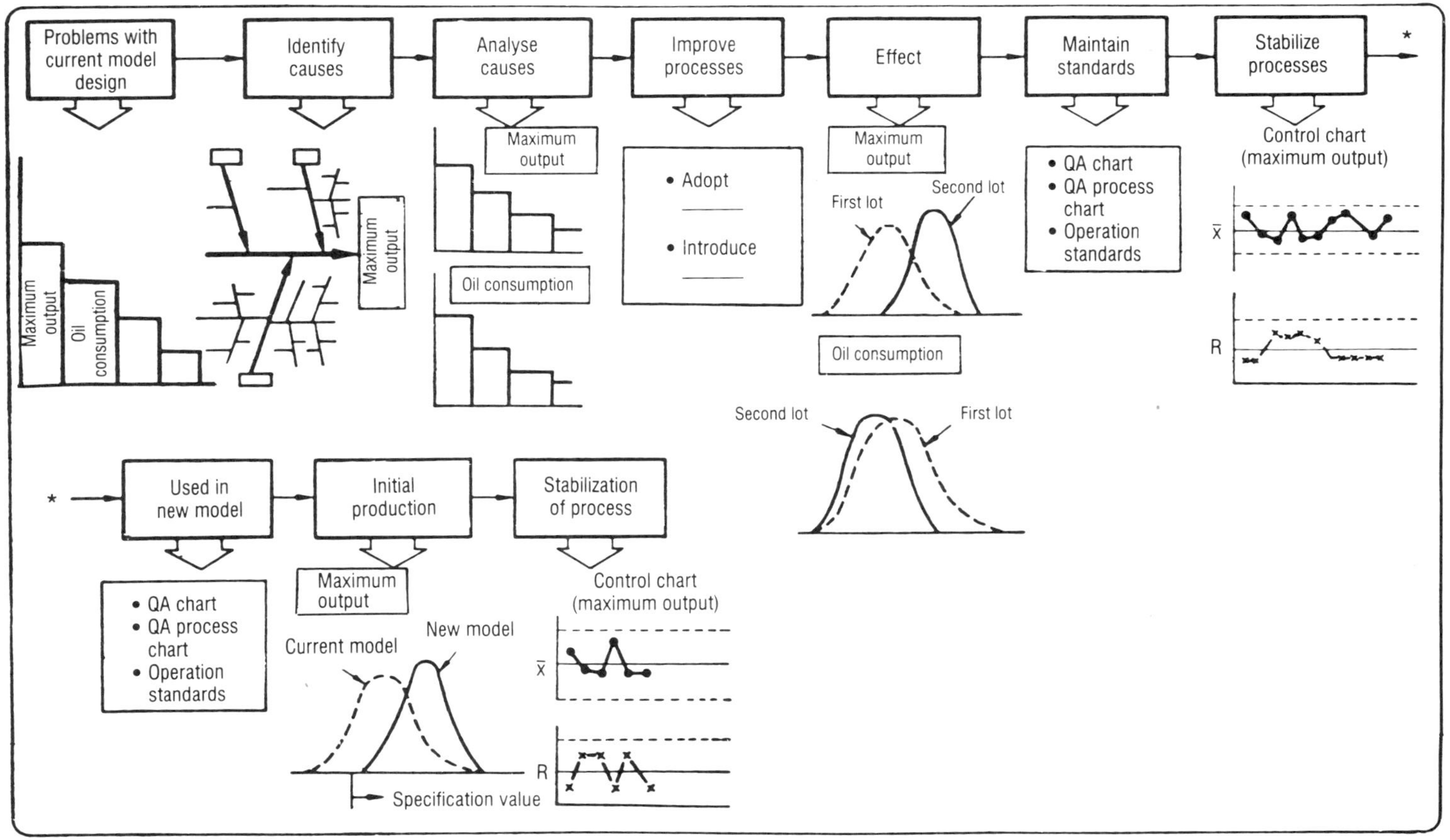

FIGURE 8.3
Example of process improvement based on initial production run

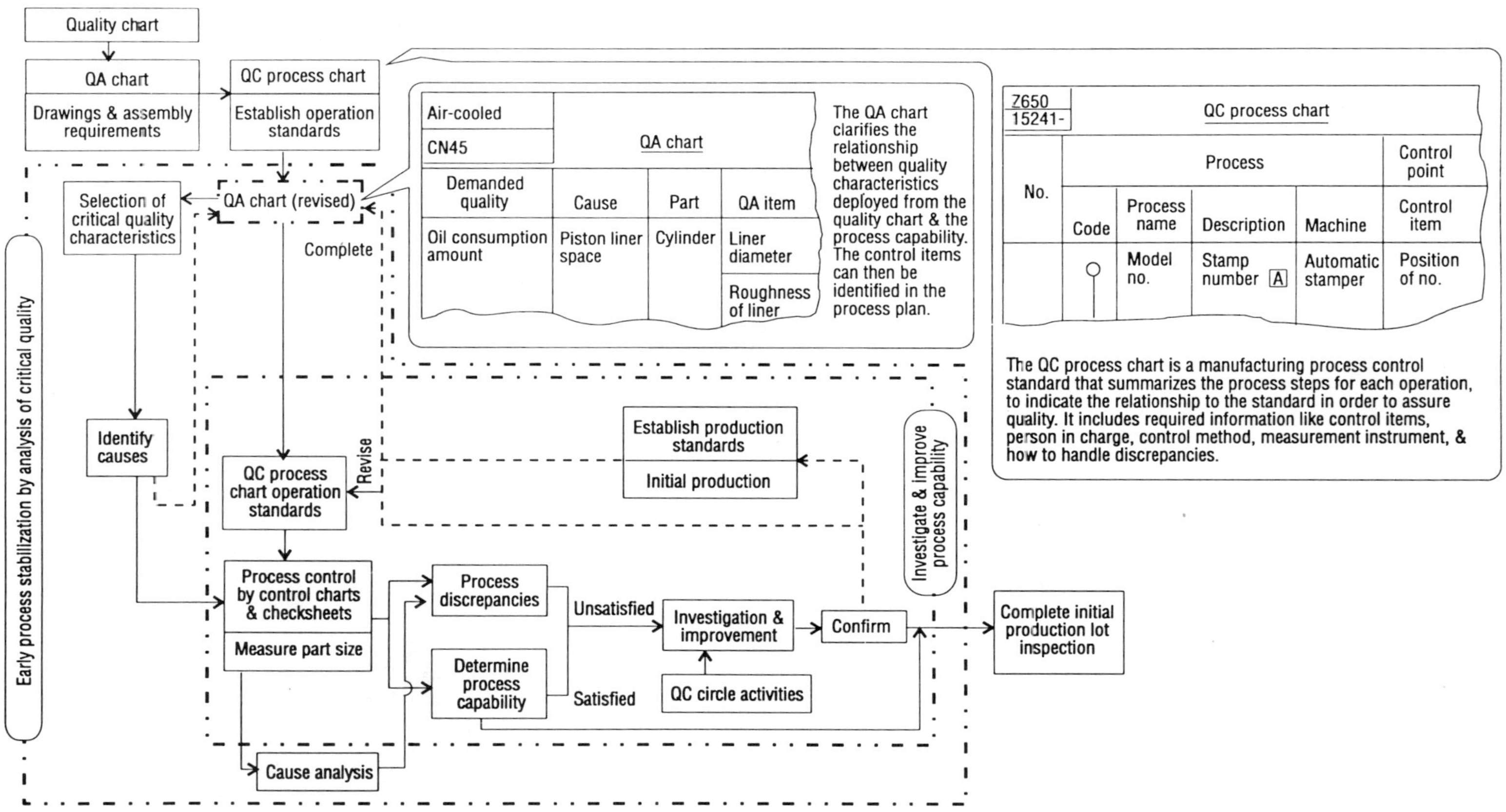

FIGURE 8.4
Development and review of the QA chart and QC process chart

	Item	[S] process	[A] process	General process
Machine	Machine used	Limited to critical equipment: critical equipment daily inspection chart	Nothing special	None
	Chart used			

	Item	[S] process	[A] process	General process
Operator	Assignment	Assignment limited to qualified operators: operator confirmation chart	Assign operators: operator confirmation chart	Not applicable
	Training			

	Item	[S] process	[A] process	General process
Method	Control items	[S] process control standards deployed from QA chart	[A] process control standards deployed from QA chart	Nothing on drawings
	Production standards	Established by analysis	Established by analysis	Use values based on experience
	Check	Checksheet for initial lot production; daily sampling	Checksheet for initial lot production; daily sampling	Not specified
	Person in charge	Foreman	Unit leader	Unit leader or group leader
	Measuring instruments	[S] mark display • Control chart for measuring instruments • Measurement standards	• Control chart for measuring instruments • Measurement standards	None
	Records	Control chart, data sheet	Control chart, data sheet	Not specified
	Determine process capability	Graph of C_p drift (C_p target)	Graph of C_p drift (C_p target)	

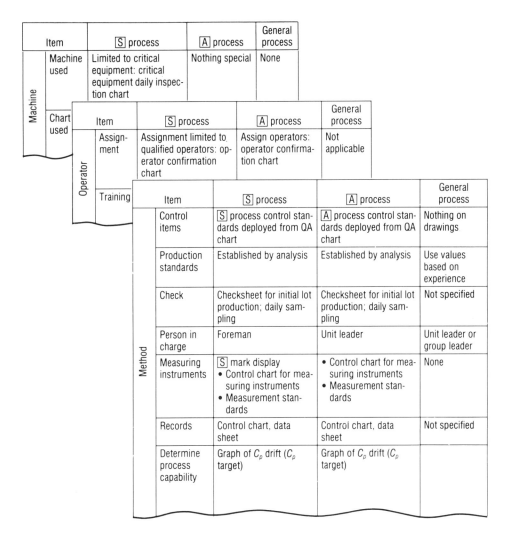

FIGURE 8.5
Example of control by prioritization of manufacturing processes

tion of quality at an early phase. Emphasis was on start-up production through an analysis of causes. Evaluation and review have been effectively conducted to improve process capability. These actions have facilitated quality analysis to improve the system of deploying quality, process analysis, and effective communication of information on process capability to the product development department.

Figure 8.9 outlines how the system works when quality evaluation uncovers documented quality problems and a project is initiated to investigate and to improve the process capability. An example of reduction of noise level in air-cooled engines is detailed in *Quality Control* (28 [June 1977]:120).

(Text continues on p. 205)

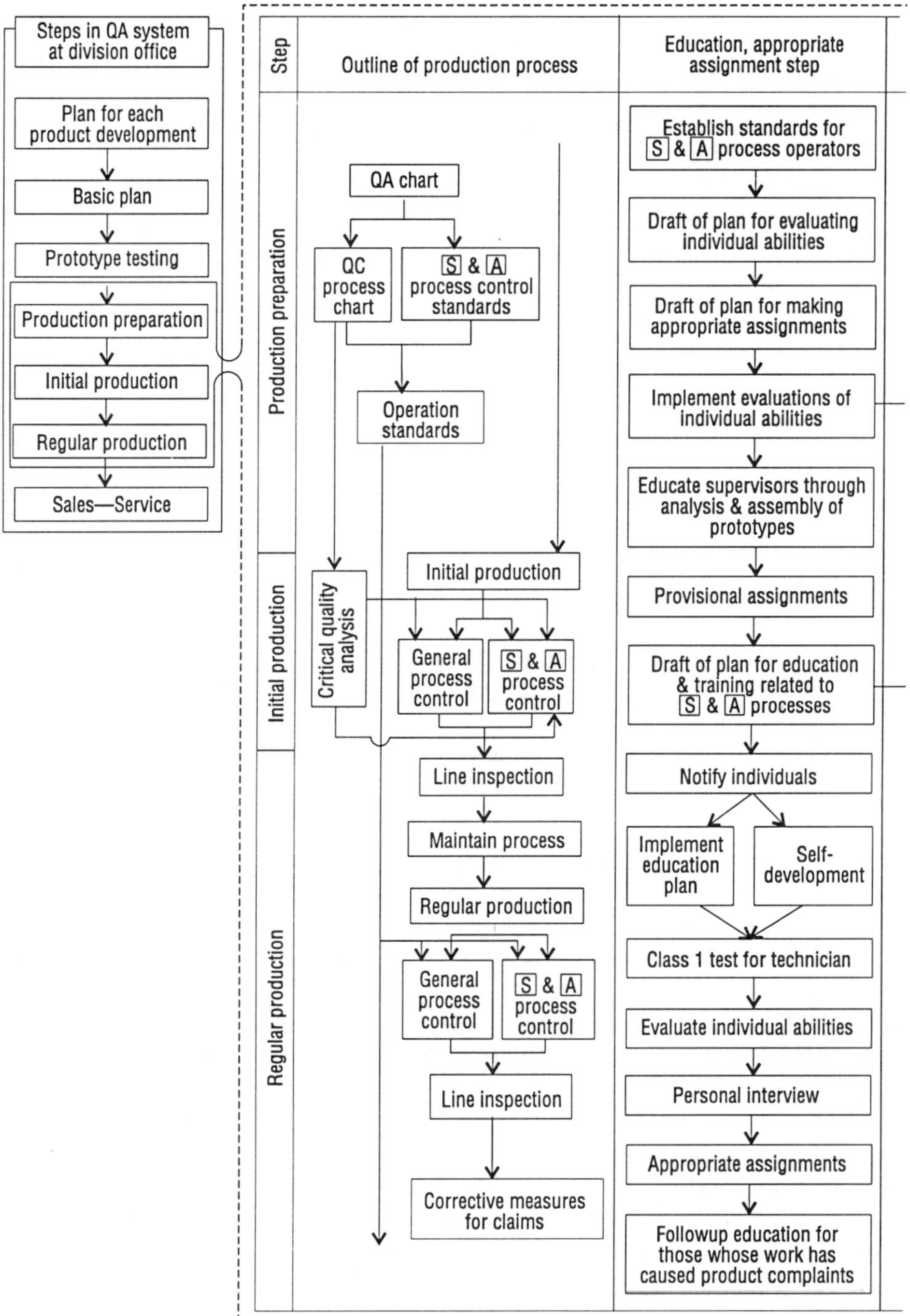

FIGURE 8.6
Implementation of education and operator assignment for control by prioritization

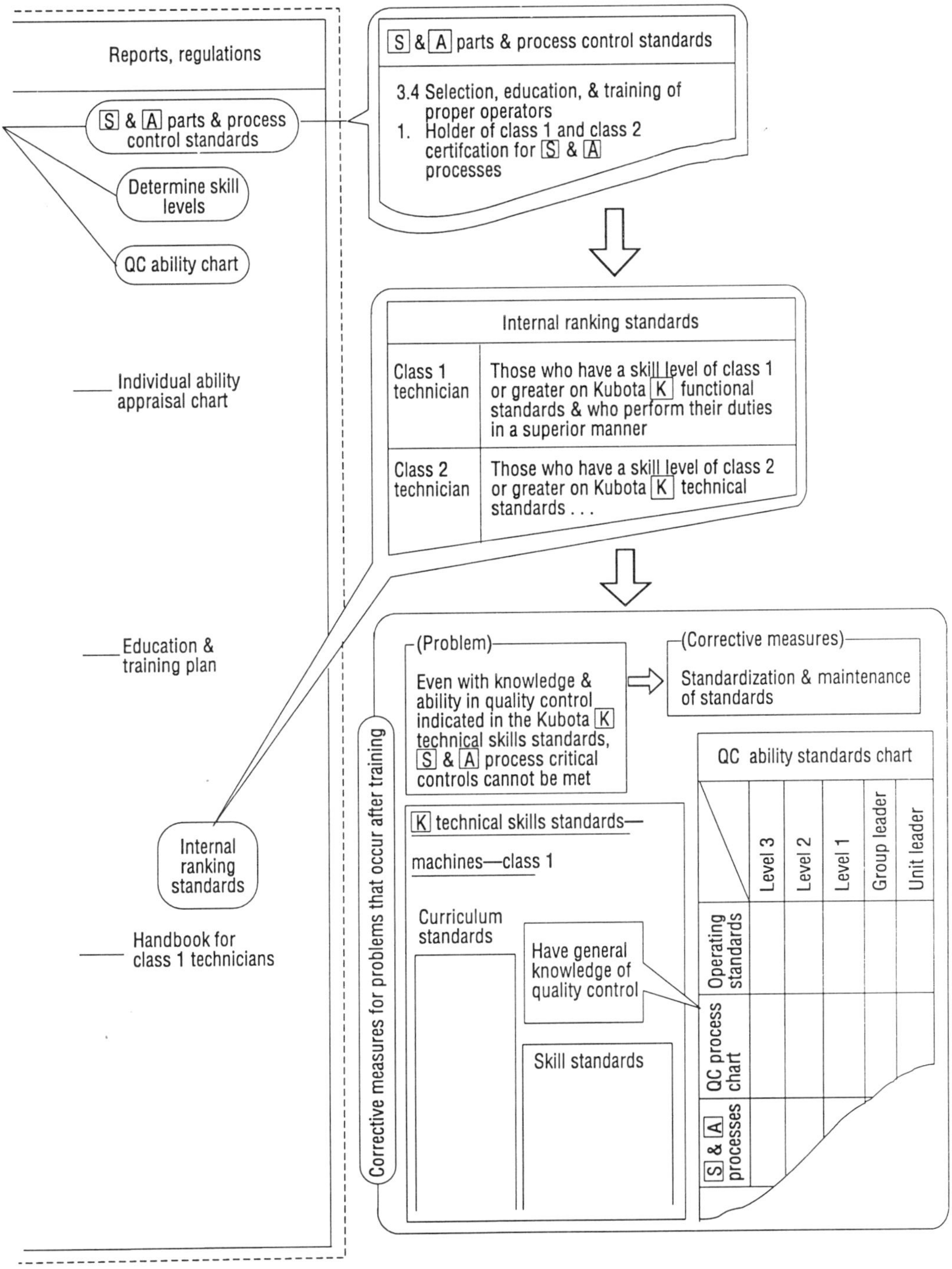
Reports, regulations
S & A parts & process control standards
Determine skill levels
QC ability chart
Individual ability appraisal chart
Education & training plan
Internal ranking standards
Handbook for class 1 technicians
S & A parts & process control standards
3.4 Selection, education, & training of proper operators
1. Holder of class 1 and class 2 certifcation for S & A processes
Internal ranking standards
Class 1 technician
Those who have a skill level of class 1 or greater on Kubota K functional standards & who perform their duties in a superior manner
Class 2 technician
Those who have a skill level of class 2 or greater on Kubota K technical standards . . .
Corrective measures for problems that occur after training
(Problem)
Even with knowledge & ability in quality control indicated in the Kubota K technical skills standards, S & A process critical controls cannot be met
(Corrective measures)
Standardization & maintenance of standards
K technical skills standards—machines—class 1
Curriculum standards
Have general knowledge of quality control
Skill standards
QC ability standards chart
Level 3
Level 2
Level 1
Group leader
Unit leader
Operating standards
QC process chart
S & A processes

For qualification For education & training	S & A processes individual ability evaluation form (machine)	7/16/76	Section manager (approval)	Foreman (evaluation)	Date	Section manager (approval)	Foreman (evaluation)
		S process qualification			A process qualification		

Dept.	Manufacturing dept.	Job no.	Name	Assistant foreman rank	Qualification date	

	Element (item)	Details of requirements (observed guidelines)	1 Unsatisfactory	2	3 Average	4	5 Above average
Skill standards	1. Operating skills	1. Quick & reliable operation of one's machine tool equipment & speed controls					●
		2. Ability to react quickly to & discover problems with one's machine tools					●
	2. Good job setup skills	1. Quick & reliable setup of appropriate tooling; knowledge of standards					●
		2. Able to perform job properly in time allotted					●
		3. Knowledge of prior & next processes; able to apply skills quickly				●	
	3. Good cutting & grinding skills	1. Able to load workpiece & perform cutting (grinding) operations quickly & accurately					●
		2. Able to maintain optimum standard operating conditions when cutting (grinding) workpiece					●
		3. Able to judge wear & life of cutting (grinding) tools, predict when defects are likely to occur, & can take appropriate action			●	×	
		4. Exhibits skills in satisfying process capability for one's own machine & should a malfunction occur, seeks the cause & prevents recurrence		●		×	
	4. Has measurement instrument skill	1. Able to select proper measuring instrument & can take measurements quickly & accurately					●
		2. Able to judge surface finish intuitively & fit as specified in the Japanese Industrial Standards				●	
capability standards	5. Standards related	1. Able to understand & follow operating standards					●
		2. Able to identify mistakes & propose improvements in operating standards				●	
		3. Understands contents of QC process chart & can identify problems	●			×	

●—● Actual performance
×—× Target performance

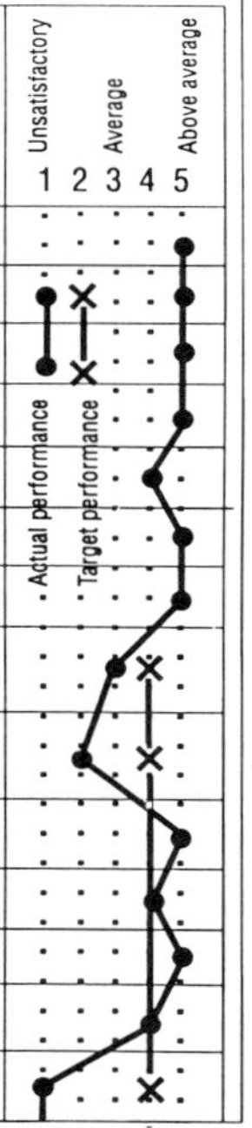

Quality control	6. Data related	1. Able to calculate process capability index & understands how to improve upon it
		2. Able to analyze causes of certain effects
		3. Able to determine from control charts when process is stable or out of control
		4. Understands basic QC tools (7 QC Tools) by name & usage
Safety	7. Safety related	1. Can perform safety operations
Critical	8. Knowledge of control standards	KS002–0002 1. Classify critical parts & processes; KS041–0006 Indicated classification of critical parts & processes; KS943–001 General control of critical safety parts

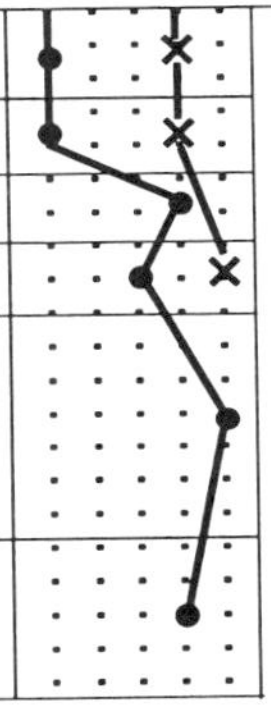

[S] & [A] parts & process control standards (manufacturing dept.) established 5/16/76 (excerpt)
1. For performing [S] processes, those holding class 1 or class 2 levels, someone selected by the workplace supervisor, & authorized by the appropriate manufacturing section manager
2. For performing [A] processes, someone selected by the workplace supervisor & authorized by the appropriate manufacturing section manager

Date evaluated	7/20/76	Evaluation points	76

Critical training areas	Achievement standard (expected level)	Training method	Achievement training period	Trainer	Training materials	Achievement level	Remarks
Items where training is required to achieve planned level	Which level must be attained?	What method is used for training?	By when will it be accomplished?	Who will train?	What training materials will be used?	What training objectives were reached?	Specific training methods or retraining items needed
6. Data related	4. Level	Man-to-man	( ) days ( ) weeks one month (circled) two months ( ) months	Foreman Unit leader (circled) Group leader QC person (circled) Other worker Staff	Operating standards (circled) QC process chart Engineering standards (circled) Setup cards (QC methods) ( )		

FIGURE 8.7
Individual ability evaluation form

Chart of appropriate personnel assignments — Line name: Crank B

○ Technician with sufficient setup skill

⦶ Technician with sufficient operation skill

S A classification						(A)	(A)	(A)	(A)	(A)						
Equipment no.	SP142	L521 L522	L477 L478	L200 L103	L527	L488	L514 L516	M215	M251	M268		D515 D503 D481	D32	M156 M170 M246 M242	PH124	G146
Equipment (process) / Operator name	Centering	Copying lathe—KDM	Copying lathe—Ikegai	Lathe	Ohsumi NC lathe	Ikegai NC lathe	Niigata lathe	Heller RFK 800	Heller RFK 600	Heller RFK 250	Gun drill	Jokoku multiple spindle milling machine	Self-feeder	Key milling machine	Tsugami rolling machine	Mitsubishi hobbing machine
A	○	⦶	○	(T•)	(⦶)	(⦶)	○					⦶			⦶	⦶
B	○	○	○			○										
C	○	○	○	○	○	○		⦶			⦶			⦶	○	○
D				○	○	○	○									
E				○	○	○	○				⦶	⦶			⦶	⦶
F				⦶	(T•)	(T•)		○	○		⦶	⦶	○	⦶	⦶	⦶
G	⦶		⦶	⦶	○	○		○	○	○	⦶			○	○	○
H								○	○	○		⦶	○	⦶		
I	⦶	⦶						○	○					⦶		
J											○	○				
K											○	○	○	(T•)		
L											⦶	○	○			
M				⦶	⦶•	⦶•		⦶				⦶		○	⦶	○
N				(T•)	(T•)	(T•)		(T•)	(T•)		⦶			○	⦶	⦶
O												⦶		○	○	○
P					(T•)	(T•)	○			(T•)						

(T•) =Training

FIGURE 8.8
Chart of appropriate personnel assignments

◯ Needs skills for setup & operation

Manufacturing section 1

Dept. manager	Foreman	Supervisor	Unit leader
Matsumoto	Kugitani	Iwasawa	Umeki

Documentation history

Checked 7/1/76

Remarks column

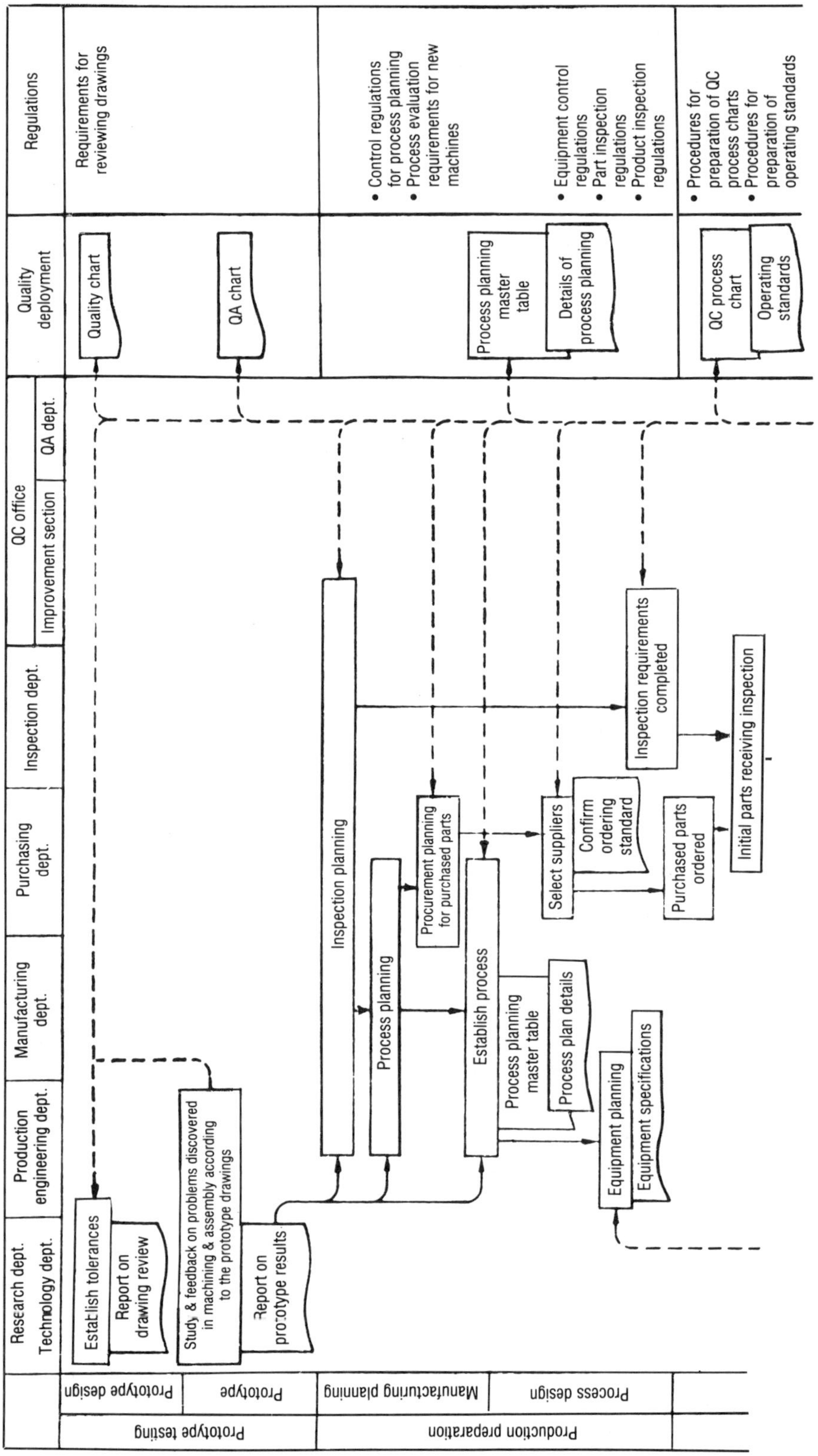
Research dept.
Technology dept.
Production engineering dept.
Manufacturing dept.
Purchasing dept.
Inspection dept.
QC office
Improvement section
QA dept.
Quality deployment
Regulations
Prototype testing
Prototype design
Prototype
Production preparation
Manufacturing planning
Process design
Establish tolerances
Report on drawing review
Study & feedback on problems discovered in machining & assembly according to the prototype drawings
Report on prototype results
Quality chart
QA chart
Requirements for reviewing drawings
Inspection planning
Process planning
Establish process
Procurement planning for purchased parts
Process planning master table
Process plan details
Equipment planning
Equipment specifications
Select suppliers
Confirm ordering standard
Purchased parts ordered
Inspection requirements completed
Initial parts receiving inspection
Process planning master table
Details of process planning
QC process chart
Operating standards
• Control regulations for process planning
• Process evaluation requirements for new machines
• Equipment control regulations
• Part inspection regulations
• Product inspection regulations
• Procedures for preparation of QC process charts
• Procedures for preparation of operating standards

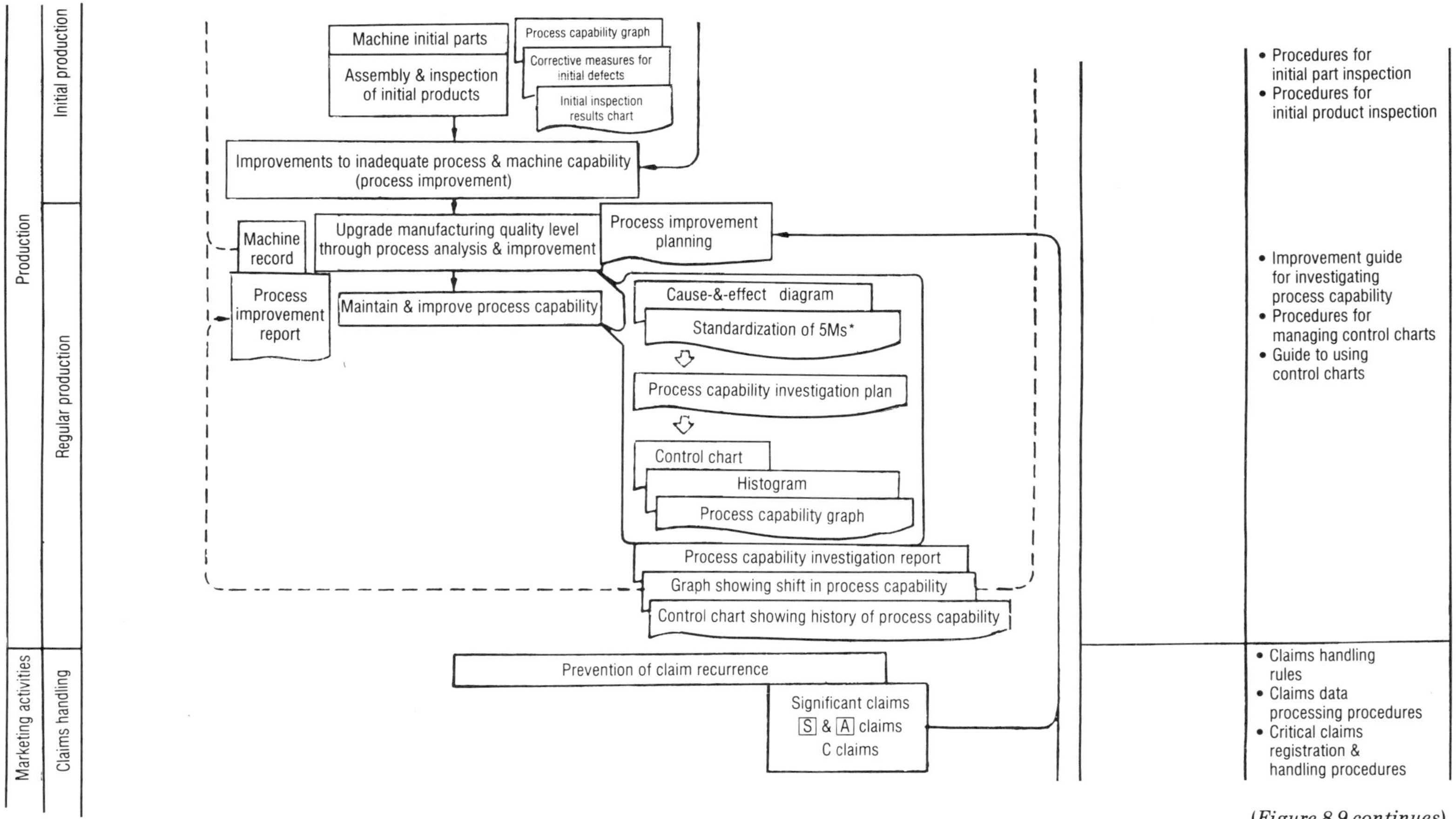
Production
Initial production
Regular production
Marketing activities
Claims handling
Machine initial parts
Assembly & inspection of initial products
Process capability graph
Corrective measures for initial defects
Initial inspection results chart
Improvements to inadequate process & machine capability (process improvement)
Machine record
Upgrade manufacturing quality level through process analysis & improvement
Process improvement planning
Process improvement report
Maintain & improve process capability
Cause-&-effect diagram
Standardization of 5Ms*
Process capability investigation plan
Control chart
Histogram
Process capability graph
Process capability investigation report
Graph showing shift in process capability
Control chart showing history of process capability
Prevention of claim recurrence
Significant claims
S & A claims
C claims
• Procedures for initial part inspection
• Procedures for initial product inspection
• Improvement guide for investigating process capability
• Procedures for managing control charts
• Guide to using control charts
• Claims handling rules
• Claims data processing procedures
• Critical claims registration & handling procedures

(*Figure 8.9 continues*)

(continued)

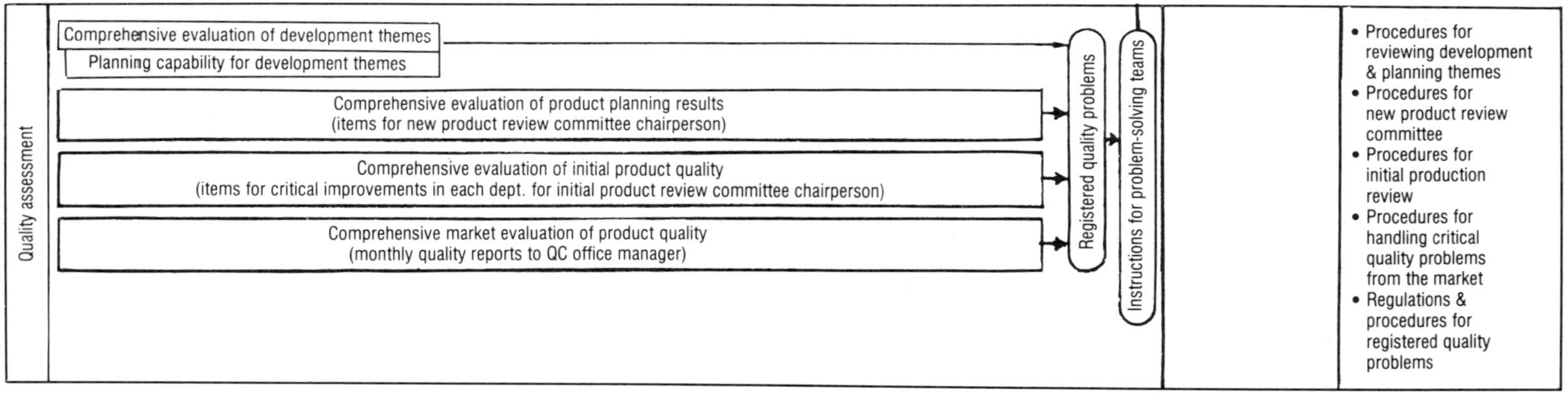

*5Ms = man, machine, method, materials, measurement

FIGURE 8.9
System for investigation and improvement of process capability

CONCLUSION

Kubota's internal combustion division's system to control high-priority [S] and [A] parts and processes during product development, production preparation, and manufacturing is supported by the special activities described. The sales department, however, needs to become more active.

Kubota's target is zero claims in the marketplace with regard to [S] and [A] parts and processes. To achieve this goal, further system upgrading for the control of critical parts and processes is required. To further this, the [S] and [A] items currently established, which are based on past quality information, are to be selected more carefully through the reliability control activities to be explained in the introduction to Chapter 11. They are being promoted as TQM activities for control of [S] and [A] parts and processes to reduce risk.

9

Quality Deployment and Manufacturing Methods Deployment

Takao Tanisawa

INTRODUCTION

Changes in the social structure and environment have brought about a marketplace that increasingly demands products that exhibit higher performance, more diversity, better safety and fewer hazardous effects, and greater economy. This is particularly true for large and medium-size trucks and buses because of the wide range of applications in which they are used. Assuring a company's survival and continued success under such business conditions requires predicting changes in this environment, proactively keeping pace with trends, and delivering to customers products that fit changing social norms.

From the concepts based on quality assurance described earlier, the identification and implementation of assurance items, and gathering market requirements, to final sales and service, this "market-in" approach is vital.

THE PHILOSOPHY OF QUALITY FUNCTION DEPLOYMENT

Quality function deployment brings the market-in concept to the entire company's quality assurance activities, including all phases of market research, R&D, product planning, product design, production preparation, purchasing, production sales, service, and marketing. Essentially it is a system linking all activities to one objective: quality. Figure 9.1 is a concept diagram of such a system.

At Hino Motors, deployment of the quality function is employed to guide companywide quality assurance activities. Quality function deployment is a concrete way of managing market-demanded quality through a system of purposeful links by deploying the demand into

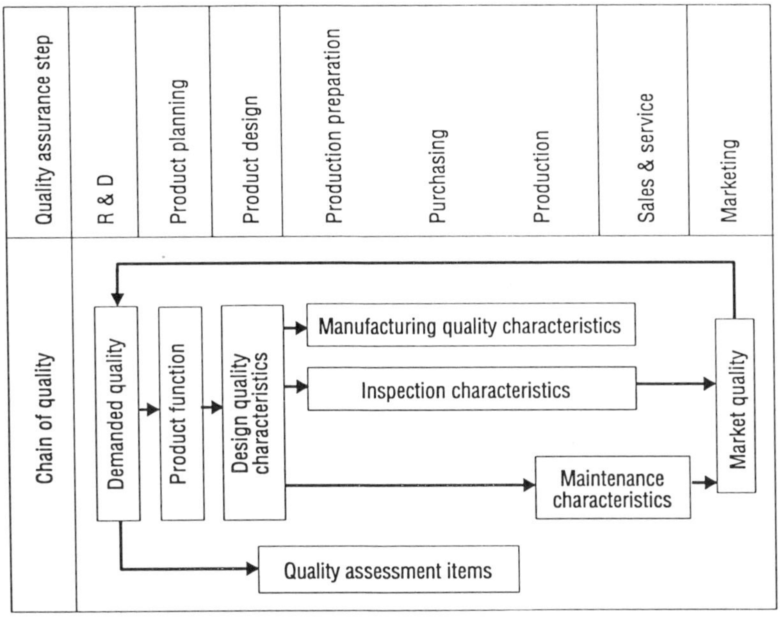

FIGURE 9.1
Linking a system for quality

design quality characteristics, manufacturing control characteristics, inspection characteristics, and maintenance characteristics. By managing these characteristics through each phase from market research to sales and service, quality that will be acceptable to the market is produced.

Hino Motors received the Deming Prize in 1971 for improvements made in its quality assurance system. Even so, from the results of market research on the initial quality of new products it was clear that (1) the interrelationships of quality characteristics was inadequate and (2) the design department's intentions were not being communicated sufficiently to the production department. To come up with implementable corrections, the product development department has been promoting the objective of clearly identifying tolerance stackup issues that lead to day-to-day quality problems.

Additional activities were employed to improve communication of design intentions to the production department and to develop appropriate control characteristics for them. In time, through developing successive new products, specific methods and means were perfected. These activities not only have brought greater precision against tolerance stackup but also have led to deployment of market requirements into better means of communicating design intent and cooperation among departments within the company.

QUALITY FUNCTION DEPLOYMENT AND PRODUCTION PREPARATION

Background of Quality Function Deployment at Hino Motors

The main purpose of the quality function deployment system is to assure the survival and prosperity of the company by ensuring that its products are acceptable to the marketplace. This is accomplished by strengthening the links between the multitude of departments involved – product planning, design, production preparation, production, and marketing – so that quality can be built into production methods, equipment, and so on by the production preparation department in an objective and economical way. This is called manufacturing methods deployment and has been systematically introduced in the company.

Conventional quality assurance activities in the production preparation department focused on satisfying design quality characteristics while attempting to assure cost and production volume objectives. Market data were used primarily to address complaints, a far cry from being used to predict trends in market requirements.

The real incentive for introducing manufacturing methods deployment was that a major cause of market complaints was the inadequate control of tolerance stackup (i.e., the precision of assembling a succession of components and subsystems) and a poor understanding of how this related to overall product function. Even though the manufacturing process could focus on controlling the precision of individual parts, it could not adequately control the stackup of precision errors in assemblies of these parts. Thus, the quality chain would break down. Further, in an attempt to alleviate this, the precision of individual parts was often pursued so relentlessly that the cost was driven up, even though the means to achieve quality objectives must optimize the relationship between quality and cost. A further problem was that the system to understand the relationship between product function and the precision of the component parts was inadequate, as was the ability to predict future market needs, so that these activities relied mostly on the insights of individual managers.

In this light, the production preparation department directed its efforts to linking the quality characteristics in the manufacturing methods and the other manufacturing processes: from raw materials to machining to parts assembly to component units to system assembly. By linking design quality to manufacturing methods and final assembly, the product can be made at minimum cost. This is the beginning of a system of linking quality to manufacturing methods (manufacturing methods deployment).

An example of this system is given in Figure 9.2 for performance

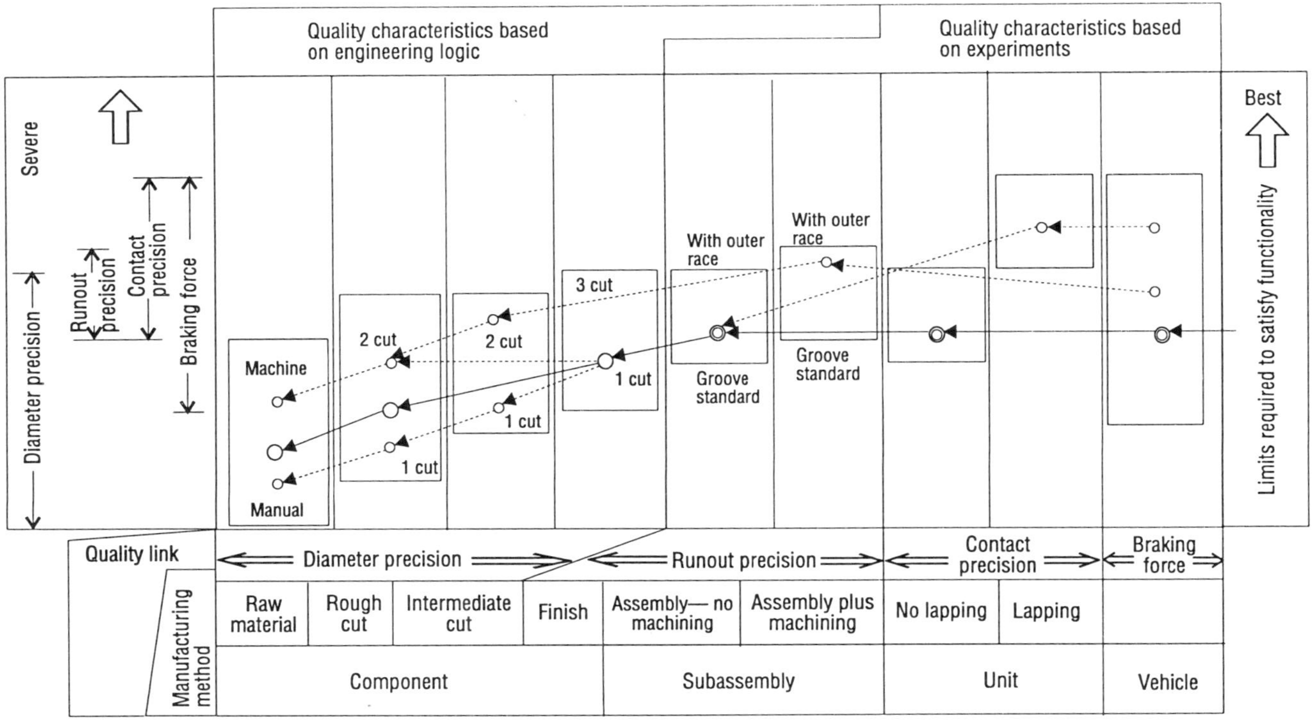

FIGURE 9.2

Linking quality and manufacturing methods

Note: This figure depicts the concept of objectively transforming quality links into manufacturing methods. Quality is carried to vehicle-to-unit-to-subassembly-to-component structural levels, and causal relationships are linked to the functional quality characteristics, the assembly quality characteristics, and component quality characteristics. In terms of a process, based on different manufacturing methods, process sequences, and a combination thereof, a machine sequence can be linked to a manufacturing method. These two links are illustrated in this example as the quantitative limits required to achieve product quality.

of a vehicle brake system. Braking force is known from experiments to rely upon how precisely the brake shoe contacts the brake drum as a unit, and upon the trueness of the inner diameter of the drum and the outer diameter of the shoes as a subassembly. From the viewpoint of manufacturing methods and engineering logic, however, the level of precision to be assured for each manufacturing method can be linked to other processes, from raw materials to machining to assembly. By linking these, defect-free manufacturing can be done in the most cost-effective manner.

The basic philosophy behind establishing minimum-cost manufacturing methods begins with the fact that there are many links in the manufacturing methods that can be tied to quality in order to achieve a single target. From among those that best meet these objectives, a selection is made on the basis of cost. This can be likened to a manufacturing method "menu" that becomes the quality-cost graph illustrated in Figure 9.3.

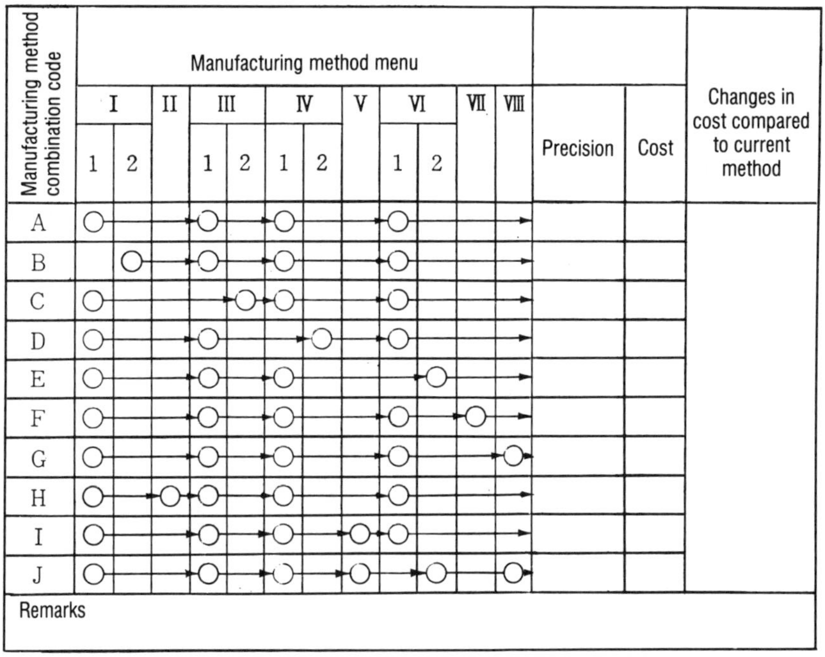

Manufacturing method combination code
Manufacturing method menu
I
II
III
IV
V
VI
VII
VIII
1 2 1 2 1 2 1 2
Precision
Cost
Changes in cost compared to current method
A
B
C
D
E
F
G
H
I
J
Remarks

FIGURE 9.3
Manufacturing method menu

Note: In this figure, a multitude of manufacturing methods are organized like a menu, showing precision and cost. Then, linking the manufacturing methods into a sequence by the type of method, the processes sequence, and the combination of these gives A, B, C, ... Each method is then reviewed in terms of precision and cost, and the optimal method is selected.

Details and Purpose of Manufacturing Methods Deployment

Manufacturing methods deployment can be loosely divided into three stages. The first occurs during the product design phase and is synchronized with productivity studies. The second stage is in the production preparation phase, where it is synchronized with manufacturing methods, equipment investigations, procurement, and facility planning. The third stage occurs during production and introduction of the product to the market. During all three stages it is critical that market-in approaches drive the plan-do-check-act cycle of control. Details of this flow can be seen in Figure 9.4.

The intent of manufacturing methods deployment can be summed in five steps.

1. Promoting research in manufacturing methods and a search for well-founded quality characteristics, and negotiating with the designers to optimize the manufacturing methods and processes, in order to deliver quality at the lowest possible cost
2. Objectively and systematically arranging the relationship between quality characteristics and manufacturing methods, and checking their continuity as a process
3. Employing the manufacturing methods deployment chart to communicate the design and manufacturing intent when establishing processes
4. Establishing in the manufacturing processes inspection items and inspection processes, and communicating those requirements to manufacturing
5. Following up after production has begun, so that manufacturing research studies based on improvements and market application data can be made to improve the manufacturing processes, develop new processes, and predict future requirements for both internal and external customers.

STEPS FOR IMPLEMENTING MANUFACTURING METHODS DEPLOYMENT

This is an example of specific steps to implement manufacturing methods deployment activities.

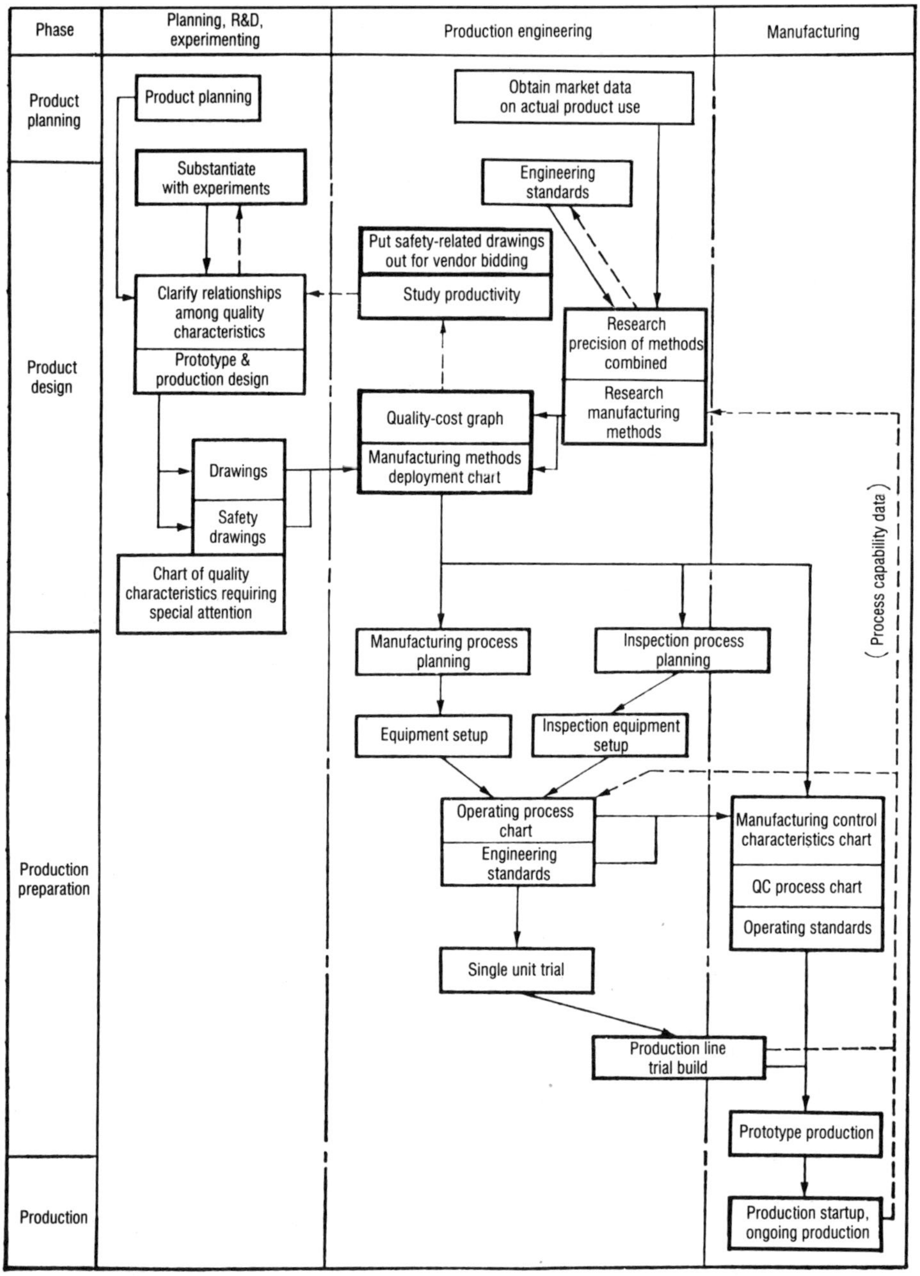

FIGURE 9.4
Manufacturing methods deployment flow chart

Preliminary Manufacturing Methods Deployment Chart

Function Deployment Chart and Cause-and-Effect Diagram for Quality Characteristics

To better understand how product functions link in a system, diagram quality characteristics to structural levels of the product. This can be done as in Figure 9.5, with a cause-and-effect diagram of quality characteristics or a function deployment chart.

Function Quality Characteristics vs. Component Parts Matrix

Figure 9.6 is a quality characteristics vs. component parts characteristics matrix for the vehicle assembly components, derived from the function deployment chart and quality characteristics cause-and-effect diagram. This matrix depicts the cause-and-effect relationship between function quality characteristics and component parts characteristics, and aids in the process of identifying critical quality characteristics.

Selecting Quality Items for Manufacturing Methods Deployment

Based on the cause-and-effect diagram and the matrix, the next step is to prioritize specific items and to select the quality characteristics that will be used for manufacturing methods deployment.

1. New manufacturing methods, mechanisms, and parts
2. Quality characteristics for which there is great market demand
3. Design quality improvements, quality characteristics that demand improvements in manufacturing quality
4. Quality characteristics that would dramatically increase product value
5. Where there will be large investments in facilities
6. Other critical quality characteristics

Researching Manufacturing Methods

The research into manufacturing methods at this phase is still preliminary, so quality and cost issues must be critically examined from

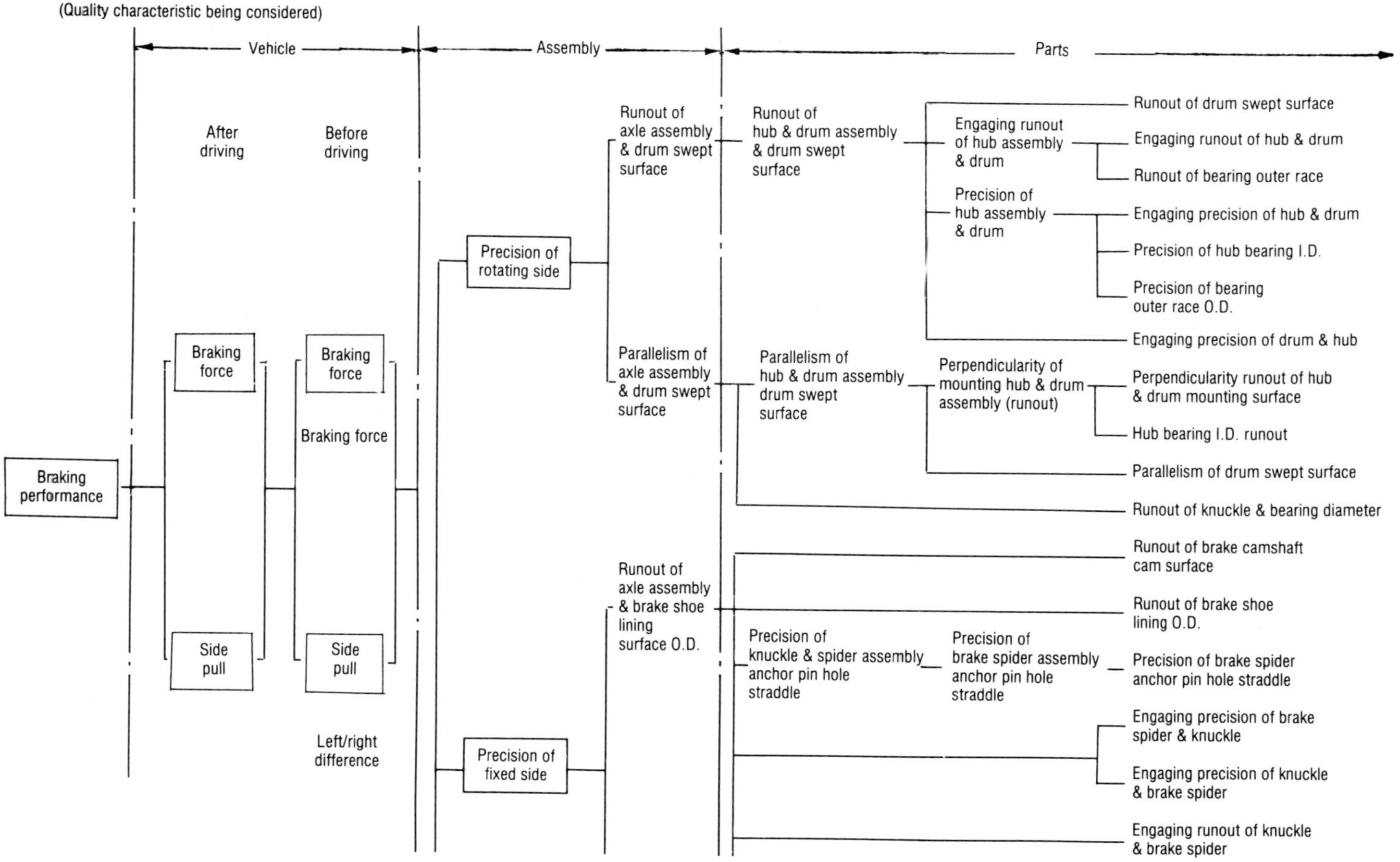

(Quality characteristic being considered)
Vehicle
Assembly
Parts
After driving
Before driving
Braking force
Side pull
Braking force
Side pull
Braking force
Left/right difference
Braking performance
Precision of rotating side
Precision of fixed side
Runout of axle assembly & drum swept surface
Parallelism of axle assembly & drum swept surface
Runout of axle assembly & brake shoe lining surface O.D.
Runout of hub & drum assembly & drum swept surface
Parallelism of hub & drum assembly drum swept surface
Precision of knuckle & spider assembly anchor pin hole straddle
Engaging runout of hub assembly & drum
Precision of hub assembly & drum
Perpendicularity of mounting hub & drum assembly (runout)
Precision of brake spider assembly anchor pin hole straddle
Runout of drum swept surface
Engaging runout of hub & drum
Runout of bearing outer race
Engaging precision of hub & drum
Precision of hub bearing I.D.
Precision of bearing outer race O.D.
Engaging precision of drum & hub
Perpendicularity runout of hub & drum mounting surface
Hub bearing I.D. runout
Parallelism of drum swept surface
Runout of knuckle & bearing diameter
Runout of brake camshaft cam surface
Runout of brake shoe lining O.D.
Precision of brake spider anchor pin hole straddle
Engaging precision of brake spider & knuckle
Engaging precision of knuckle & brake spider
Engaging runout of knuckle & brake spider

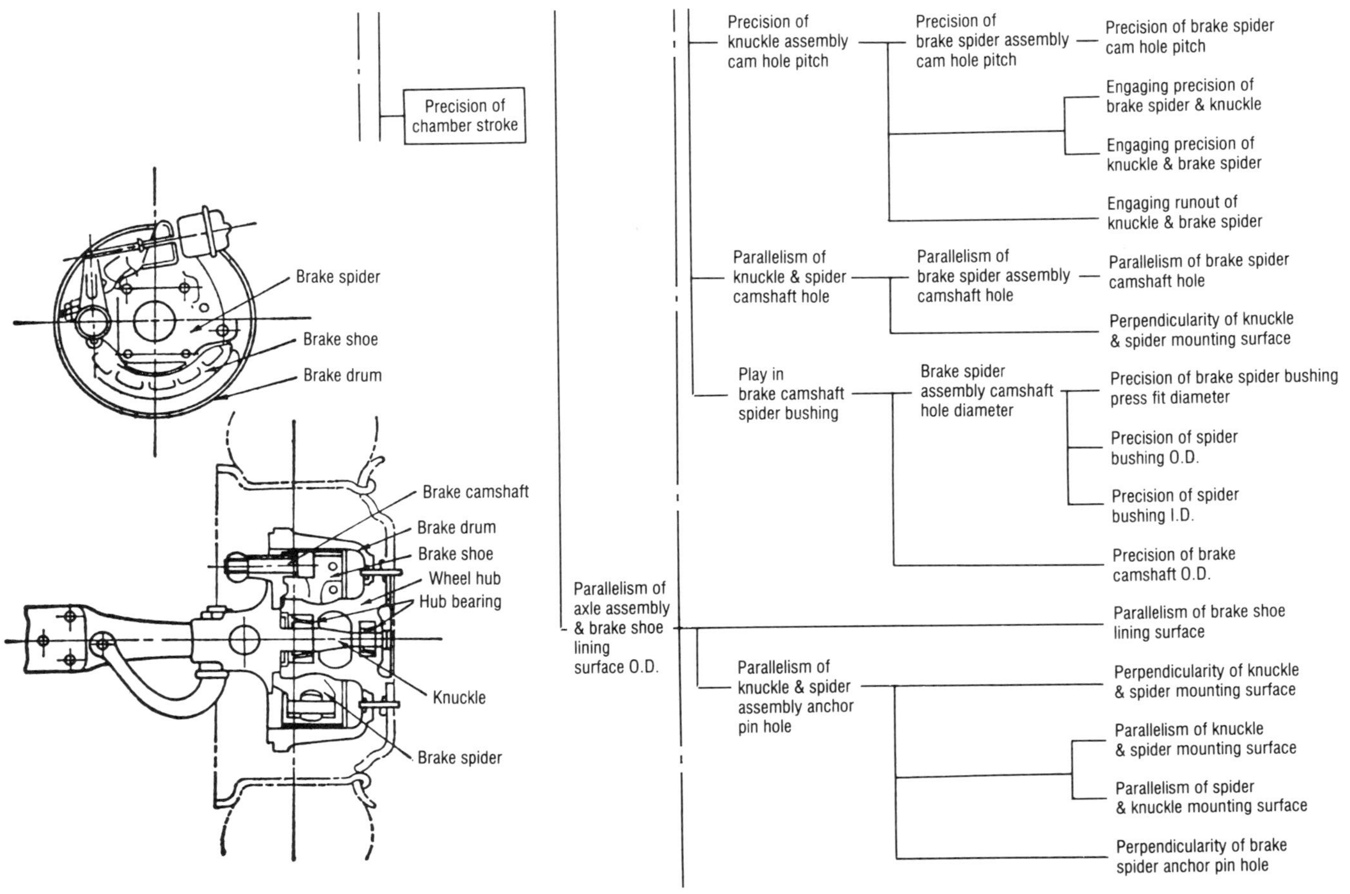

FIGURE 9.5
Quality characteristics cause-and-effect diagram

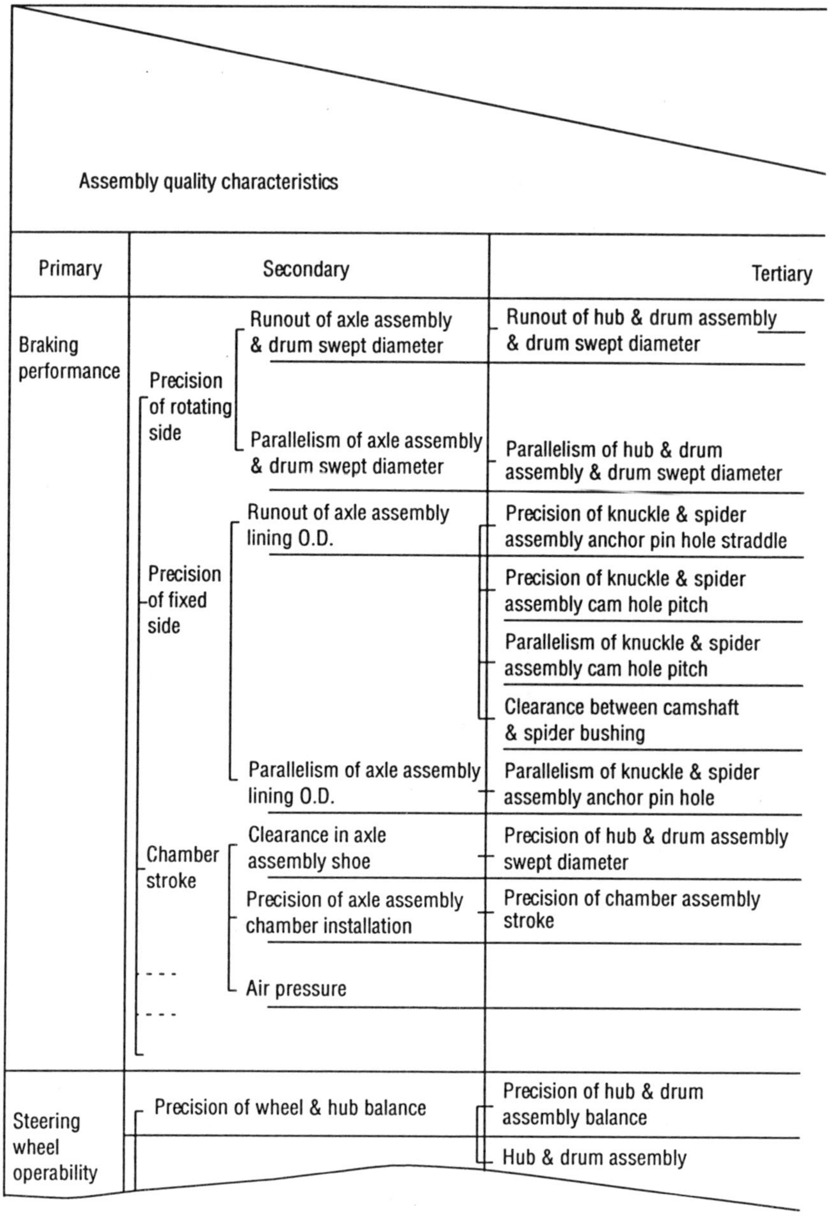
Assembly quality characteristics
Primary
Secondary
Tertiary
Braking performance
Precision of rotating side
Runout of axle assembly & drum swept diameter
Runout of hub & drum assembly & drum swept diameter
Parallelism of axle assembly & drum swept diameter
Parallelism of hub & drum assembly & drum swept diameter
Precision of fixed side
Runout of axle assembly lining O.D.
Precision of knuckle & spider assembly anchor pin hole straddle
Precision of knuckle & spider assembly cam hole pitch
Parallelism of knuckle & spider assembly cam hole pitch
Clearance between camshaft & spider bushing
Parallelism of axle assembly lining O.D.
Parallelism of knuckle & spider assembly anchor pin hole
Chamber stroke
Clearance in axle assembly shoe
Precision of hub & drum assembly swept diameter
Precision of axle assembly chamber installation
Precision of chamber assembly stroke
Air pressure
- - -
- - -
Steering wheel operability
Precision of wheel & hub balance
Precision of hub & drum assembly balance
Hub & drum assembly

FIGURE 9.6
Function quality characteristics vs. component parts quality characteristics matrix

Component parts / quality characteristics	Wheel hub: Runout of drum engagement diameter	Wheel hub: Precision of drum engagement diameter	Wheel hub: Precision of bearing I.D.	Wheel hub: Perpendicularity of drum mounting surface	Wheel hub: Runout of bearing I.D.	Brake drum: Runout of swept diameter	Brake drum: Precision of hub engagement diameter	Brake drum: Parallelism of swept surface	Knuckle: Runout of bearing O.D.	Knuckle: Precision of spider engagement diameter	Knuckle: Runout of spider engagement diameter	Knuckle: Perpendicularity of spider mounting surface
Runout of hub assembly & drum engagement diameter	///	///				///	///					
Precision of hub assembly & drum engagement diameter												
Perpendicularity of hub assembly & drum mounting surface			///	///	///			///	///			
Precision of brake spider assembly anchor pin hole straddle										///	///	
Precision of brake spider assembly cam hole pitch										///		
Parallelism of brake spider assembly cam hole pitch												///
Brake spider assembly cam hole diameter												
Engaging runout of hub assembly & drum	///	///		///		///	///					
Precision of hub assembly balance	///	///		///		///	///	///				
Hub assembly, hub bolt hole . . .												

many aspects. Five items in particular should be sufficiently addressed.

1. The ability to interchange parts, should additional machining or selective combinations become necessary after assembly
2. Serviceability, in case of adjustments during assembly
3. Other elements that could negatively affect quality characteristics
4. Machining or assembly that exists only in the "twilight zone" between work units or shops
5. Securing quality that creates function only in combination with other units

When deciding on manufacturing methods, four types of documentation should be consulted.

1. Engineering standards for proposing processes, for manufacturing processes, and for process capability
2. Documents of past investigations into the precision of tolerance stackup
3. Current process capability
4. Market data on product use

Procedure for Proposing Manufacturing Methods

The principle behind the procedure for proposing manufacturing methods is to follow the structural levels of the product from final assembly to unit assembly to subassembly to machining individual parts to raw materials, in order to link the quality characteristics from the vehicle to assemblies to subassemblies and to the precision of the parts.

1. Quality characteristics for each major process are clarified.
2. The sequence of the processes is determined so that the quality characteristics within major processes are rationally satisfied.
3. The correlation between quality characteristics is studied, particularly between the quality of assemblies and the precision of component parts.
4. The combined precision of "twilight zone" activities between work units is studied.

5. Inspection processes are developed by selecting inspection classifications, methods, and instruments and devices that support the criticality of the quality characteristics.

On the basis of these procedures, a preliminary manufacturing methods deployment chart can be made. See Figure 9.7 for a filled-in example of such a chart.

Research into Manufacturing Methods

Each manufacturing method that was studied when the preliminary manufacturing methods deployment chart was constructed is reviewed in terms of engineering standards, effects on precision of tolerance stackup, and process capability data; if necessary, experiments are made that are summarized in a manufacturing methods research chart and quality-cost graphs.

Investigation and Analysis of the Precision of Tolerance Stackup

The precision of individual component parts and the precision resulting from assembling the component parts must be investigated and analyzed statistically. The cause-and-effect relationships of the function to assembly precision to component parts precision must be identified. A typical study of tolerance stackup is shown in Figure 9.8.

Detailed Study of Manufacturing Methods

Based on the above analysis, a detailed study of a variety of manufacturing methods is made that emphasizes quality characteristics with a strong effect on product function. The degree of precision that each component part and assembly must maintain throughout the manufacturing process must be assured; this is determined through engineering standards, analysis reports of tolerance stackup, and examination of records of process capability. When determining an assurance value of a manufacturing method that involves a number of processes and assembly, the use of statistical methods to aid understanding cause-and-effect relationships and the manipulation of data on individual manufacturing methods allows values to be estimated.

Manufacturing methods deployment chart

Issue no.	Revision:				
	Date issued:				
Issuing dept.: production engineering dept., machine engineering section	Sect. mgr.	Chief eng.	Supv.	Sect. memb.	Page
					/

Part name	Front axle assembly with wheel brake	Part no.	3 307 6606 00 (representative)
Function	Braking force		
Quality characteristics	Place built-up chassis on brake tester; braking force at each wheel should exceed standard values		
	Difference between left & right sides should be within standard values		

Manufacturing method deployment

Process	Machining precision	Manufacturing method	Pre-machining conditions
Vehicle			
Inspection of completed vehicle	Braking force each wheel: $\geq$ a kg ◎ left/right difference: $\geq$ b kg ◎	Measure with brake tester 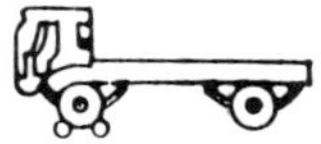	1. Chamber stroke: $\leq$ c 2. Precision of brake shoe to drum swept surface contact
Chamber stroke adjustment (end process of final line)	 Chamber stroke ◎	To replicate actual driving conditions, operate brake pedal & adjust with slack adjuster	Installation dimensions for clevis pin 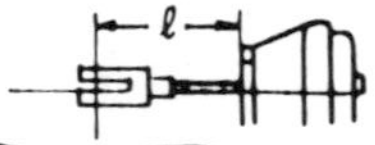

Assembly			
Install hub & drum assembly on front axle 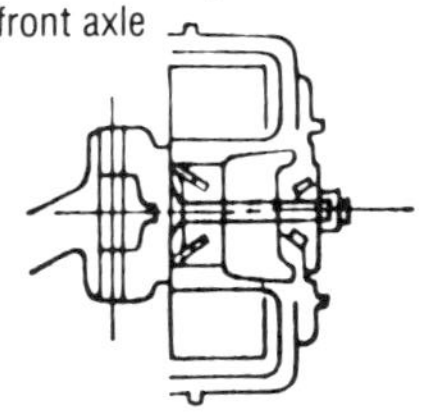	Precision of brake shoe to drum swept surface contact (rotating side) 1. Runout of brake drum swept surface: ≤ d ○ 2. Parallelism of brake drum swept surface: ≤ e ○ 3. Hub bearing start torque: f kg/cm ◎	1. When pressing (hydraulic) bearing inner race onto hub & drum assembly, avoid striking bearing 2. Do not use hammer 3. Tighten lock nut	1. Runout of brake shoe lining O.D.: ≤ g 2. Parallelism of brake shoe lining O.D.: ≤ h 3. Runout of drum swept surface in relation to hub & drum assembly bearing center: ≤ i 4. Parallelism of drum swept surface in relation to hub & drum assembly bearing center: ≤ j
Install brake hardware 	Precision of brake shoe to drum swept surface contact (fixed side) 1. Runout of brake shoe lining O.D.: ≤ g ○	Manual assembly	1. Runout of brake camshaft cam surface: ≤ k 2. Runout of brake shoe lining O.D.: ≤ g 3. Knuckle & spider assembly

(*Figure 9.7 continues*)

(continued)

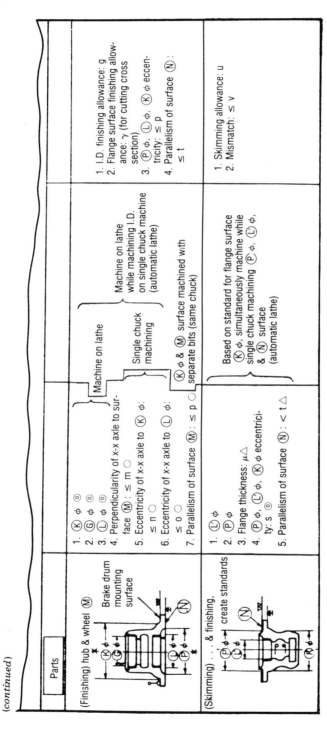

Parts			
(Finishing) hub & wheel (M) 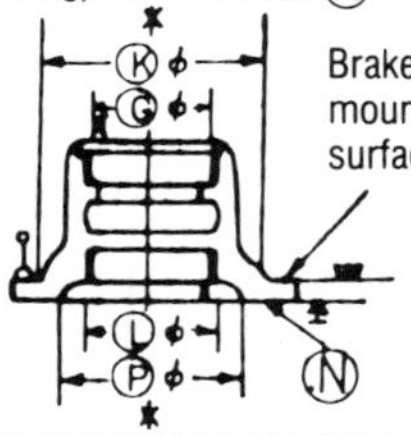	1. (K) ϕ ◎ 2. (G) ϕ ◎ 3. (L) ϕ ◎ 4. Perpendicularity of x-x axle to surface (M) : ≤ m ○ 5. Eccentricity of x-x axle to (K) ϕ: ≤ n ○ 6. Eccentricity of x-x axle to (L) ϕ: ≤ o ○ 7. Parallelism of surface (M) : ≤ p ○	Machine on lathe (items 1–3); Single chuck machining (items 4–6); Machine on lathe while machining I.D. on single chuck machine (automatic lathe) (K) ϕ & (M) surface machined with separate bits (same chuck)	1. I.D. finishing allowance: g 2. Flange surface finishing allowance: γ (for cutting cross section) 3. (P) ϕ, (L) ϕ, (K) ϕ eccentricity: ≤ p 4. Parallelism of surface (N) : ≤ t
(Skimming) . . . & finishing, create standards 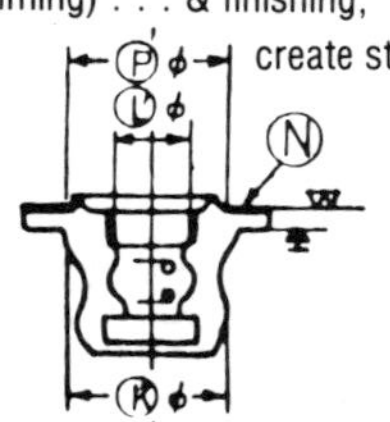	1. (L') ϕ 2. (P) ϕ 3. Flange thickness: μ△ 4. (P) ϕ, (L') ϕ, (K) ϕ eccentricity: s ◎ 5. Parallelism of surface (N) : < t △	Based on standard for flange surface (K) ϕ, simultaneously machine while single chuck machining (P) ϕ, (L') ϕ, & (N) surface (automatic lathe)	1. Skimming allowance: u 2. Mismatch: ≤ v

Inspection classification: ◎ 100% inspection ○ sample inspection (*n*/month) △ inspection at startup (*n*/shift) □ periodic inspection (*n*/month)

FIGURE 9.7
Manufacturing methods deployment chart

Experiments with Manufacturing Methods

Manufacturing method experimentation should not be restricted to the product development phase; experiments can be performed as part of the daily routine. They are done to test new component parts or subsystems; to understand the strength, durability, or performance of new materials; to change methods in order to lower costs; or to improve running costs. Further, such activities help justify engineering decisions to link basic production research to manufacturing methods and are invaluable for performing basic manufacturing studies. Some results of manufacturing methods experiments and a cost comparison are shown in the quality vs. cost graph in Figures 9.9 and 9.10.

Negotiating with Design

Linking and combining manufacturing methods to achieve the quality characteristics in the final product at the lowest possible cost first requires understanding the quality characteristic values. To understand them, the production preparation department must be involved. When there are a number of cost-effective ways to perform a manufacturing process, the question of other limitations must be addressed, such as balance of the quality characteristic values, distribution, interchangeability, and correlation with other characteristics. This necessitates some negotiation of these characteristic values with the appropriate members of the design team.

The traditional influence of the design team is to specify manufacturing methods in the drawings, but this often leaves the production department with little opportunity to reduce cost. For example, in the brake system case, a quality characteristic is the runout of the brake drum's inner diameter after assembly. If this is achieved, one function of the automobile is satisfied. In the past, the precision of the component parts was calculated mathematically and recorded on the drawings, and though there may have been opportunities to lower cost because the precision was higher than needed, this was not possible. The demanded quality and the associated control points required of function parts in order to achieve the function of the whole vehicle can be achieved through any number of manufacturing processes. From among those, the lowest-cost one should be linked to quality in order to achieve cost reduction.

The tolerance of the critical quality of function parts (for example, the runout of the brake drum's inner diameter) is determined in the design phase from the point of view of the critical functions of the entire vehicle. The tolerances of the individual components, however,

Performance of front axle brake resulting from precision of tolerance stackup

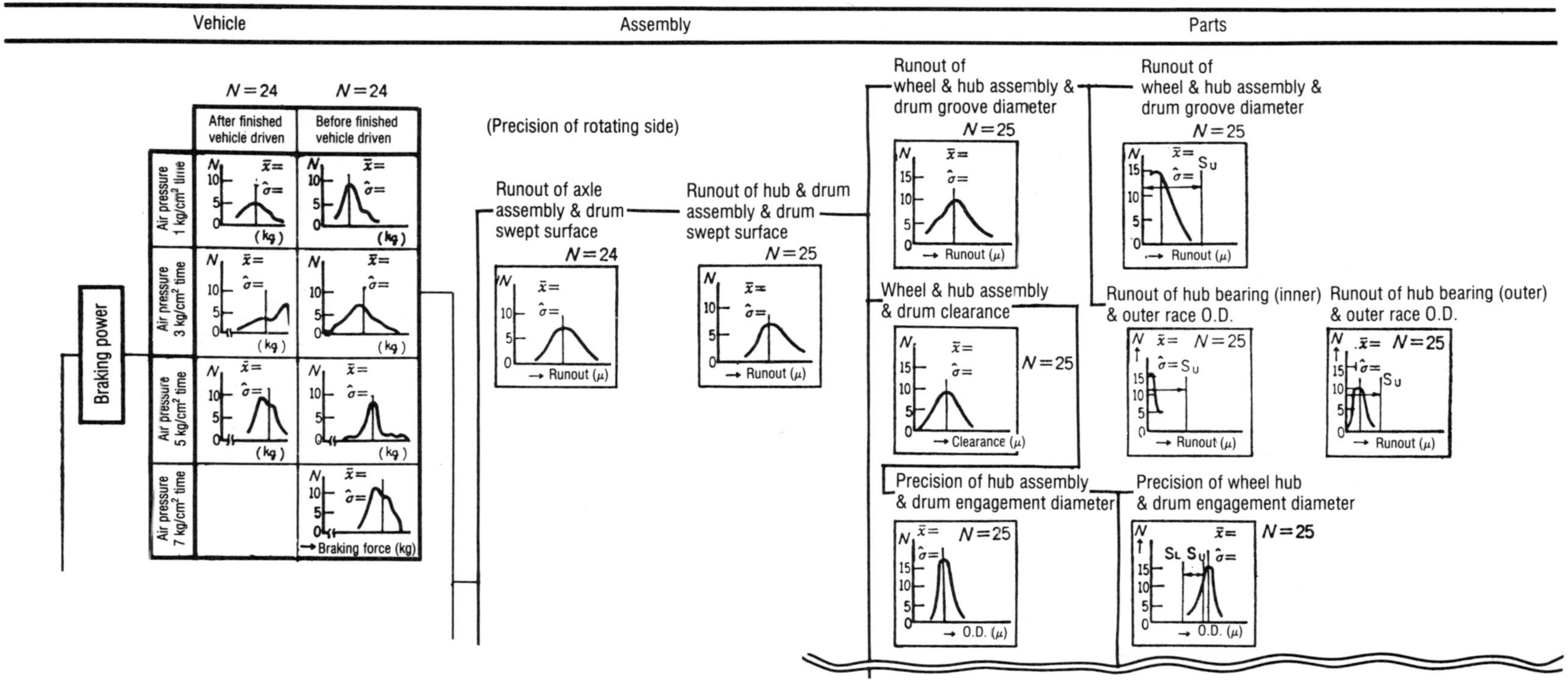

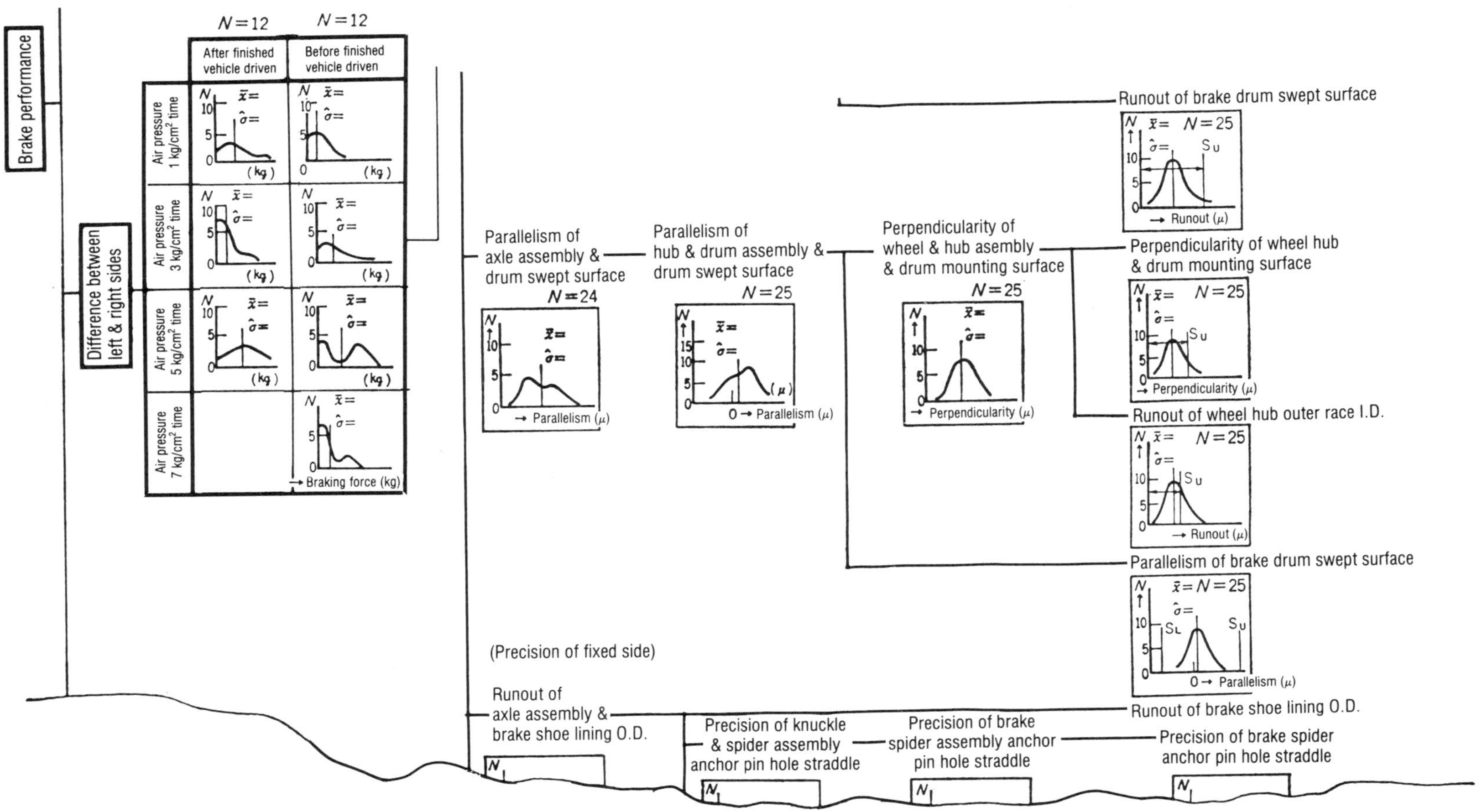

(Figure 9.8 continues)

(*continued*)

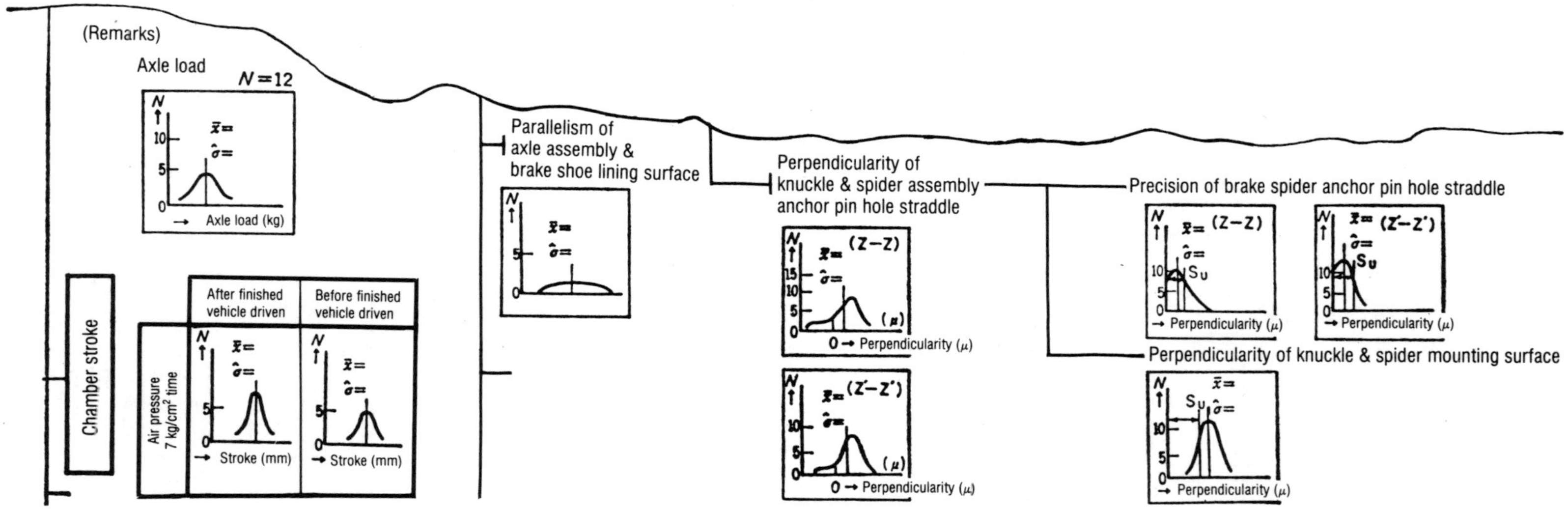

FIGURE 9.8
Investigation into the precision of tolerance stackup

are determined in the production engineering phase by referencing the machining process capabilities of the processes selected in the manufacturing methods deployment. Normally, all problems that occurred could be associated with decisions made in the design phase.

Preparation and Issuance of the Manufacturing Methods Deployment Chart

The manufacturing methods deployment chart is most required in the production preparation phase. First, a provisional chart should be prepared that reflects the negotiations with the design department and other manufacturing studies.

Follow-up after Production Startup and Consideration of Market Data on Product Usage

Once production has begun, follow-up is another important activity in the production phase. During the year after the equipment is installed and tried out, maintaining process capability must be confirmed and improvements made, if necessary. Consideration of manufacturing methods and equipment in light of market data should emphasize three points.

1. Items that require improvement of both design quality and manufacturing quality
2. Items for which market demand is high
3. Items that increase product value significantly.

Such data are obtained by a reliability analysis team from the department that is responsible for each machine. (This team must promote horizontal communication across what normally are vertically structured departments.)

Improving Engineering Standards

Data from manufacturing methods deployment and documentation used to support the selection of these methods become a normal part of the ongoing engineering standards for the manufacturing methods, as well as process capability standards and proposals for new engineering standards. Then the design department can "buy into" these engi-

Manufacturing methods research on runout of front axle brake drum swept surface

	Manufacturing methods study		Precision of runout after assembly	Cost of finishing process	Remarks
Hub unit machining	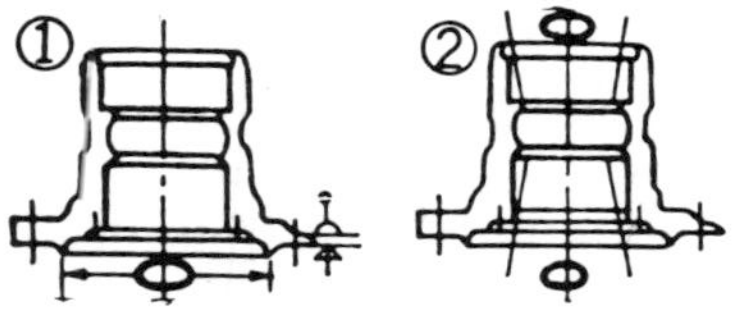	1. Simultaneous finishing of outer race I.D. 2. After pressing on outer race, mount drum to taper datum, & finish drum swept surface & mounting surface or disc mounting surface.	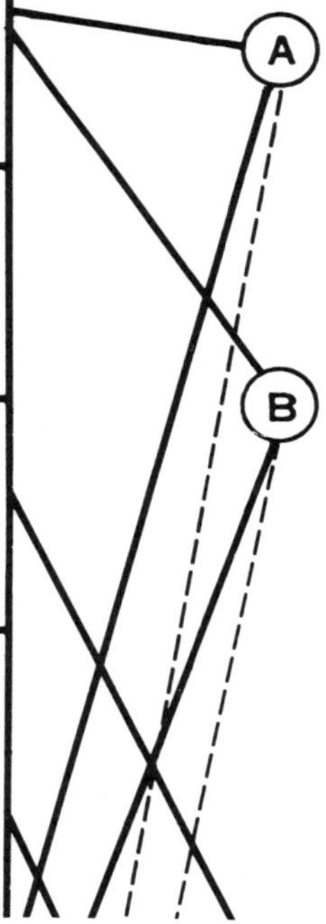		
	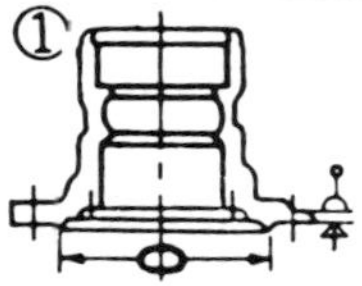	"One chuck machining": simultaneously finishing outer race I.D., drum mounting swept surface, & drum mounting surface			
	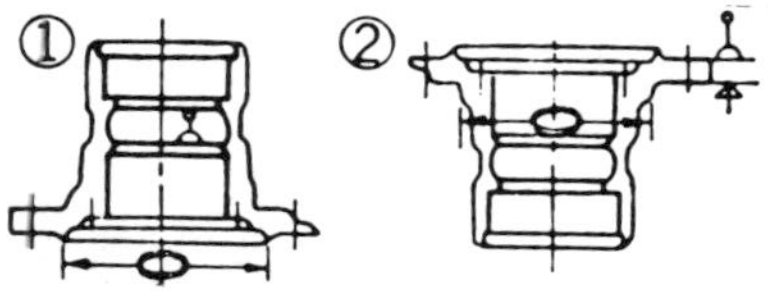	1. Finish drum mounting swept surface & drum mounting surface 2. Simultaneously finish outer race I.D. to drum mounting swept surface datum line			
	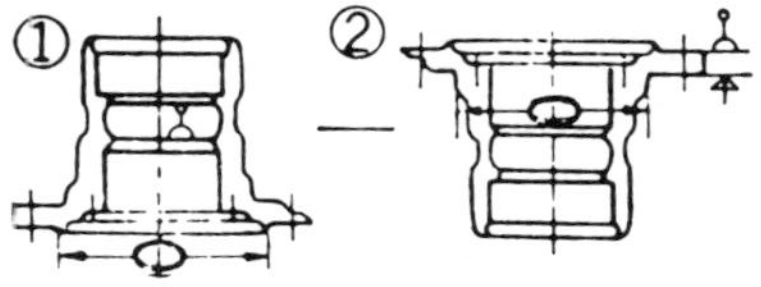	1. Finish drum mounting swept surface, drum mounting surface, & outer race I.D. (one side) 2. Finish outer race I.D. (one side) to drum mounting swept surface & drum mounting surface datum line			

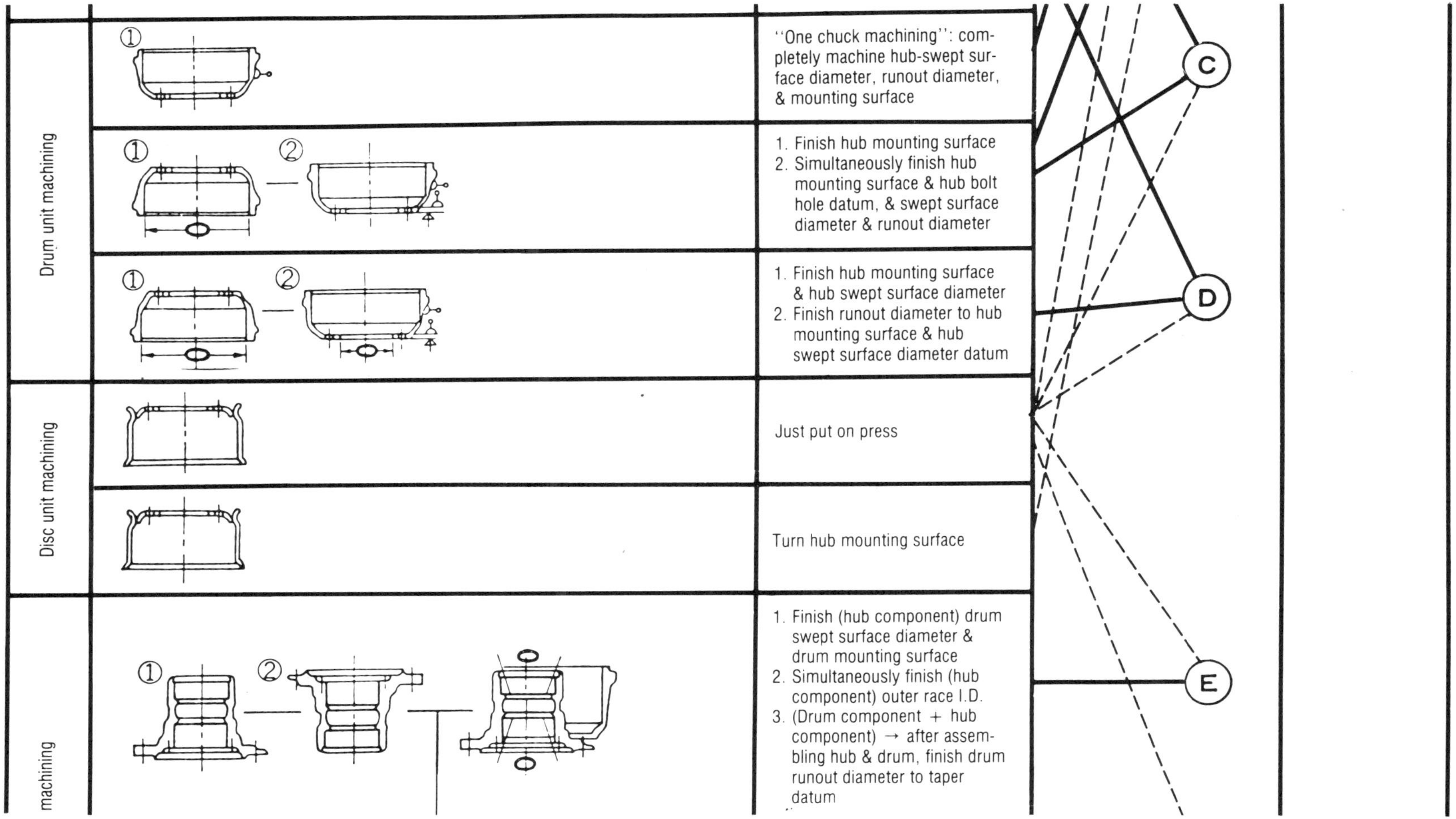
Drum unit machining
①
"One chuck machining": completely machine hub-swept surface diameter, runout diameter, & mounting surface
① ②
1. Finish hub mounting surface
2. Simultaneously finish hub mounting surface & hub bolt hole datum, & swept surface diameter & runout diameter
① ②
1. Finish hub mounting surface & hub swept surface diameter
2. Finish runout diameter to hub mounting surface & hub swept surface diameter datum
Disc unit machining
Just put on press
Turn hub mounting surface
machining
① ②
1. Finish (hub component) drum swept surface diameter & drum mounting surface
2. Simultaneously finish (hub component) outer race I.D.
3. (Drum component + hub component) → after assembling hub & drum, finish drum runout diameter to taper datum
C
D
E

(*Figure 9.9 continues*)

(*continued*)

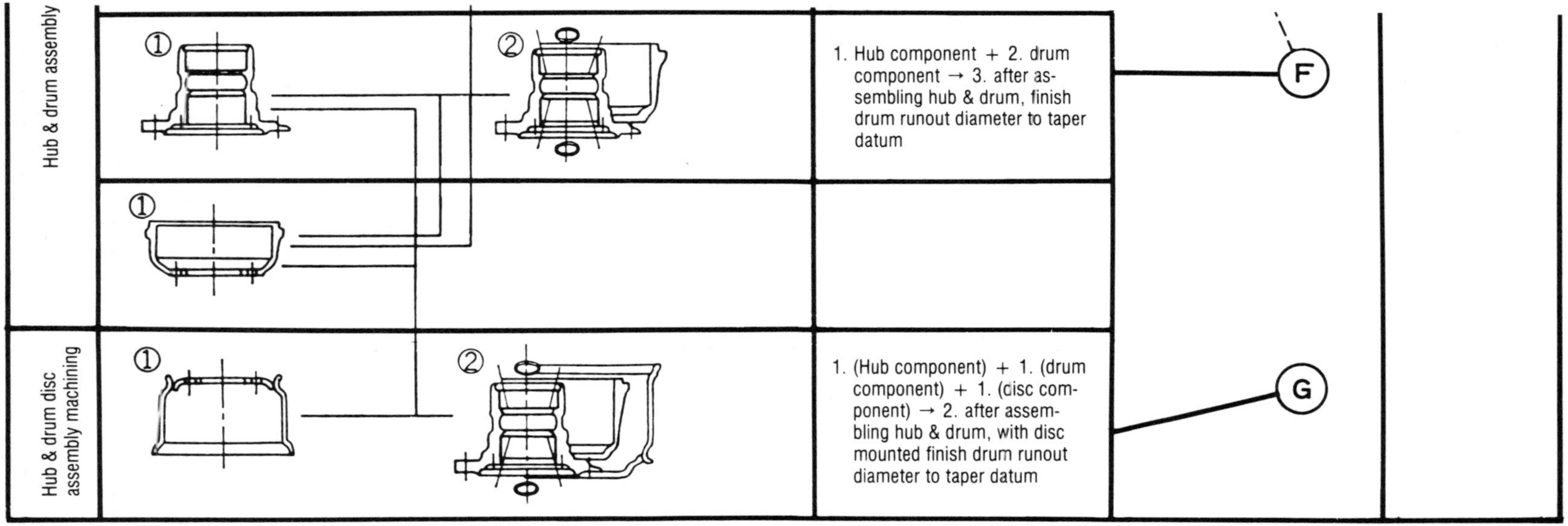
Hub & drum assembly
①
②
1. Hub component + 2. drum component → 3. after assembling hub & drum, finish drum runout diameter to taper datum
F
①
Hub & drum disc assembly machining
①
②
1. (Hub component) + 1. (drum component) + 1. (cisc component) → 2. after assembling hub & drum, with disc mounted finish drum runout diameter to taper datum
G

FIGURE 9.9
Manufacturing methods research chart

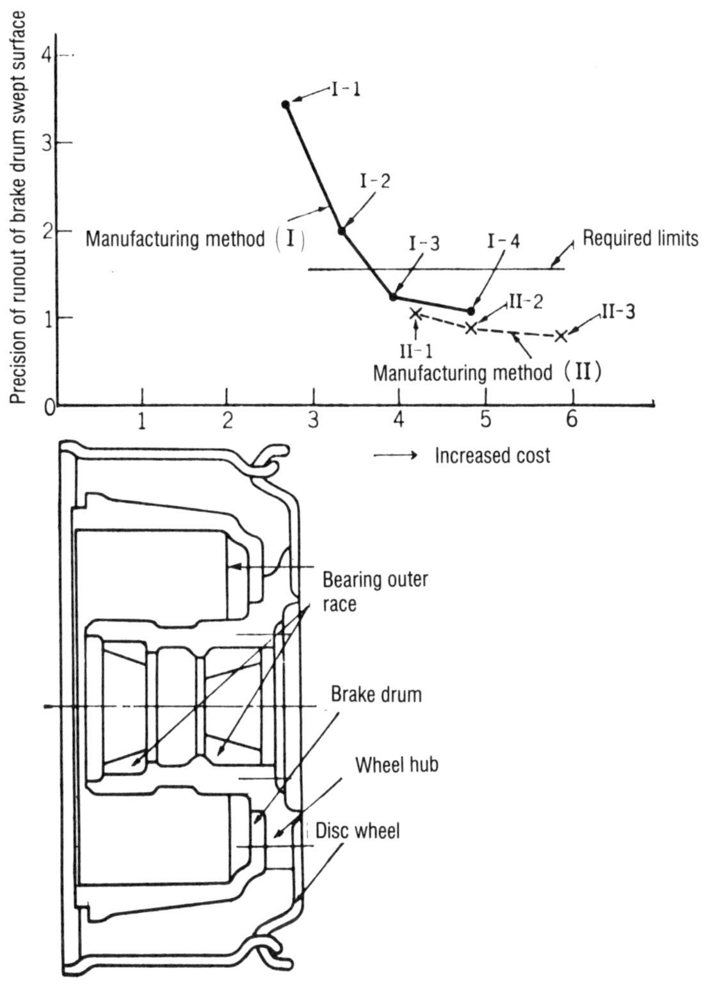

FIGURE 9.10
Quality-cost graph

neering standards so that they become part of their basic information resources.

CONCLUSION

An outline of the activities for deployment of manufacturing methods has been described with an emphasis on quality function deployment. The history at Hino Motors is still brief at this point. One of the major challenges is how to measure the effect of these activities. While the necessity and importance of these activities are fully recognized qualitatively, they require a great amount of time and effort. The costs incurred also cannot be ignored. It is thus necessary to quantify their effects.

The use of computers is an important task for the future. Hino Motors has almost reached its limits of manual methods of quality and manufacturing methods deployment, and there is a coming necessity for an electronic approach. In the area of quality deployment, computers can be used to prepare and to manage the function deployment chart, and to determine quantitatively the causal relationships in the chain of quality. Second, use of computers will be effective in deployment of manufacturing methods if computers are employed in the preparation and management of the manufacturing methods deployment chart, identification of the link between quality and manufacturing methods, and understanding of the causal relationship among quality characteristics based on studies of tolerance stackup. Computers can also play a role in linking the results of all these activities into a comprehensive and optimal system of manufacturing methods and processes.

To accomplish these goals, the Computer Study Group of the Japanese Society for Quality Control has addressed the matter and initiated a research program. The project at Hino Motors was reviewed by this group.

10

Preparation and Use of the QC Process Chart

Katsuyoshi Ishihara

This volume has been concerned primarily with establishing, based on quality functions, control points for subsystems, parts, and processes. Those involved with manufacturing processes possess a certain know-how about building quality into products, and this knowledge must be put to good use. This chapter addresses methods for pushing functions in reverse, that is, back to higher levels focused on manufacturing activities. This should be studied from the viewpoint of the methods described in other chapters of this volume. The method proposed here relates to quality characteristics by using a quality characteristics cause-and-effect control process chart. (Editor)

INTRODUCTION

Quality, it has been said, must be *built into* a product. This can happen only when the operating methods and conditions are clearly identified in such quality standards as product specifications, production specifications, and others. In manufacturing, normally the production process is based on quality standards related to receiving materials and parts needed to produce the final product that undergo machining and assembling, which requires equipment, tools, and labor. This requires that a control system be established to keep track of the history of the product's quality issues, such as who, when, what control methods, and what results were involved. It is also necessary to equate these with product safety and product responsibility.

Role of Quality-Related Tasks for Manufacturing in the Manufacturing Function

Preparation of the QC process chart first requires correct analysis of the manufacturing functions. Consideration is given to what role departmental tasks must play in these manufacturing functions. Figure 10.1 is one example. A function analysis of manufacturing tasks varies significantly, depending on how the secondary functions are handled.

Updating Control Points for Managing Quality-Related Tasks in the Manufacturing Function

A factor critical to the success of process control is determining the control points and where in the process they will exist. At Matsushita Electronic Components, the method of selecting control points was so poor that even when they were selected, gaps existed in their effectiveness. These gaps led to frequent problems in which even the painstakingly prepared control charts were useless.

To solve these problems, a function analysis of the manufacturing activity was made. The first attempt identified control points for third-level functions. Figure 10.2 shows both check items and control items, which together are referred to as control points. These definitions are important to understanding the meaning of the system described here.

DETERMINATION OF CONTROL POINTS IN MANUFACTURING FUNCTIONS AND IN UNIT PROCESSES

Determining control points for the manufacturing function requires careful research into what level of detail is appropriate. It is recommended that rather comprehensive control points to three levels of detail be used. Important considerations are explained below.

First, from the standpoint of quality assurance, control points for all the processes are selected mainly on the basis of quality characteristics given in product specifications. Or they may be selected from the standpoint of whether such processes are being followed per the standards. Previously, control points seemed to be determined the first way. Often this meant that some control points were not determined until near the end of the entire process. If abnormalities were discovered, there was insufficient time for corrective measures.

To correct this, it was thought that controlling the unit processes could allow control of the entire process. Subsequent analysis was directed primarily to establishment of control points for unit processes. It was thought that this would upgrade the level of all the processes. Deployment was performed with proper consideration for control points of the basic manufacturing functions.

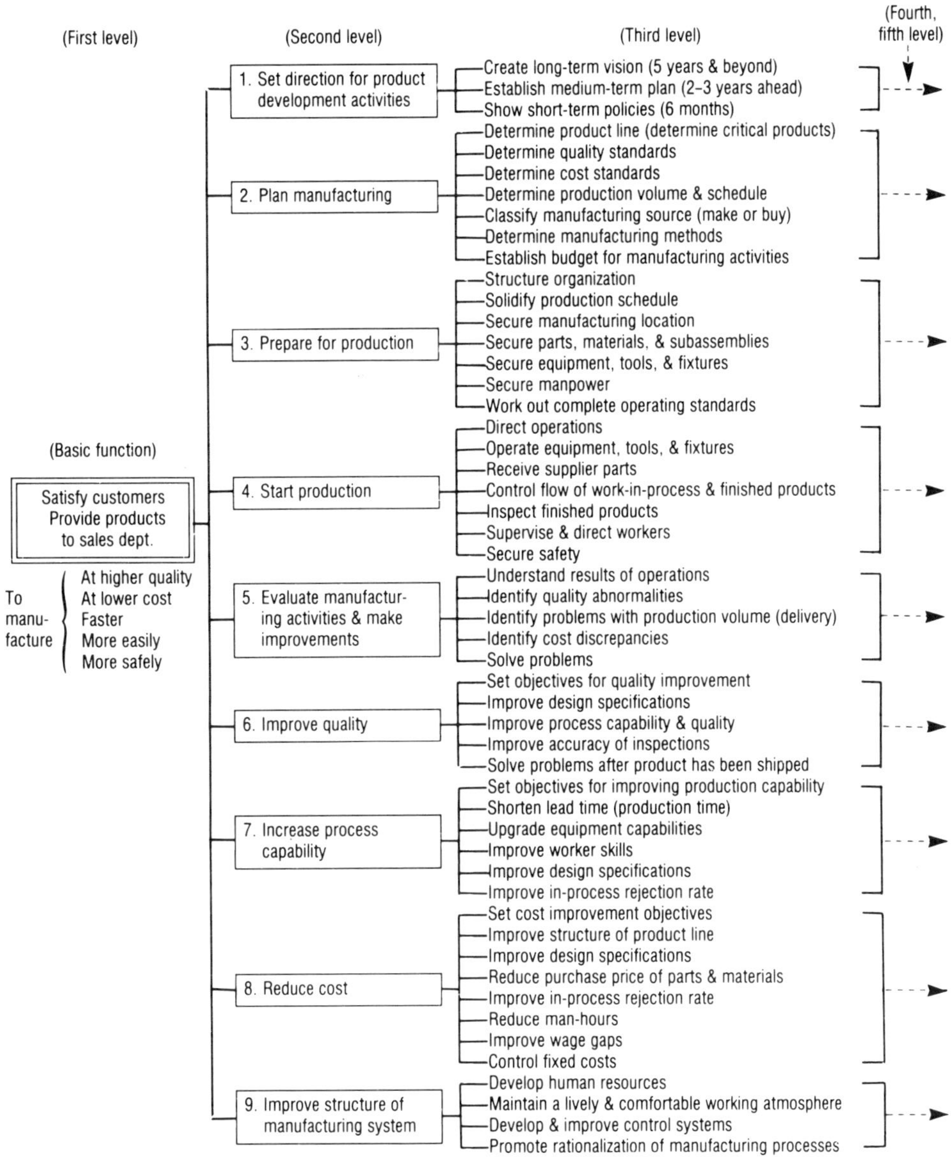

FIGURE 10.1
Manufacturing function tree

Note: Fourth- and fifth-level details would encompass chemical, assembly, machining, and other processes. It is essential that each company develop this. Previous analyses indicate that 4th-level details number approximately 400 functions and 5th-level details number approximately 1,000 functions. These 4th- and 5th-level detail items should be used explicitly in QC process charts.

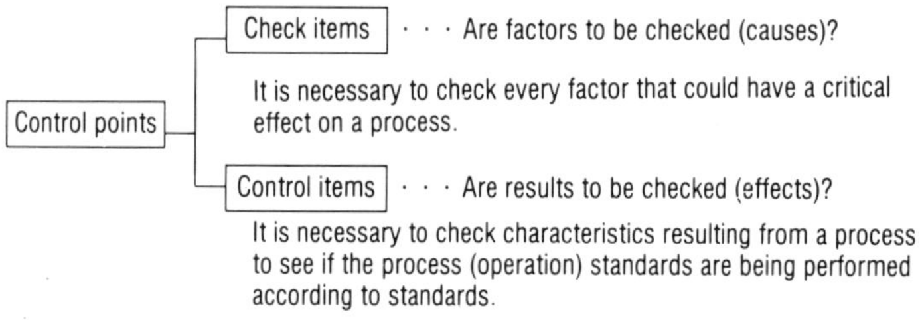

FIGURE 10.2
Concept of control points for manufacturing processes

Determination of Control Points for Unit Processes

Construction of a QC process chart first requires determination of control points for unit processes. Control points can be set up according to two methods.

One method uses the value engineering (VE) technique of function analysis to determine control points. Research on this use began in late 1966. Among the first questions asked were "What is the purpose of control points?" and "Why must control points be determined?" Setting goals and selecting methods to accomplish them requires a system that confirms, by use of control items, whether the goals have been fulfilled.

The other way is to select control items by using the industrial engineering (IE) technique of operations analysis. Figure 10.3 shows such a system of selecting control points. This system was developed using an IE technique known as the module method. It is described in detail below.

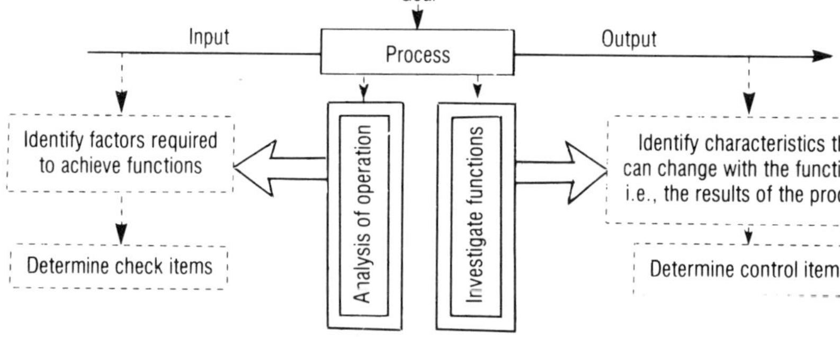

FIGURE 10.3
System to determine control points

Determination of Control Points by Investigating Process Functions

This method defines and investigates process functions based on the function analysis used in VE. In this method, basic functions are identified, and the goals of and the means to accomplish the basic functions are explored. The means that have been determined are converted to goals, and lower-level functions are sought. The system of converting goals to means is arranged such that functions are investigated on the same, lower, or higher level to clarify the relationships among them. After they are organized into a function systematic diagram, or function tree, investigation of the control points selected takes place. The methodology is to look at the effects of the higher-level functions that have been studied, to extract from them the characteristics and control points necessary to control them, and from the latter to determine control items.

The first step is to define in a verb plus object statement of the form "The process does ____ to ____." For example, in the process of applying a flux coating to a printed circuit board, function analysis would define the process as "apply flux to circuit board with a roller."

Next, ask why this process is necessary. This clarifies the purpose or role of this function in the process. With the process thus defined, characteristics can be extracted from the verb of the process function statement. These characteristics substitute for the process, and if they are measurable, they can be used as control items. Figure 10.4 is a conceptual diagram of this system of determining control items based on investigation of the functions.

From this investigation of higher-level functions thus defined, the question "Why is this function necessary?" is asked to clarify the purpose that is its next higher-level function. In the same way, this can be defined using the verb plus object statement. From this higher-level function, then, final characteristics can be extracted and their relationship to the function can be better understood.

Using this high- and low-level approach to organizing subordinate relationships between functions defined as explained above, the correlations between final characteristics and the interrelationships of processes can be identified (see Figure 10.5). By using this approach, the control items for the complete process can be determined.

The main issue is not only to investigate the higher-level functions but also to clarify the relationships to same-level and lower-level functions. Once these higher-lower relationships are understood, higher-level functions can be investigated. The basis for this is illustrated in Figure 10.6.

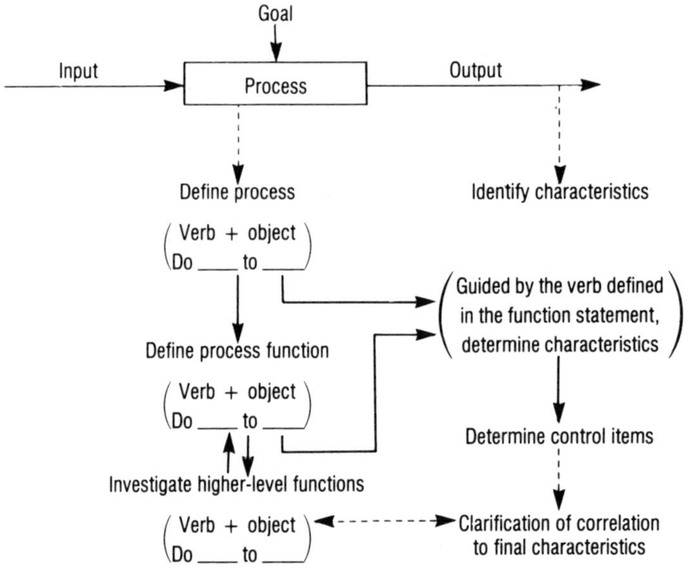

FIGURE 10.4
System to determine control items by investigating functions

Procedure for Determining Control Items

The five specific steps to establish control items are given below.

Step 1: Determination of Unit Processes and Process Classifications

The unit process can be determined either on a process-by-process basis or on an operator-level basis. Classifications can be made based on the structure of the production lot or on the range of responsibility of the supervisor or manager (see Figure 10.7).

Step 2: Clarification of the Unit Process Function

From the basic concept explained above, processes, process functions, and lower-level and same-level functions can be confirmed in order to define higher-level functions.

Step 3: Extraction of Characteristics

Characteristics can be extracted from the verb of the process function statement.

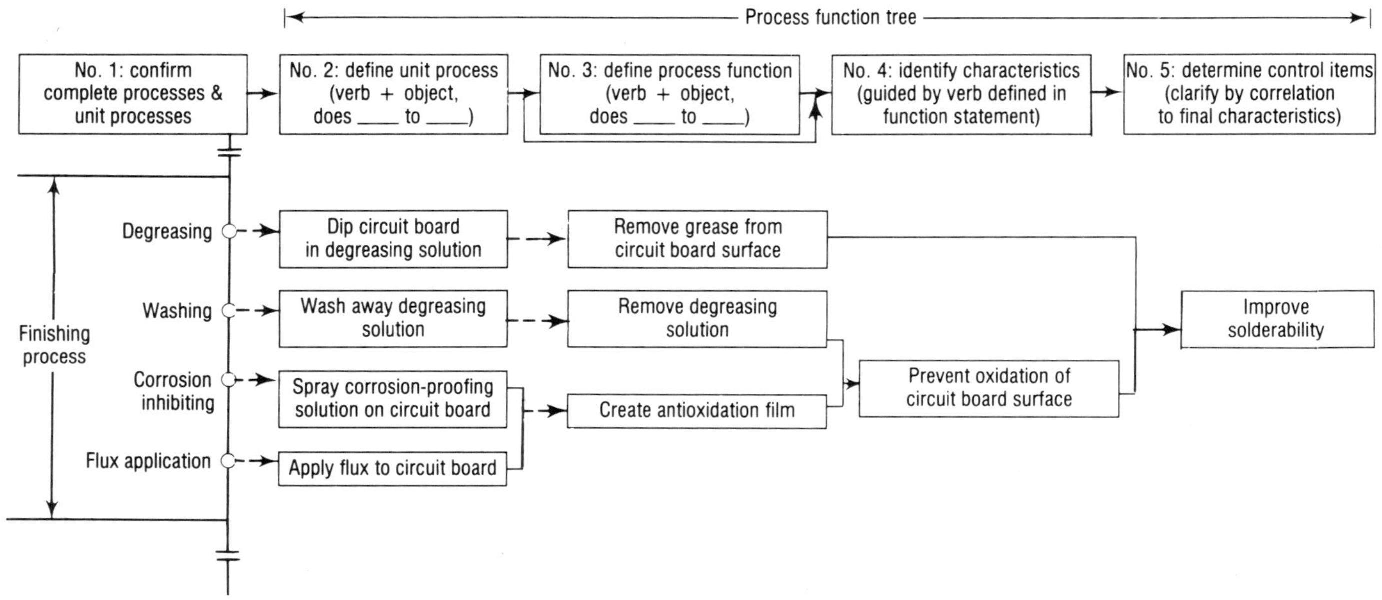

FIGURE 10.5
Interrelationships of processes based on investigation of functions

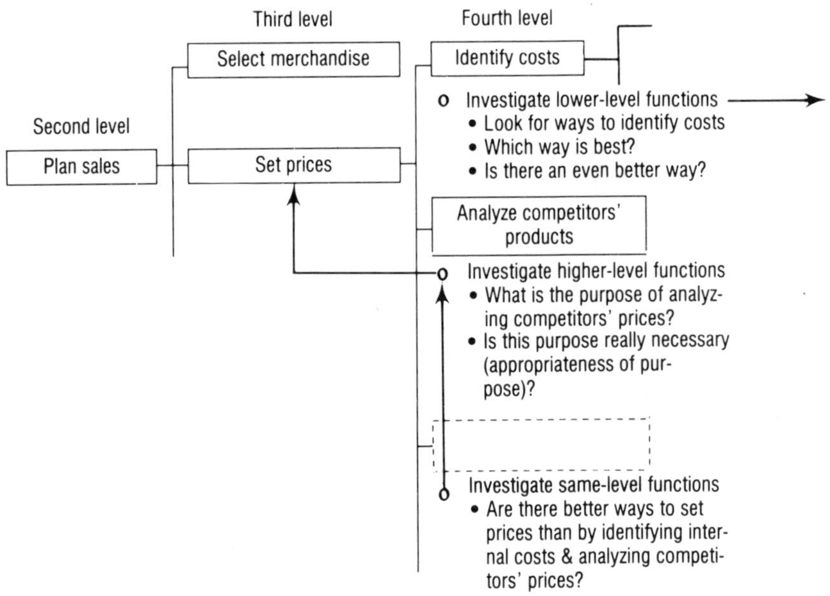

FIGURE 10.6
Investigation of higher-, lower- and same-level functions

Note: This example is one of a second-level function for sales planning. This method is equally suitable for investigating functions of manufacturing processes. This case study for sales functions is intended to encourage the reader to explore other examples of functions.

Step 4: Establishment of Control Items

The characteristics extracted in Step 3 are used in the flow to determine control items (see Figure 10.8).

Step 5: Review of Control Methods

Control methods for the selected control items are reviewed and established (person responsible, frequency, control document to be used, corrective measures). Control items are established by following these steps.

Determination of Check Items by Operations Analysis

In this technique, operations involved in individual processes (unit processes) are analyzed by operations analysis used in industrial engineering to clarify elements of the operation and their sequence. On this

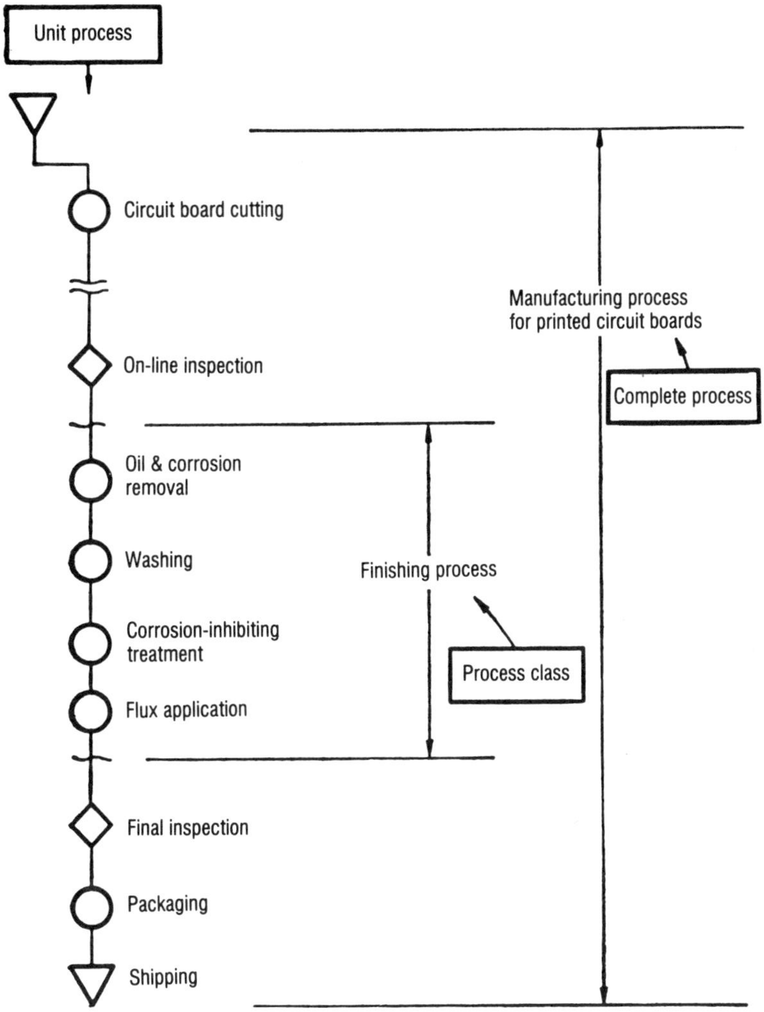

FIGURE 10.7
Determining unit processes and process classifications

basis the number of workers, parts and materials, machines, tools and fixtures, method of operation, and its contents and conditions are extracted for each element of operation to determine check items.

First, the process is categorized into elements of operation and their sequence is identified. One element of operation, to accomplish the goal of the unit process, is defined as transfer of individual objects (parts, materials, finished parts, tools, etc.) by the operator from one location to another. For example, such operating units can be "mount part on machine," "cut," or "mix liquid." From this, the number of work-

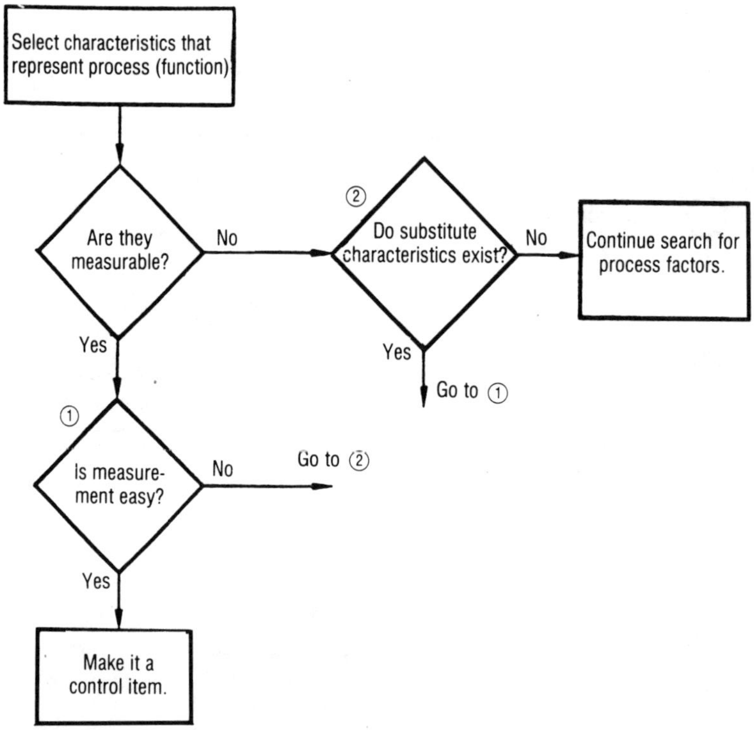

FIGURE 10.8
Decision flow to determine control items

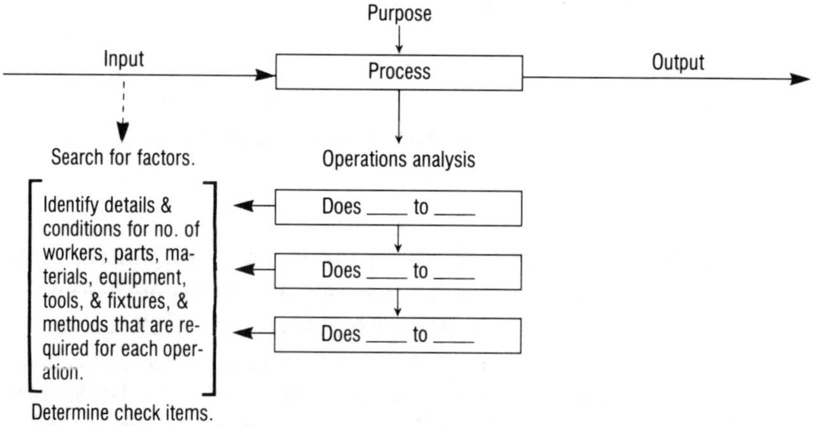

FIGURE 10.9
System to determine check items using operations analysis

ers, parts and materials, machines, tools and fixtures, methods used, and their contents and conditions are determined for each element.

1. Manpower: Qualifications, length of the training period, and so on
2. Materials and parts: Parts, materials, and semifinished products required for the process and their characteristics (conditions)
3. Machines, tools, and fixtures: Machines, tools and measuring instruments, their capability, and their precision
4. Methods: Methods and operating conditions.

Figure 10.9 shows the system to determine check items using operations analysis. With this method, all factors that can be thought of are listed and reviewed, thus reducing the chance of some important factor being missed.

The process of establishing check items consists of five steps.

Step 1: Determination of Unit Processes and Process Classifications

The unit process can be determined either on a process-by-process basis or on an operator-level basis. Classifications can be made on the basis of structure of the production lot or of the supervisor or manager's range of responsibility.

Step 2: Identification of Operation Sequence of Unit Processes

Based on Step 1, elements of operation and their sequence are clarified (refer to Figure 10.10).

Step 3: Extraction of Factors

Necessary inputs for each element of operation are identified. Factors are manpower, materials and parts, machines, tools and fixtures, and contents and conditions of methods.

Step 4: Determination of Check Items

The degree of effect and importance for control items is established, and those with a large impact are determined to be check items. Even when the cause-and-effect relationships to control items are fuzzy, they can be tentatively designated check points on the basis of engineering

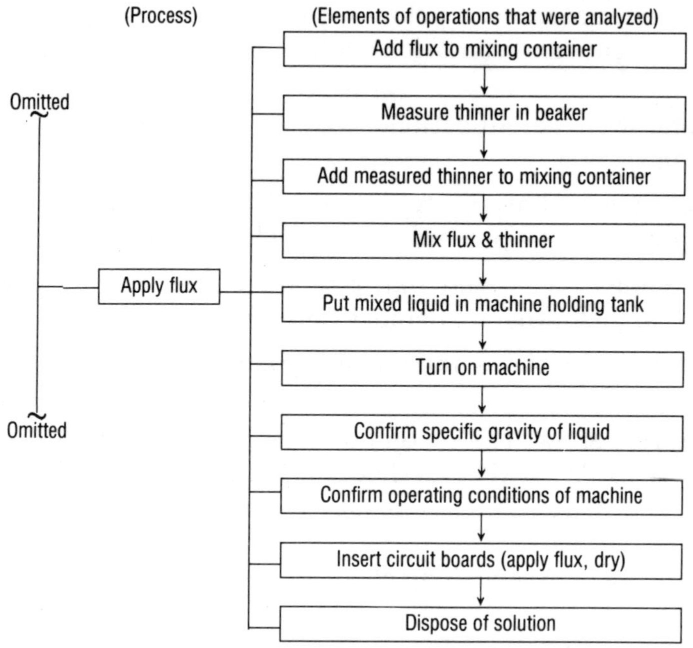

FIGURE 10.10
Operations analysis

experience. They are most needed in operations that are most likely to have mistakes and need foolproofing.

Step 5: Review of Check Items

Checking methods for the selected check items are reviewed and established (person responsible, frequency, control document to be used, corrective measures).

IMPROVEMENT OF CONTROL POINTS FOR THE QC PROCESS CHART

The procedure to improve control points consists of seven steps.

Step 1: Selection of Target Products and Processes

Products and processes to be subjected to this activity are selected. Upon approval of the supervisor, the procedure begins.

Step 2: Formation of a Promotion Organization

An organization to promote the activity is structured around the "frontline" supervisors responsible for the products and processes. It includes related personnel from engineering, production engineering, quality control, and purchasing.

Step 3: Investigation of Current Process

The current status of the process is compared against manufacturing specifications, since processes are often managed differently than specifications. Participation of the operators is important to understanding current practice.

Step 4: Review of Control Points and Control Methods

Based on Step 3 and on the process control methods review chart for each unit process (Figure 10.11), control points and control items are studied. Once selected, control points are included in the QC process chart (Figure 10.12) and the entire process is comprehensively reviewed.

Step 5: Identification of Problems

Problems resulting from the review of current practice in Step 3 and evaluation of control points and control items in Step 4 are entered in the follow-up chart for investigation of problems (Figure 10.13) to determine the corrective measures, importance, person in charge, and timing of completion.

Step 6: Implementation of Improvements for Problems

Step 7: Management of Improvement Activities with the Follow-up Chart for Investigation of Problems

The frequency of checking Step 5 improvement activities is set and followed up. Figure 10.13 is an example of a control document for this follow-up.

Process classification	Finishing	Process name	Flux application

Factors \ Items	Contents	A B C	Degree of difficulty	Item	Person responsible	Frequency, etc.	Documentaton	Action (by individual responsible)
				Inspection method				
Manpower								
Materials, parts	1. Flux							
	• Components	A	X	Brand selected	Kajiya	Confirm brand when mixing	—	Report to supervisor
	2. Thinner							
	• Components	A	X	Brand selected	〃	〃	—	〃
Machines, tools, & fixtures	1. Mixing container							
	• Volume	→	→	Container chosen				
	2. Beaker							
	• Volume	→	→	Container chosen				
	3. Flux machine							
	• Distance from roller	B	○	Distance from roller	Kajiya	Operation startup	—	Adjustment by operator
	• How flux applied	B	○	How flux applied	〃	〃	—	〃
	4. Dryer							
	• Temperature	A	○	Temperature	〃	2/month	Checksheet	Report to supervisor
				Periodic inspection	Production engineering	1/3 months	Periodic inspection report	
	5. Hydrometer							
	6. Mixer							
Method	1. Solution mix							
	• Correct mixture ratio	→	→	→	Fool-proofing			
	2. Adjust specific gravity of solution							
	• Specific gravity	A	○	Specific gravity	Kajiya	1/30 minutes	Graph	Report to supervisor
	3. Volume of liquid	B	○	Volume of liquid	〃	Operation startup	Checksheet	Addition by operator
	4. Period solution used	A	○	Period of use	〃	Change once every 15 days		Enter date refilled in checksheet

FIGURE 10.11
Review of process control methods

Date: 7/20/73 Date:

Date: Date:

Function (purpose)	Characteristics (characteristic value)	A B C	Degree of difficulty	Item	Person responsible	Frequency, etc.	Documentation	Action (by individual responsible)
	Results (output)			Control method				
(High-level function)								
Increase solderability	Solderability	A	○	Solderability	Kitasaka from QC section	n = 5/lot	Test data	QC & manufacturing sections study corrective measures
				Control test				
Prevent oxidation	Degree of oxidation inhibition	A	X					
(Process function)								
Coat with antioxidant	State of oxidation inhibition	A	X					
(Corrosion-inhibiting flux)								
	(Antioxidant + flux)							
(Process)								
Apply flux	State of flux coating	A	○	State of flux coating	Kajiya	2/day	Checksheet	Report to supervisor corrective measures
	Uniform							
	No clogged holes							
Mix solution								
Add flux to mixing container ↓								
Measure thinner into beaker ↓								
Add thinner to mixing container ↓								
Mix flux & thinner ↓								
Add mixed solution to machine holding tank								
Apply flux								
Turn on machine ↓								
Adjust specific gravity ↓								
Confirm operating conditions of machine ↓								
Insert circuit boards, apply flux, dry								
Change solution								
Dispose of used solution								

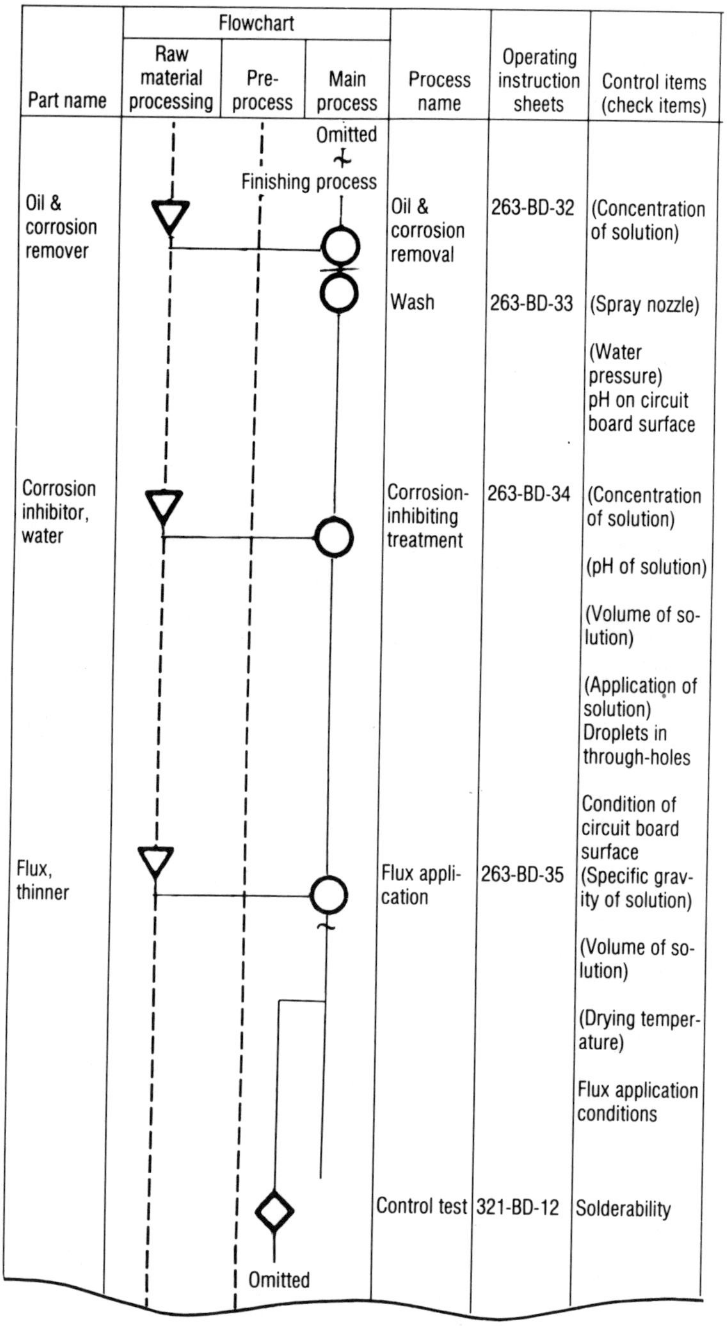
Flowchart
Part name
Raw material processing
Pre-process
Main process
Process name
Operating instruction sheets
Control items (check items)
Omitted
Finishing process
Oil & corrosion remover
Oil & corrosion removal
263-BD-32
(Concentration of solution)
Wash
263-BD-33
(Spray nozzle)
(Water pressure)
pH on circuit board surface
Corrosion inhibitor, water
Corrosion-inhibiting treatment
263-BD-34
(Concentration of solution)
(pH of solution)
(Volume of so-lution)
(Application of solution)
Droplets in through-holes
Condition of circuit board surface
Flux, thinner
Flux appli-cation
263-BD-35
(Specific grav-ity of solution)
(Volume of so-lution)
(Drying temper-ature)
Flux application conditions
Control test
321-BD-12
Solderability
Omitted

FIGURE 10.12
QC process chart for printed circuit boards

Dept: printed circuit board dept., plant no. 2 mfg. section, printed circuit board division	Section manager:	Sakashita	Made by:
Date established:	No		Nakamura

Control method							
Control instruction sheets	Control charts, etc.	Person responsible	Action by	Sampling, measurements	Inspection items	Inspection method	Remarks
	Checksheet	Kajiya	Nakamura	1/day concentration analysis			
	Checksheet	Kajiya	Nakamura	2/day visual inspection			
	〃	〃	〃	2/day gauge confirmation			
273-BD-22	〃	〃	〃	2/day n = 5 with pH test paper			
	Checksheet	Kajiya	Nakamura	2/day with colorimeter			
	〃	〃	〃	2/day pH test paper			
	〃	〃	〃	2/day visual check of solution level			
	〃	〃	〃	2/day visual inspection			
273-BD-23	〃	〃	〃	2/day visual inspection n = 5			
273-BD-24	〃	〃	〃	2/day n = 5 visual inspection			
	Graph	Kajiya	Nakamura	1/30 minutes check with hydrometer			
	Checksheet	〃	〃	1/day check with level gauge			
	〃	〃	〃	2/day check with thermometer			
273-BD-25	Checksheet	Kajiya	Nakamura	2/day n = 5 visual inspection			
	Test data	Kitasaka	S. Iwashita	n = 5/lot solderability test			

The rest is omitted

Process classification	Finishing	Process name	Corrosion inhibitor

Date: ______

Classification	Problems	Proposed corrective action	Priority	Person responsible	Target date	Action details, effect	Confirmed 7/24	Confirmed 8/10	Confirmed	Done
Method	1. Incorrect mixture ratio of solution (undiluted solution + water → 2% 20 liters)	1. Standardization of mixing methods								
		1.1. Add fill line to holding tank	B	Manufacturing (Nakamura)	7/20	7/23 completed	✓			O
		1.2. Add fill line to measuring device	B	〃	7/20	7/23 completed	✓			O
Materials	2. Method of solution control is unclear	2. Clarification of solution control method								
	2.1. Method of checking concentration (measuring method, frequency) must be clarified	2.1. Check twice a day with colorimeter	A	Manufacturing (Nakamura)	7/20	7/20 started	✓			O
	2.2. Checking oxidation of solution must be clarified	2.2. Check twice a day with pH test paper	A	〃	7/20	7/23 started	✓			O
Machine	3. Because holding tank is fixed, it cannot be washed	3. Improve way of disassembling holding tank	A	Production engineering	8/8	Improvement of holding tank	In-process	✓		O
						(8/3–7)				
Machine	4. Wash water from prior process can enter tank with corrosion inhibitor & dilute it	4. Investigate dripping circuit boards; prevent	A	Manufacturing	8/20	7/23–8/10 investigate dripping circuit boards	Under investigation	Under investigation		
	↑			Quality control						
	Drips from circuit board on conveyor; droplets clogging holes			Production engineering						

FIGURE 10.13
Follow-up chart for investigation of problems

PREPARATION AND USE OF THE QC PROCESS CHART

Correctly Understanding the QC Process Chart

The QC process chart has a long history in industry. Since it is used by different companies in different ways, it is called by many names. Among them are QC process diagram, control process diagram, quality chart, QC process chart, and process control detail chart; here it will be referred to by its most common name, the QC process chart.

Definition of the QC Process Chart

The QC process chart illustrates the process (or part of a process) that a product undergoes from the time parts and materials are delivered to the time it is shipped as a finished good. It shows specific control points and control methods for each process, the arranged sequence of unit processes, and which characteristics are to be controlled by whom and where, supported by what kind of data.

Structure of the QC Process Chart

For the QC process chart shown in Figure 10.12 to be understood properly by all shop floor personnel and to be used correctly, it must be formalized into a widely available manual that explains how to prepare a QC process chart. The manual should include special symbols to show the flow of the processes, directions on how to write a process flow, items to be identified as control methods, the reason for dividing control points into control items and check items, and so on. It is this attention to determining control points that makes the QC process chart so necessary.

How to Construct the QC Process Chart

Selection of Target Products and Processes

It is important first to select the products and processes that will be the subject of examination (all processes? critical processes only?) and to begin the work with the supervisor's approval. A process is a chain of unit processes, and determining the control points for each of these requires that all unit processes first be identified according to either the manufacturing method or the operator. Process classifications must be further clarified on the basis of the makeup of the production lot and of the areas of responsibility of managers and supervisors.

Investigation of Current Process

The engineering, quality control, production engineering, and manufacturing departments should jointly conduct research on the current status of each unit process, to make certain that manufacturing specifications are being followed.

Review of Control Points and Control Methods

Follow the procedure for determination of control points described above and review the control points and control methods.

Determine Control Items

Using the procedures for determining control items, examine the characteristics extracted from process function definitions. Determine whether control items can be created. If the characteristics are measurable, they can be used as control items as is. If they are not, it is necessary to identify additional process factors.

Review Control Methods

Control methods for the selected control items are based on four items.

1. Person responsible: Person who checks the control items (characteristics) and reports results to the person responsible for taking corrective actions
2. Frequency: How often checks are made, sample size, sampling method
3. Control documents: Documents for finding discrepancies and initiating corrective measures – control charts, graphs, checksheets, and so on
4. Corrective measures: Criteria for abnormalities, corrective measures (emergency measures, prevention of recurrence, routing of

communication), and person responsible for taking these measures

Determine Checkpoints

Check items are based on the steps mentioned. They are assigned an importance ranking (A, B, C) by the level of effect on the control items, and those having potential major effects are the tentative control items. The processes are later analyzed again for their effect and to eliminate those with little effect.

Review Check Methods

For the selected check items, the person responsible, frequency, control documents, and corrective measures are finalized according to the inspection methods review chart.

Filling in the QC Process Chart Diagram

The control points (control items and check items) of Step 3 are entered in the QC process chart for each process and reviewed before registration for continued control.

Improvements of Problem Areas

In order to improve assigning of problem areas from a review of the current process, the control points and control methods, and plans of improvement are finalized by cooperation with other departments. The QC process chart can be completed after corrective measures are taken.

Use of the QC Process Chart

The QC process chart generally serves to apply control standards to quality of the manufacturing processes. As a result (1) determination of quality control is on the shop floor; (2) the control characteristics are clearly related to the preceding and succeeding processes; (3) the control supervisor can divide the entire process into preparation, main process, and so on, and monitors the conditions by means of control points to guide subordinates.

Methods in other companies include (1) promotion of quality

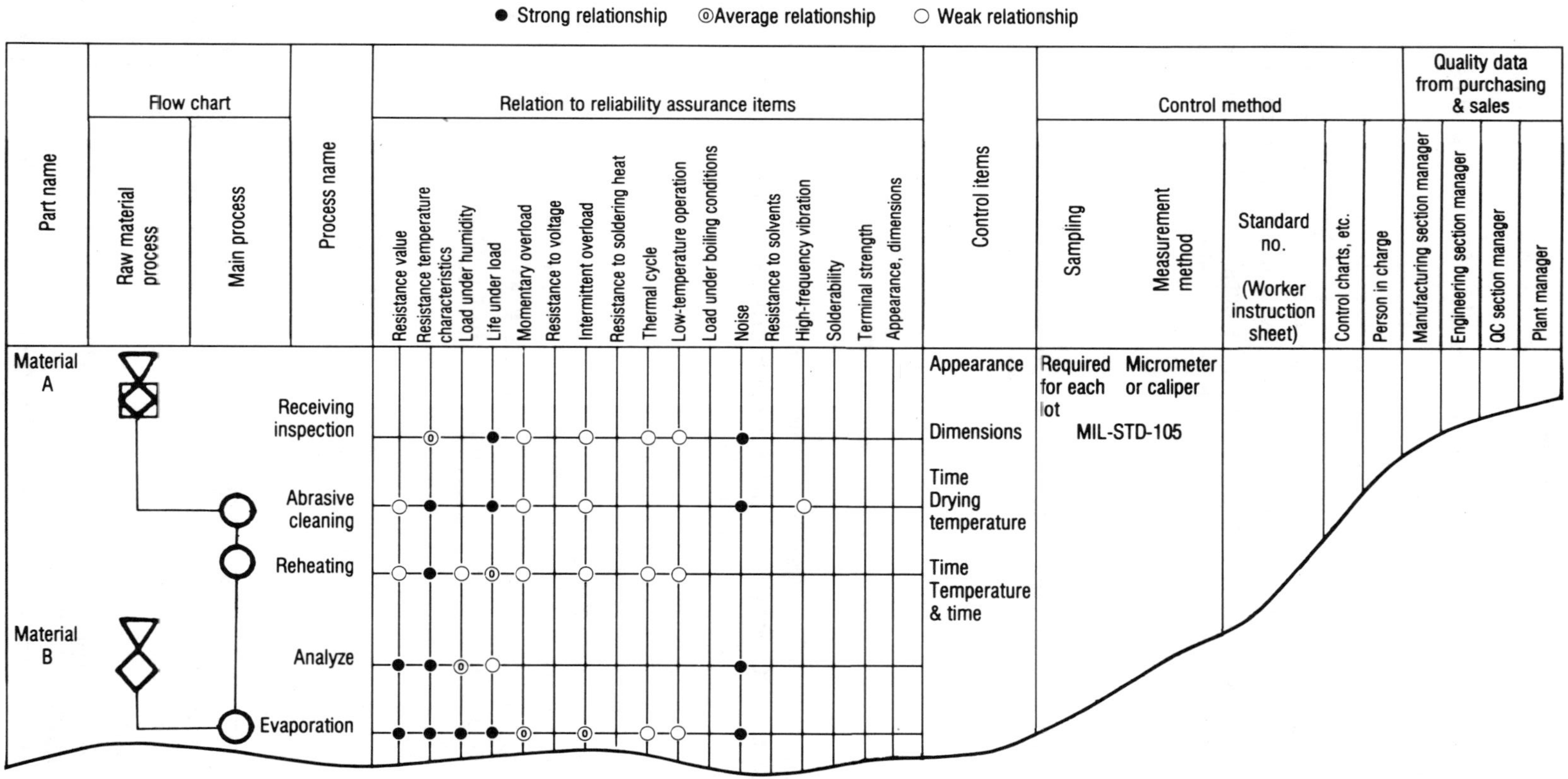

● Strong relationship
◎Average relationship
○ Weak relationship
Part name
Flow chart
Raw material process
Main process
Process name
Relation to reliability assurance items
Resistance value
Resistance temperature characteristics
Load under humidity
Life under load
Momentary overload
Resistance to voltage
Intermittent overload
Resistance to soldering heat
Thermal cycle
Low-temperature operation
Load under boiling conditions
Noise
Resistance to solvents
High-frequency vibration
Solderability
Terminal strength
Appearance, dimensions
Control items
Control method
Sampling
Measurement method
Standard no.
(Worker instruction sheet)
Control charts, etc.
Person in charge
Quality data from purchasing & sales
Manufacturing section manager
Engineering section manager
QC section manager
Plant manager
Material A
Material B
Receiving inspection
Abrasive cleaning
Reheating
Analyze
Evaporation
Appearance
Dimensions
Time
Drying temperature
Time
Temperature & time
Required for each lot
Micrometer or caliper
MIL-STD-105

FIGURE 10.14
Quality characteristics factor control process diagram

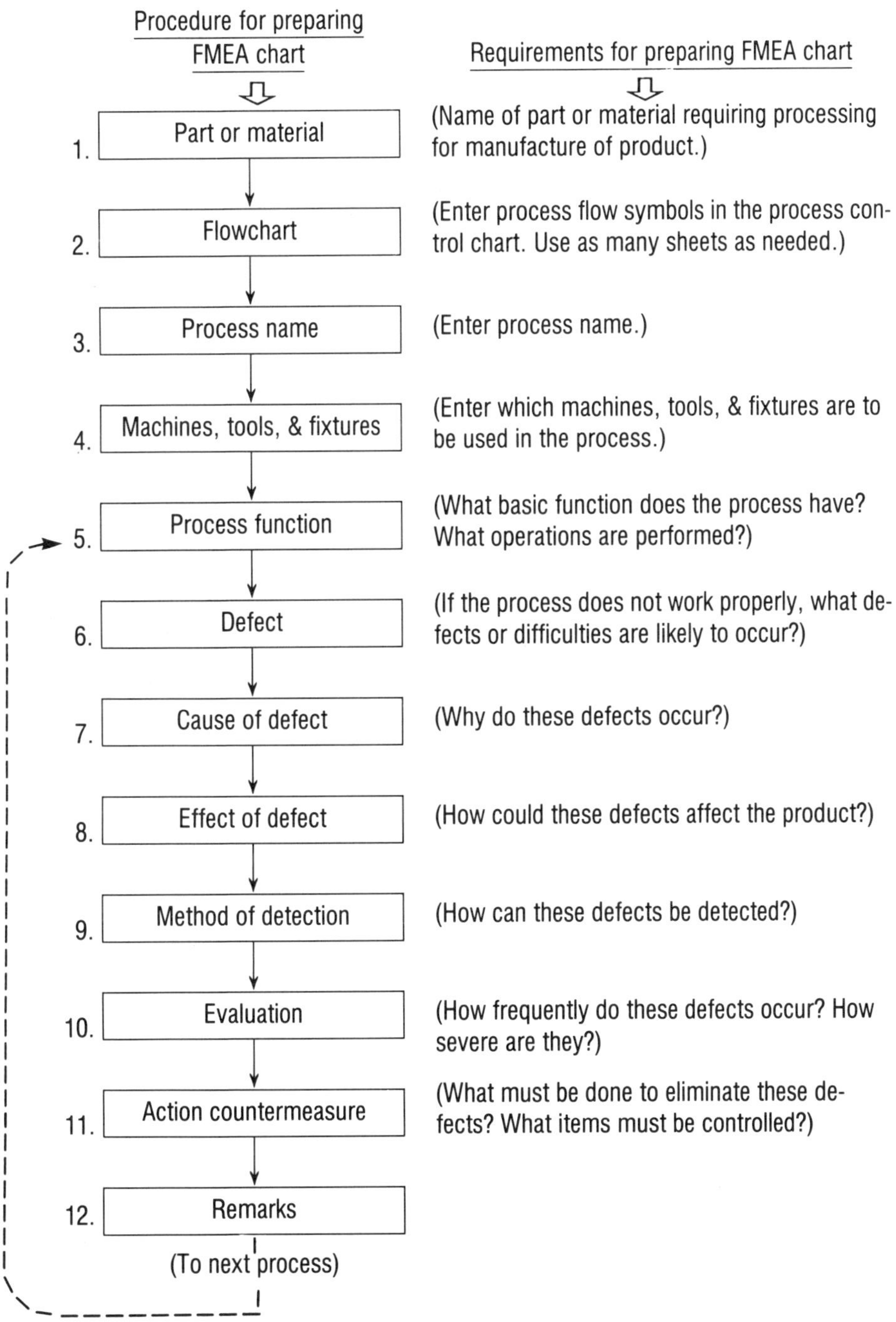

FIGURE 10.15
Process FMEA basic procedure

No.	Product name	Process FMEA chart	Division	Plant	Name	Approved by	Initials	Made by
1	New stop light switch		Quality control section	Team				

1. Part name	2. Flow chart: Raw material process	2. Flow chart: Main process	3. Process name	4. Equipment, tools	5. Process function	6. Defect	7. Cause of defect	8. Effect of defect: Effect on product	8. Effect of defect: Effect on system	9. Method of detection	10. Evaluation: Occurrence	10. Evaluation: Severity	10. Evaluation: Detection	10. Evaluation: Risk priority	11. Action, countermeasure, control method	12. Remarks
	▽	○	Crimping set screw	Circuit board set screw Crimper (crank type)	Attach set screw to circuit board 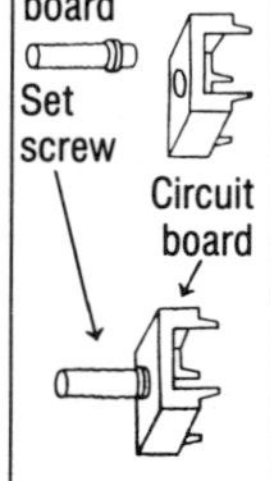	1. Loose set screw	• Worn punch • Broken punch (several out of six) • Incomplete stroke • Worn crank • Punch too high • Lower die mispositioned	• Unstable operation (cannot switch on/off) • On position changes	Brake lights don't illuminate	Self-inspection during operation	3	3	3	27	(Control method) • Change punch after 100,000 shots • Check crimping condition at change of lower punch die, operation startup, 10 a.m., 3 p.m. n = 5 Checklist	
						2. Mispositioned crimp	• Poor placement on lower die	Shaft not inserted Too much force applied	—	Confirm procedure when inserting shaft	2	3	1	6	• Control of crimping force n = 5 1/day $\bar{x}$–R control chart (Action, countermeasures) • Install feed detect microswitch	
						3. Misformed circuit board	• Overcrimped; punch too low	• Unstable operation (cannot switch on/off)	Brake lights do not illuminate	Self-check during operation	2	3	2	12	• Change shape of punch 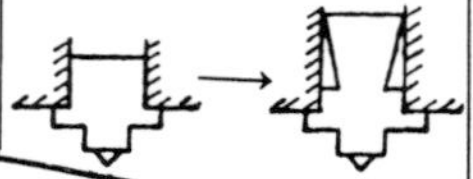	

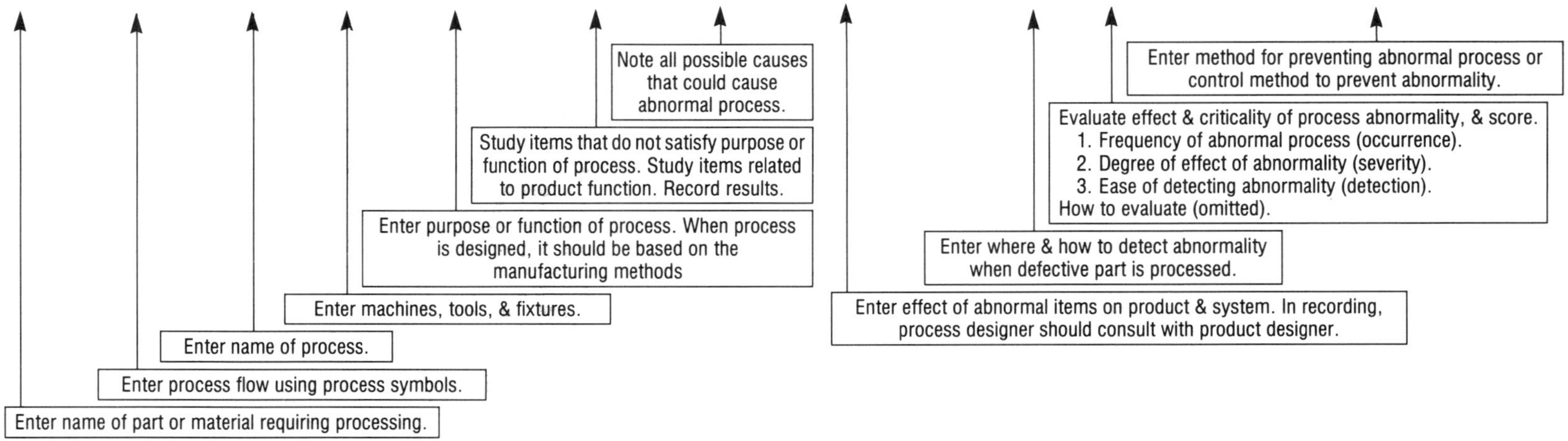

Enter name of part or material requiring processing.
Enter process flow using process symbols.
Enter name of process.
Enter machines, tools, & fixtures.
Enter purpose or function of process. When process is designed, it should be based on the manufacturing methods
Study items that do not satisfy purpose or function of process. Study items related to product function. Record results.
Note all possible causes that could cause abnormal process.
Enter effect of abnormal items on product & system. In recording, process designer should consult with product designer.
Enter where & how to detect abnormality when defective part is processed.
Evaluate effect & criticality of process abnormality, & score.
1. Frequency of abnormal process (occurrence).
2. Degree of effect of abnormality (severity).
3. Ease of detecting abnormality (detection).
How to evaluate (omitted).
Enter method for preventing abnormal process or control method to prevent abnormality.

FIGURE 10.16
Sample of a filled-out process FMEA chart

assurance in daily management activities; (2) analysis of quality problems in the factory; (3) improvement of control points, including manufacturing volumes and cost; (4) deployment to operating standards manual and improvement of daily management activities of the operators; (5) identification of problem areas to be solved by voluntary QC circles.

Application of QC Process Chart

The QC process chart is not always associated with an ideal quality assurance system. Sometimes complaints exist, an investigation fails to realize results, and new control points are required for the QC process chart.

To resolve this situation, studies and analyses led to the quality characteristics factor control process diagram (Figure 10.14). The objectives of this chart, with the characteristics to be assured on the horizontal axis, are to analyze those characteristics and to select the control points. I called this matrix QC process chart a matrix of horizontal control vs. control by prioritization. I contend that perfect quality assurance is not possible without this control based on cause and effect.

Creation of Control Points in the QC Process Chart: Process FMEA

Procedures for deployment from the function analysis of manufacturing to the QC process chart, and the preparation and use of this chart, have been explained. Process failure mode and effects analysis (FMEA) is also a system for applying function deployment.

Objective of Process FMEA

The purpose of process FMEA is to identify defective conditions associated with the process and to assess the effects on the final product. This is another method for applying function deployment, and it is also an adaptation of the function analysis method that was introduced from the United States for skills training in 1956. By this method predictable problems are analyzed in relation to the control item characteristics and check items of the QC process chart. It is one use of the QC process chart.

Procedure for Filling out the Process FMEA Chart

This FMEA analysis uses the procedure illustrated in Figure 10.15. It is also important to make an analysis with a process FMEA chart (Figure 10.16). Each item must be filled in according to the procedure.

CONCLUSION

The preparation and use of the QC process chart have been introduced. In the present industrial climate, in which the emphasis is on safety and reliability, it is increasingly difficult to achieve effective quality assurance from the conventional QC process chart alone. It is advisable to identify fully and in detail the characteristics of quality demanded by the consumers and to deploy them as quality characteristics. The quality characteristics control process diagram is deployed into a matrix relating it to control points from the QC process chart for each unit process. It is used to develop improved systems control by prioritization of targeted areas, manpower, methods, machines, materials, and quality characteristics. The value of the process FMEA lies in its improvement of the QC process chart.

It is my firm belief, based on activities that have been carried out, that a truly useful "living" QC process chart can be achieved only through the cooperative efforts of the many groups and functions within the organization.

PART IV
Applications

11

Applications of Quality Function Deployment

Toshio Iwahashi

INTRODUCTION

The internal combustion division of Kubota, Ltd., has always pioneered new agricultural implements and is a leader in the industry. The oil crisis forced the division manager to introduce TQM in order to restructure the division in February 1974.

The focus of this promotion was to establish a quality assurance system. The first task was a review of the existing quality control program and an analysis of past produce successes and failures from all phases of product development through sales and marketing. The purpose of this effort was a total reworking of the QC system in order to perpetuate success and to make failures a thing of the past.

During these activities it was decided that a comprehensive program was needed to capture the quality of the market demands and to respond to those demands. A comprehensive system was developed to create the sequence quality chart → QA chart → process planning master table → QC process chart → operating standards manual. In order to build the quality demanded by the farmers into products, the quality deployment plan focused on quality analysis to upgrade the quality assurance system. This chapter outlines the activity associated with the quality assurance chart, its maintenance, and the problems experienced during its implementation.

QUALITY ASSURANCE SYSTEM AND QUALITY FUNCTION DEPLOYMENT

The quality control objectives of Kubota, Ltd. are based on the usefulness, safety, and cost effectiveness of products. A comprehensive system of quality control must cover a wide range from product planning through service and the quality audit; the proper application of such a system will provide the market with quality products that satisfy the users and their clients.

To put the plan into action after the introduction of TQM in the Kubota division, division headquarters first upgraded the quality assurance system by summarizing the problems associated with the old system, as shown in the left column of Table 11.1. Then, to respond to changes in the industry, the company established "targets of improvement" with major emphasis on problems 1 through 4 and "Details of activities" to achieve these targets, as summarized in the table. In the far right column, "Tasks to be performed" is the action required to achieve the "Details of activities."

For the deployment of quality functions or control activities to assure quality, the individual departments in the table traditionally assumed responsibility for the maintenance of the quality assurance system. Division headquarters centralized and organized "tasks to be performed" (1) and placed the responsibility for quality assurance activities (Table 11.2) on the headquarters and on the individual departments. Based on the activities of Table 11.1, "Tasks to be performed" (2) and (3), the comprehensive system of quality assurance was defined in Figure 11.1.

Activities that were the responsibility of individual departments were now clearly defined and evaluated at each step, to assure quality through the succeeding steps. Problems across several steps were present, including difficulties with the specifications in the transition from development to production and claims caused by nonconformance of the inspection items and standards to the market-demanded quality. The causes were traced to the basic deficiencies of the quality assessment system of the division.

The solution to this problem was the implementation of the items in Table 11.1, "Tasks to be performed" (4). With emphasis upon upgrading the quality assessments in each step, the quality assessment system was overhauled and replaced with the system of quality assessment and inspection of Figure 11.2. At this time the table of assignment of responsibilities for quality assessment and inspection in Table 11.3 was formally implemented and attached to the quality assurance provisions, which linked the assessment and inspection to items (6), (9), (10), and (11) of "Tasks to be performed" in Table 11.1.

As a result, the activities to measure market quality and quality evaluation and the quality chart, QA chart, and QC process chart are linked.

RELIABILITY MANAGEMENT ACTIVITIES

The quality and cost of a product determine its value; the quality is a function of the product and its reliability. Figure 11.3 extends

(*Text continues on p. 275*)

TABLE 11.1
Major activities to maintain the quality assurance system

Problems	Purpose of activities	Details of activities	Tasks to be performed
1. Many problems result from responsibility & authority not being defined or not achieved at steps such as planning, design, production, etc.	To upgrade activities of assurance at each step	To clarify responsibility & authority in quality assurance at each step of quality assurance activities	1. Promotion of upgrading of quality assurance at each step & perpetuation of control
			2. Clarification of items of quality assurance & persons responsible
2. Independent of problems at each step, many problems are created due to unclear interrelationship between steps. Also, troubles continue because of unclear standards of evaluation.	To improve interrelationship between steps	To clarify interrelationship between steps & upgrade quality evaluation to secure assurance for succeeding processes; to feed back information on quality & quality intelligence, & by using such information, to promote solution of problems that involve various depts.	3. Upgrading of quality assurance system
			4. Upgrading of quality assessment Implementation of review system for development theme planning Improvement of evaluation of results of product development Upgrading quality assessment of first lot Implementation of evaluation of market quality
			5. Maintaining the system to use the quality information
3. It is not known what must be done to solve quality problems. Even if it is known, it is not communicated to related depts. & therefore problems persist. (Problems are not solved logically & systematically.)	To clarify control items for quality through steps	To clarify interrelationship between product quality & parts quality, or quality characteristics & inspection characteristics in designing, & control characteristics in processes; also, to deploy quality with the quality sheet at its center so that the best available technologies are used	6. Preparation of quality sheet
			7. Improve basic planning manual
			8. Implement simultaneous multidimensional design
			9. Preparation of QA chart
			10. Preparation of master table for process planning
			11. Review of QC process
			12. Upgrading of QC circle activities
		To perform analysis by using statistical methods so that each quality characterisic that has evolved can be weighed	13. Implementation of quality analysis
			14. Implementation of process analysis
		To determine critical-to-function [A] parts & processes & conduct control differentiated from ordinary parts & processes	15. Implementation of special control of [A] parts & [A] processes
4. System is not fully developed to cope with rise of new problems.	To establish a system to cope with PL problems	To determine critical-to-safety [S] parts & [S] processes & conduct control especially on critical processes	16. Implement special control for [S] parts & [S] processes

TABLE 11.2
Quality assurance activities table

Step: High level	Step: Intermediate level	Step: Detail level	Assurance item	Assurance task	Person responsible		Significant standards	Control documentation
	Product planning	A. Market research	Correct understanding of market needs	1. Survey market & collect data	Sales manager (export manager)	Sales & marketing manager (export manager)	Operating guidelines for handling sales information SMAC manual	Sales reports
				2. Analyze & communicate data				
				3. Technically evaluate market needs & create ideas	Engineering manager		Operating guidelines for technology improvement	Engineering improvement committee suggestion form
				4. Research market acceptance of current products				Domestic & international business trip report
				5. Investigate competing products				Market share report Initial market quality survey Customer satisfaction report
				6. Research antipollution laws; identify future regulatory requirements				Report on competitor products
				7. Research product liability problems				Catastrophic failure report
		B. Product development themes	Appropriateness of product development themes	1. Establish product concept	Engineering manager		Review process for product development themes	Product development theme planning form, quality chart type A_1
				2. Compare with market technology trends			Quality chart type A_1	Minutes of theme review meetings
				3. Determine availability of required technology				
				4. Project market demand & product life cycle			Design calculation standards, quality chart type C	
				5. Medium-term . . .			Rules of engineering specialists subcommittee	
			Process classifications needed to achieve manufacturing quality	1. Determine make or buy decision	Plant manager		Process classifications	Process classification chart New product review committee documents
			Determine processes to satisfy manufacturing quality requirements	2. Determine processes	Production engineering manager		Control procedures for process planning	Process planning master table Process capability investigation report
				3. Procure equipment			Equipment procurement standards, equipment control procedures, equipment receiving procedures	Inspection report Machine & equipment setup inspection report

Production preparation	L. Process design	Proper vendors	4. Select vendors	Plant manager	New equipment ordering procedures Order placement standards (quality assurance) Purchasing control requirements for critical-to-safety parts	New product component report Ordering standards confirmation report QC process chart
		Prepare operations to satisfy manufacturing quality requirements	5. Prepare QC process chart	Manufacturing manager	Instructions for preparing QC process chart Instructions for QA chart deployment	QC process chart QA chart
			6. Prepare [S] & [A] process control standards		Control procedures for critical-to-safety processes Standards for selection of critical equipment	Critical-to-safety & critical-to-function processes control standards report Requisition slips for design & manufacture of special machine tools & dies
			7. Prepare checklist			
			8. Prepare operating standards		Instructions for preparing operating standards Control procedures for operating standards	Operating standards Job setup standards Tooling control standards Process diagram for machining critical areas
		Preparation of inspection procedures compatible with inspection plans	9. Determine inspection standards	Plant manager		
			10. Determine inspection items	Inspection section manager	Classification of parts & processes by degree of criticality Painting inspection standards Part inspection procedures Product inspection standards & judgment criteria Inspection control procedures Inspection drawing control procedures Initial part production inspection procedures Initial product inspection procedures	Inspection control subcommittee documentation Inspection standards
			11. Prepare samples for inspection limits			
			12. Prepare inspection acceptance forms			
			13. Prepare product evaluation check-sheet			
			14. Check inspection forms for preparing operations			

(continues)

(Table 11.2 continued)

Step: High level	Step: Intermediate level	Step: Detail level	Assurance item	Assurance task	Person responsible	Significant standards	Control documentation
Production	First	M. Sales preparation	Sales preparation supports sales plan	1. Disseminate product information to sales & service personnel through new product seminars — Planning	Sales manager (export manager) (Marketing manager (export manager))	Sales manual	Seminar plans
				Implementation	Service engineering manager	Safety manual	New product preview committee meeting minutes
				2. Prepare product iterature	Sales manager (export manager)	Catalogue & advertising display standards, service manual standards	Checklist for preparation of advertising material
				3. Begin marketing displays & demonstrations	Local SS manager (export manager)	MSK manual & display model standards	Comprehensive analysis chart of sales plans
				4. Establish sales & service locations & increase salesforce	Sales manager (export manager)	Improvement guidelines for salesforce	Planning chart for dealership expansion
		N. Service preparation	Service preparation supports service plans	1. Prepare service training & technical material	Service engineering manager	Standard service rates & technical information preparation guidelines	Service manual Service engineering data
				2. Design & manufacture service tools & equipment		Service equipment development manual	New product review committee meeting minutes
				3. Train the trainers		Trainer development manual	
				4. Make service establishment standards		Service facility setup standards, Kubota service certification standards	
			Availability of service parts to support service plan	5. Prepare parts list & price list	Parts manager		Parts list, price list
				6. Prepare suggested parts list	Parts supply manager	New product introduction literature distribution manual	
				7. Procure suggested parts			
		O. Initial production	1. Clear identification of problems in initial production 2. Conformity of initial quality to design quality	1. Secure purchased parts	Purchasing manager Operations manager (Product)		
				2. Receiving inspection of initial parts	Inspection manager (Product)		
						Control: Provisions for controlling standards	Checklists QC process chart Operating standards Worksheets Running test reports, sampling inspection monthly reports
				6.	Inspection manager	Product inspection standards Running test manual	
				7. Assess readiness for regular production			

Production	Regular production	Q. Regular production	1. Conformity of product quality to design quality 2. Ensuring proper control of processes	1. Implement standard operations carefully	Production manager	Plant manager	Worksheet standards QC circle manual	Manufacturing processes control	Operating standards, lot cards
				2. Improve & update QC process chart			QC process chart manual		
				3. Improve & maintain operating standards			Operating standards management		
				4. Train operators					Worksheet QC circle activities status chart Process problems report Quality defect memos Recurrence prevention report Control charts Original control charts [S] & [A] checksheets
				5. Feed back quality data & confirmation of no recurrence			In-house rejects handling		
				6. Improve product quality & prevent excess quality through process analysis & improvement			Process capability investigation & improvement manual Control chart maintenance manual Control chart use manual		
				7. Implement startup inspections					Progress chart of startup inspections
				8. Implement in-process inspection					In-process checksheet
			Maintenance of process & machine capabilities	9. Handle process irregularities & prevent recurrence	Production manager		Control chart maintenance manual, control chart use manual, process capability investigation & improvement manual		Process problem report Prevention recurrence report Calculation of process capability Process capability progress graph
				10. Check & take action for C_p and C_m					
				11. Maintain & improve machinery & equipment	Manufacturing engineering manager		Equipment, tooling, fixtures, maintenance standard manual		Machine reports Regular checkup records Regular inspection records
			Purchased parts quality certification	12. Receiving inspection	Inspection manager		Parts inspection standards		Receiving inspection daily report Quality defect memo
				13. Daily promotion of problem prevention	Purchasing manager		In-house rejection handling standards		
				14. Guidance for vendors with worst receiving quality					
				15. Implementation of QC diagnosis					

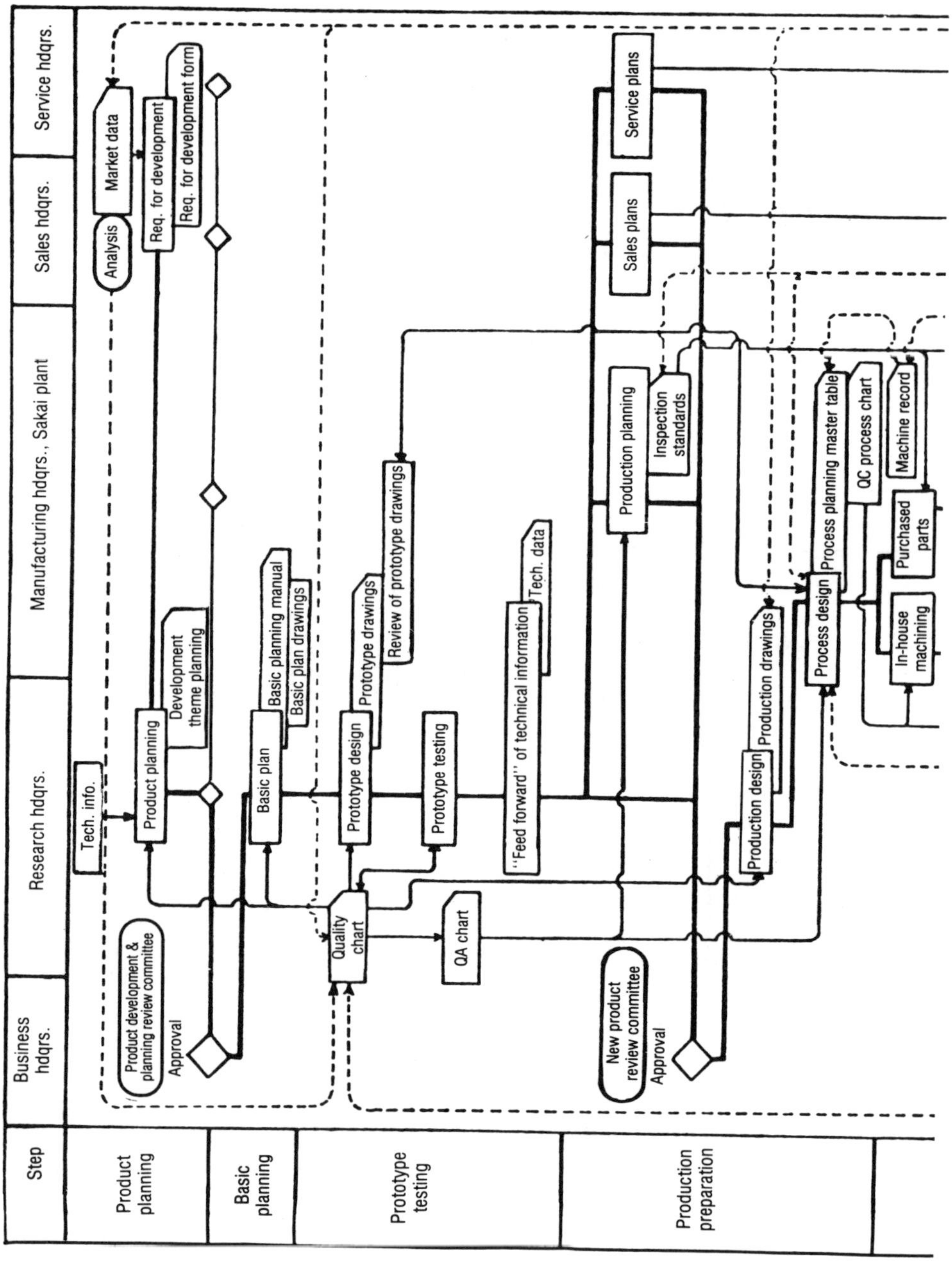

Step
Product planning
Basic planning
Prototype testing
Production preparation
Business hdqrs.
Research hdqrs.
Manufacturing hdqrs., Sakai plant
Sales hdqrs.
Service hdqrs.
Product development & planning review committee
Approval
Tech. info.
Product planning
Development theme planning
Analysis
Market data
Req. for development
Req. for development form
Basic plan
Basic planning manual
Basic plan drawings
Quality chart
QA chart
Prototype design
Prototype drawings
Review of prototype drawings
Prototype testing
''Feed forward'' of technical information
Tech. data
New product review committee
Approval
Production planning
Inspection standards
Sales plans
Service plans
Production design
Production drawings
Process design
Process planning master table
QC process chart
Machine record
Purchased parts
In-house machining

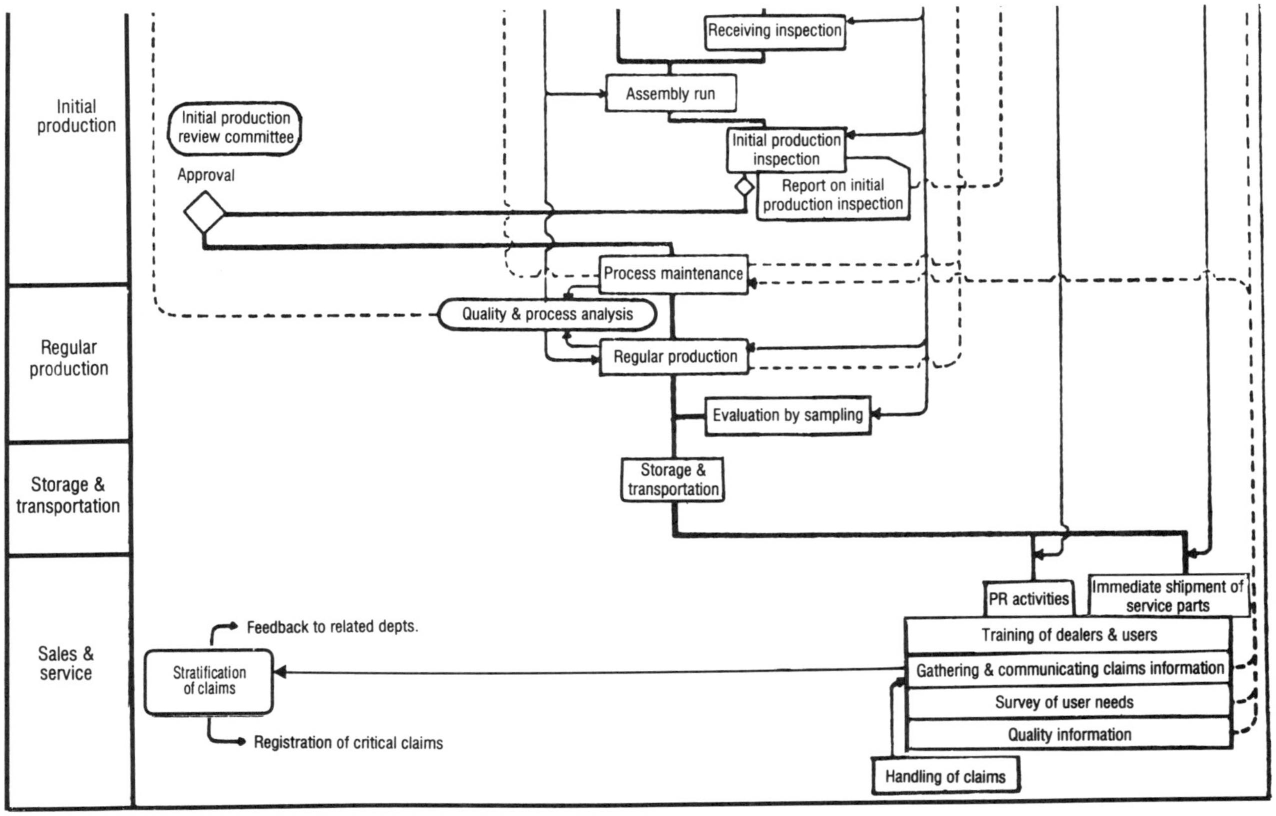

FIGURE 11.1
Outline of the quality assurance system of the internal combustion equipment division

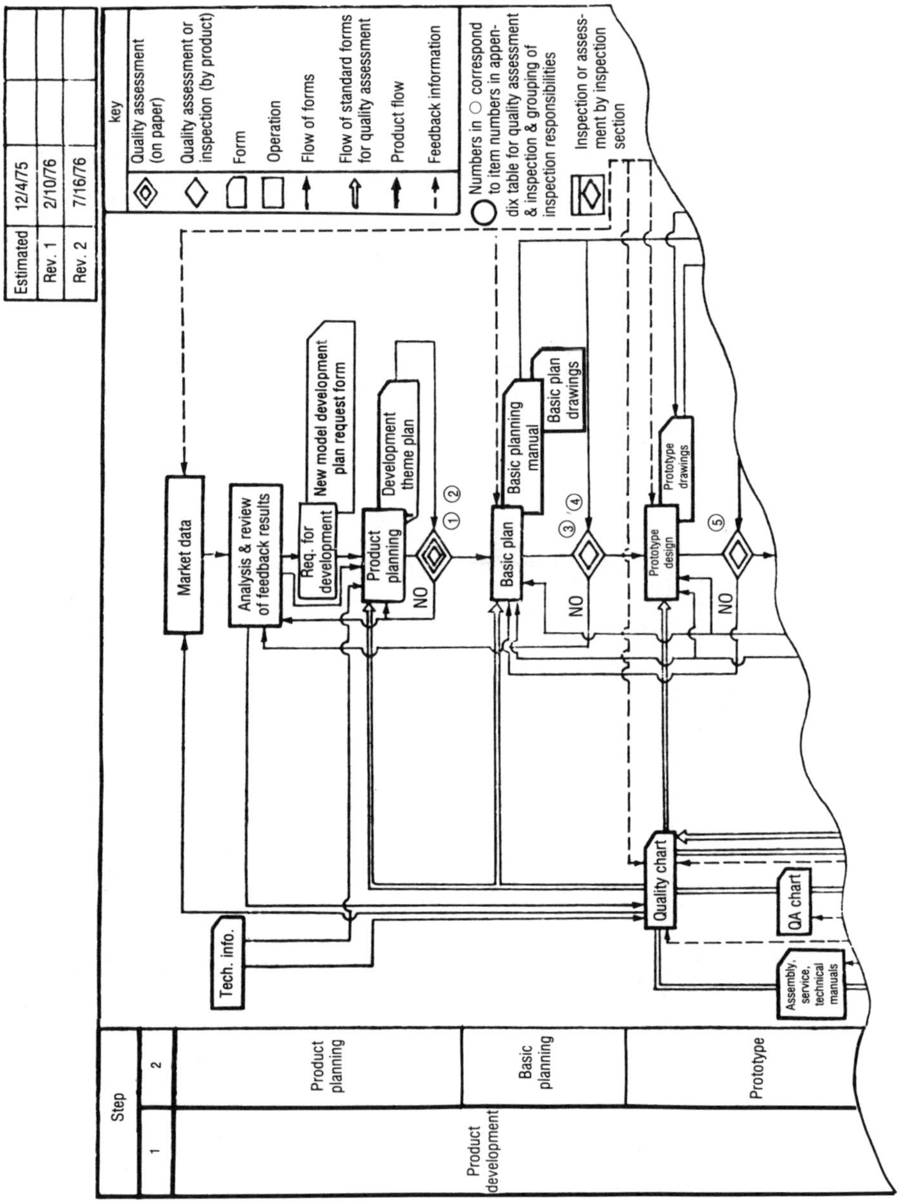
Estimated 12/4/75
Rev. 1 2/10/76
Rev. 2 7/16/76
key
Quality assessment (on paper)
Quality assessment or inspection (by product)
Form
Operation
Flow of forms
Flow of standard forms for quality assessment
Product flow
Feedback information
Numbers in ○ correspond to item numbers in appendix table for quality assessment & inspection & grouping of inspection responsibilities
Inspection or assessment by inspection section
Step
1
2
Product development
Product planning
Basic planning
Prototype
Market data
Analysis & review of feedback results
Req. for development
New model development plan request form
Product planning
Development theme plan
① ②
NO
Basic plan
Basic planning manual
Basic plan drawings
③ ④
NO
Prototype design
Prototype drawings
⑤
NO
Tech. info.
Quality chart
QA chart
Assembly, service, technical manuals

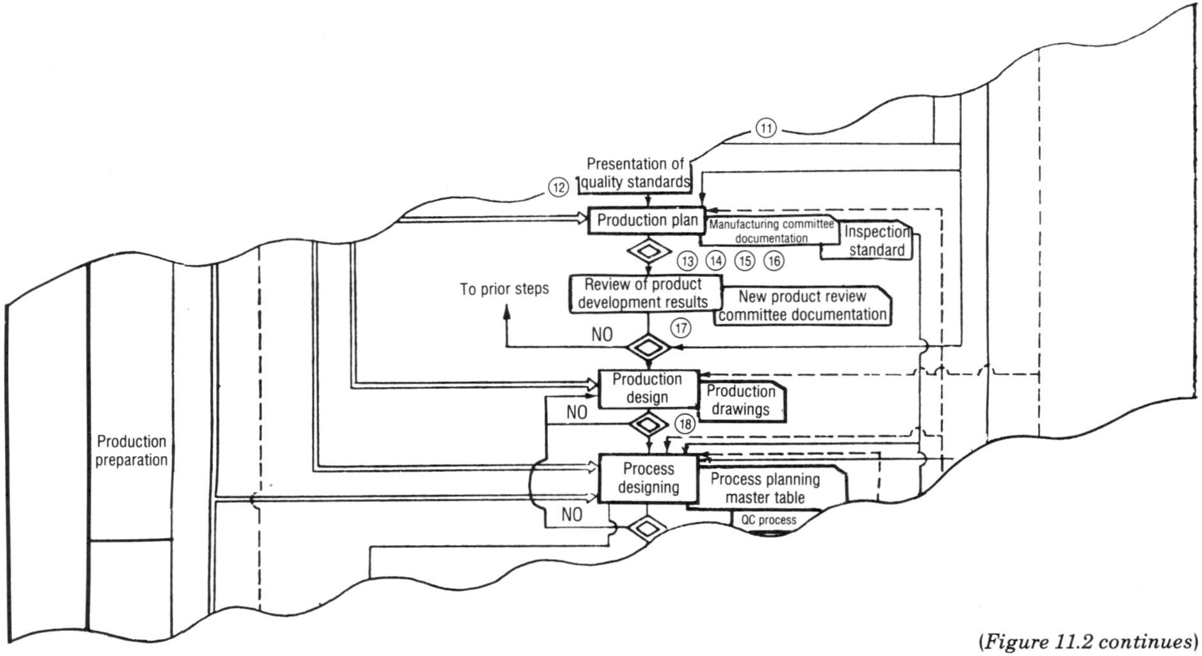

(*Figure 11.2 continues*)

(continued)

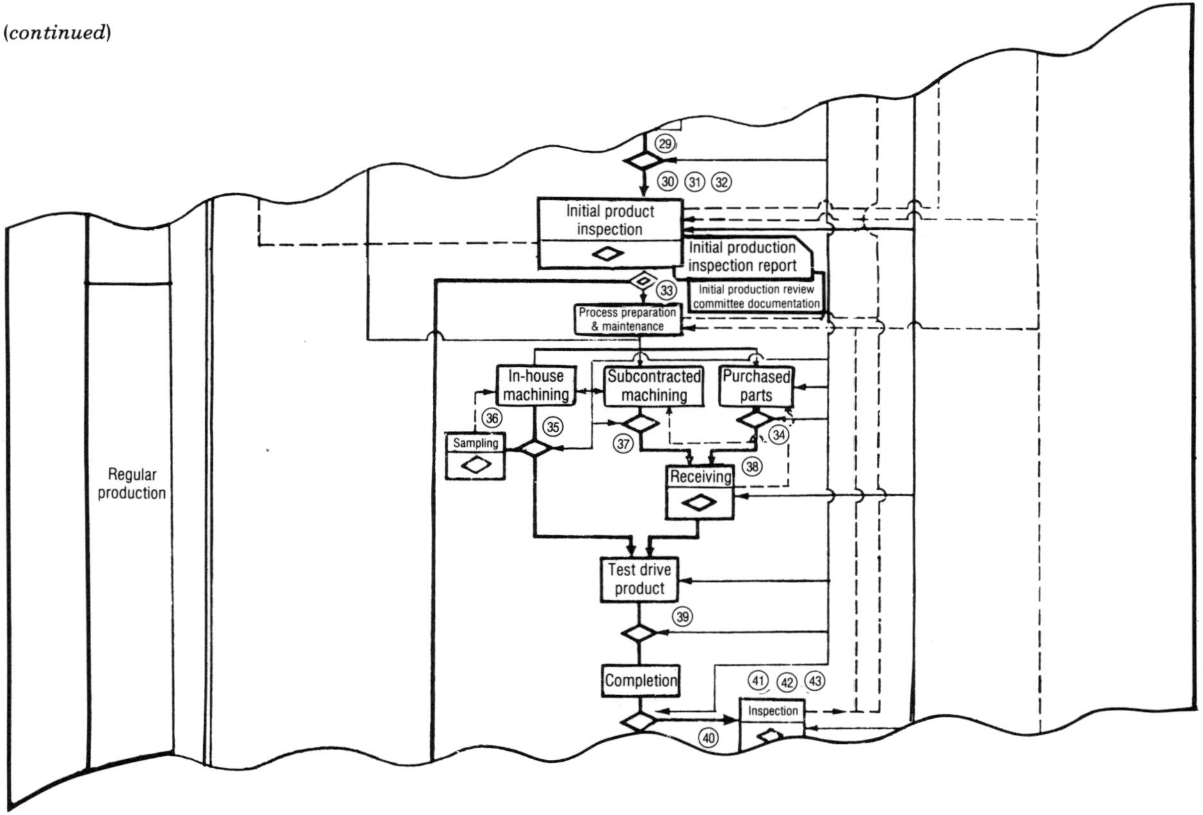

FIGURE 11.2
System of quality assessment and inspection (basic model)—subsystem for quality assurance system

[1]High level.

[2]Intermediate level.

this relationship for a combine, which is a representative agricultural implement.

At the Kubota division there is an active program to control reliability and to achieve the quality functions as described. One of the activities is the evaluation of conformity between durability-related quality (including maintenance-related quality) expected by the users and the product itself. The purpose is to design durability-related quality into the product while it is still in the design phase and to manufacture it accordingly. Figure 11.4 presents an organization to control the reliability activities in new product development in order to achieve this objective. Figure 11.5 is the current status of these activities for each step.

As a technical project to conduct activities on reliability, the engineering department uses the quality table (mainly type C) and QA chart of Figure 11.5, "Detailed Activities." The engineering and service departments also use FMEA, failure mode effects and criticality analysis (FMECA), FTA, and other tools as methods of failure analysis.

In the design and development phase, FMEA and FMECA are effective tools for failure prevention. The former is associated primarily with reliability, and the latter is related to safety. Their purpose is to reduce the potential risks in the prototype testing and production phases by identifying every predictable failure mode in the product design phase, with clarification of potential design defects. In use, function FMEA applies to basic design, detailed FMEA applies to the detail design, and final system FMEA addresses the completion of development after prototype testing. In practice they have not been used this way.

FMEA and FMECA are generally used to address areas regarded as weak in the quality chart, including the five points listed below.

1. Identification of problems and weak points in design to serve as a basis for design change
2. Acquisition of information to evaluate trade-offs
3. More accurate prediction of reliability
4. Acquisition of information to select materials in the planning phase
5. Formation of the basis for test plans (especially marginal tests) and for their implementation

FMEA is the method for considering failures modes of parts and units and for evaluating how they affect the system and subsystems. Because it applies to individual parts and units, it occasionally does not identify a system failure with multiple causes, that is, the failure

TABLE 11.3
Assignment of responsibilities of quality assessment and inspection (basic model)

Assignment of responsibilities of quality assessment & inspection (basic model)

◎	Person responsible Judgment of acceptance or failure of assigned responsibilities If acceptable, make decision to proceed to next step & any conditions. If failure, make decision on what to do & steps to be repeated. In principle, have authority to approve changes to already fixed items.
●	In charge of implementation
○	Cooperating associate
△	Receives information

Procedures for changing nonbasic models & subcontracted parts, such as land & marine diesel, etc., are stipulated separately.

- Engineering manager instructs related dept. managers
- At Sakai plant: manager of related manufacturing dept.; at Utsunomaya & Tsukuba plants: manager of related section

Step (intermediate)	Corresponding no. in system diagram	Details of assigned responsibilities	Director of business hdqrs.	General manager	Quality control office			Research hdqrs.			Production hdqrs.				Sales hdqrs.		Export director	Service hdqrs.		Major standards	Operating procedures
					Head of QC office	Quality assurance manager	Improvements manager	Director	Engineering administration manager	Engineering manager	Director	Plant manager	Inspection manager	Directors of related depts.	Director	Director of related depts.		Director	Directors of related depts.		
Product planning	①	Evaluation of planned quality						◎	○	●				○		○			○		Engineering manager, along with product planning staff prepares development theme plan & implements. Upon approving product plan, submit to plan review committee. Decide whether to proceed.
	②	Overall evaluation of development planning theme	◎	○	○	△		○	△	●	◎	△			○		○	○		Manual for review of development plans	
		Decision to proceed to next step	◎																		
Basic plan	③	Evaluation of established design quality						○		◎			○	○		○				Basic planning	
	④	Overall evaluation of basic planning	△		△	△		◎	△	△●	△	△						△			
		Decision to proceed to prototype testing																			
	⑤	Evaluation of prototype drawing																			

Stage	No.	Item	1	2	3	4	5	6	7	8	9	10	11	12	13	14	15	16	17	Manual	Description
																					design quality as the quality standard—to be submitted to the related departments along with engineering special committee documents.
																					Director of research determines in engineering special committee whether completed development should be presented to new product review committee.
											◎	●	○							Inspection control manual	
											◎	●	○							Initial production inspection manual	
Production preparation	⑮	Evaluation of				△				○		◎	●	○							Inspection manager, based on quality standards specified by engineering manager, establishes inspection standards (including purchased parts) & inspection plan, quality assessment plan (including scheduled initial production inspection, equipment, & labor) to be reviewed by plant manager.
	⑯	Evaluation of production planning for decision to proceed to production									◎	* ◎	○	○						Production special committee manual	* Plant manager, as chairman of the production special committee, reviews production plans (including inspection & materials flow). Manufacturing manager evaluates overall production planning & determines division of responsibilities & whether to submit plans to the new product review committee.
	⑯	Evaluation of sales planning													◎	○	* ◎			Marketing special committee manual	* Export manager, when the applicable product is mainly for export, evaluates sales plans as the head of the sales committee, & determines whether they should be submitted to the new product review committee.
	⑯	Evaluation of service planning																◎	○	Service special committee manual	
	⑰	Overall assessments of product development results	◎	○	○	△	△	○	△	●	○	○	△	△	○	△	△	○	△	New product review committee manual	Division directors provide overall review of quality assurance plans by each dept. at the completion of the development program along with cost, volume, & delivery plans & determine readiness to proceed to initial or regular production.
		Decision to proceed to production	◎																		
	⑱	Evaluation of production drawings & engineering information								◎										Design calculation standards, critical-to-safety & function parts control manual, general rules, safety standards.	Engineering manager confirms that assessment results have been reflected in production drawings & distributes to plant managers technical data (parts listed by criticality, process classification, QA chart, etc.) that are needed to maintain quality in production stage. Engineering manager has authority to approve changes to production drawings & specifications after release (for critical quality characteristics, director of research).

(continues)

(Table 11.3 continued)

Assignment of responsibilities of quality assessment & inspection (basic model)

◎	Person responsible Judgment of acceptance or failure of assigned responsibilities If acceptable, make decision to proceed to next step & any conditions. If failure, make decision on what to do & steps to be repeated. In principle, have authority to approve changes to already fixed items.
●	In charge of implementation
○	Cooperating associate
△	Receives information

Procedures for changing nonbasic models & subcontracted parts, such as land & marine diesel, etc., are stipulated separately.

- Engineering manager instructs related dept. managers
- At Sakai plant: manager of related manufacturing dept.; at Utsunomaya & Tsukuba plants: manager of related section

Step (intermediate)	Corresponding no. in system diagram	Details of assigned responsibilities	Director of business hdqrs.	General manager	Quality control office			Research hdqrs.			Production hdqrs.				Sales hdqrs.		Export director	Service hdqrs.		Major standards	Operating procedures
					Head of QC office	Quality assurance manager	Improvements manager	Director	Engineering administration manager	Engineering manager	Director	Plant manager	Inspection manager	Directors of related depts.	Director	Director of related depts.		Director	Directors of related depts.		
	⑲	Review design conformance of selected manufacturing processes									* ◎	◎		●[1] ○[2] ○[3]						Manufacturing process selection manual	Production engineering manager (production engineering section manager) prepares proposal on manufacturing process classes with help from related depts.; plant manager reviews & approves. * Those with special standards are to be approved by manufacturing director.
	⑳	Evaluation of conformance of established processes & design quality												◎[1]						Process planning control regulations	
	㉑	Certification of vendors, by product																			

												◎	◎	○[2]						Inspection standards for initial production	Inspection section manager conducts evaluation of problems with initial products (1) the same as initial production & checks improvements to be reviewed by plant manager, who determines whether to proceed to regular production. If not acceptable, next production lot becomes initial production (2).
Regular production	㉟	Line inspection of machined parts												◎[3]							Materials manager has suppliers inspect in accordance with regular parts inspection standards. Manufacturing manager shall determine inspection items, etc., in manufacturing process, & forward those that meet the standard to the following process. ㉔ ㉘ ㉙ 53 39 and
	㊱	Sample assessment of machined parts											◎[4]								
	㊲	Inspection of subcontracted parts & purchased parts												◎[2]						Regular production parts inspection standards	
	㊳	Receiving inspection											◎							Parts inspection	
	㊴	Product test drive												◎							
	㊵	Final inspection											◎								
	㊶	Daily sampling inspection of products				△															
	㊷	Product quality																			

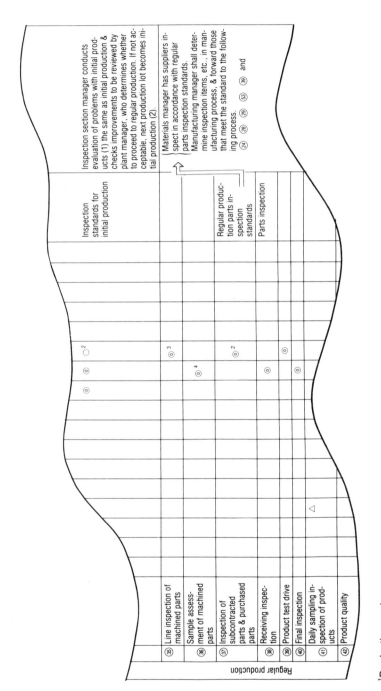

[1]Production engineer

[2]Material

[3]Manufacturing

[4]Sakai & Tsukuba plants

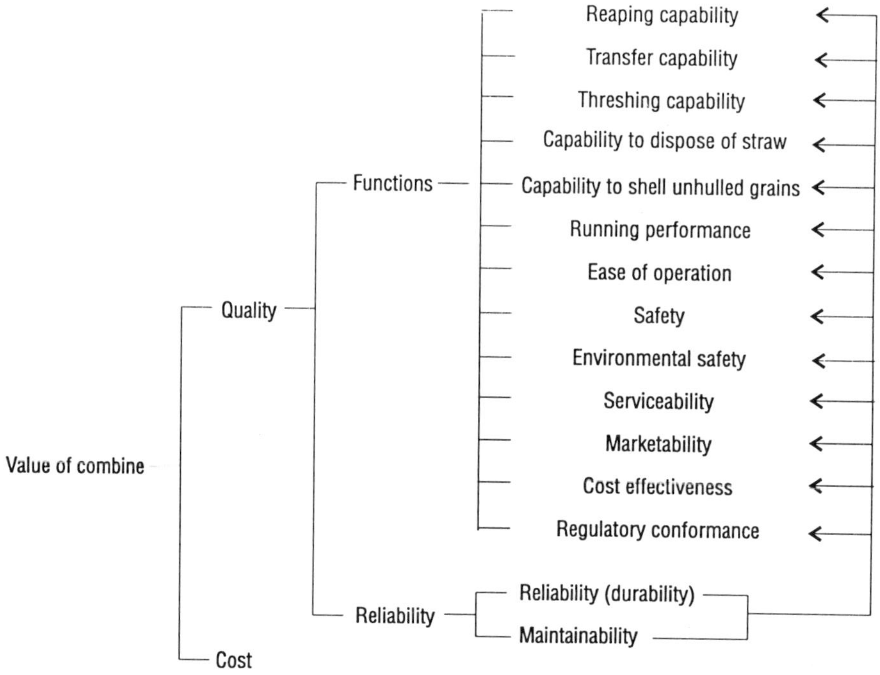

FIGURE 11.3
Positioning of reliability activities (example: combine)

of two different units or parts at the same time that cause the system to cease functioning. It is a particularly serious problem for an agricultural implement with many parts. FTA is presently being applied to solve this problem, but only qualitatively, to identify problems and areas requiring design change. In the future it will be necessary to expand its application to quantitative deployment by adding the rate of failure.

Generally, FMEA and FMECA are bottom-to-top analytical methods and FTA is a top-to-bottom approach to identify "unfavorable occurrences," and the underlying causes of the unfavorable occurrences, expanded from top to bottom. It is basically a design engineering approach (see Shigeru Mizuno, *Quality* 6, no. 2 [1976]: 3–8).

It becomes obvious that FMEA and FTA are types of quality deployment and that FTA in particular resembles the quality chart. In them quality deployment is confined to targets identified as failures or faults, and the sense of value differs from that of the quality chart, in which all aspects of product quality are targeted.

Goals for product quality are an important part of the management goals of a company. If quality targets are included in the central activ-

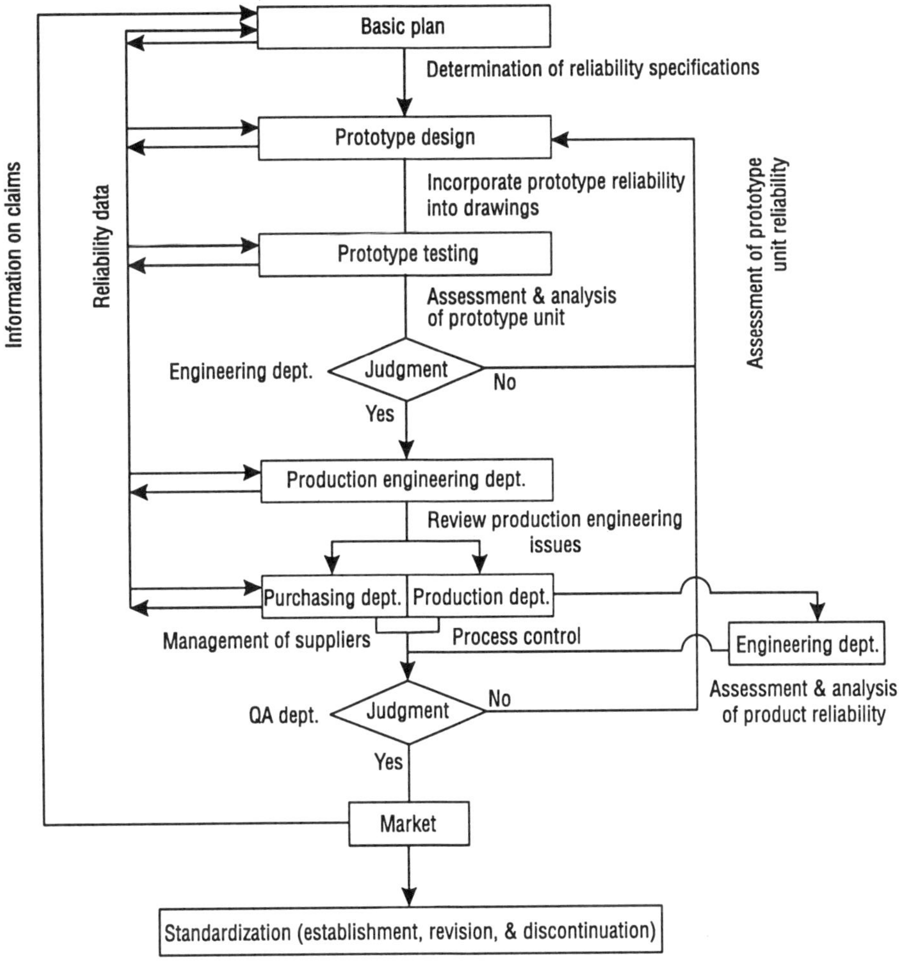

FIGURE 11.4
Organization of activities to ensure reliability in new product development

ity of quality control, the quality chart should be regarded as primary and FMEA and FTA as secondary.

APPLICATIONS OF THE QUALITY CHART AND THE QA CHART

To make the application of the quality chart and the QA chart clearly understood at the Kubota division (Figure 11.1), the system appears in detail in Figures 11.6 and 11.7, with all the steps from development to production preparation for the quality assurance sys-

(Text continues on p. 288)

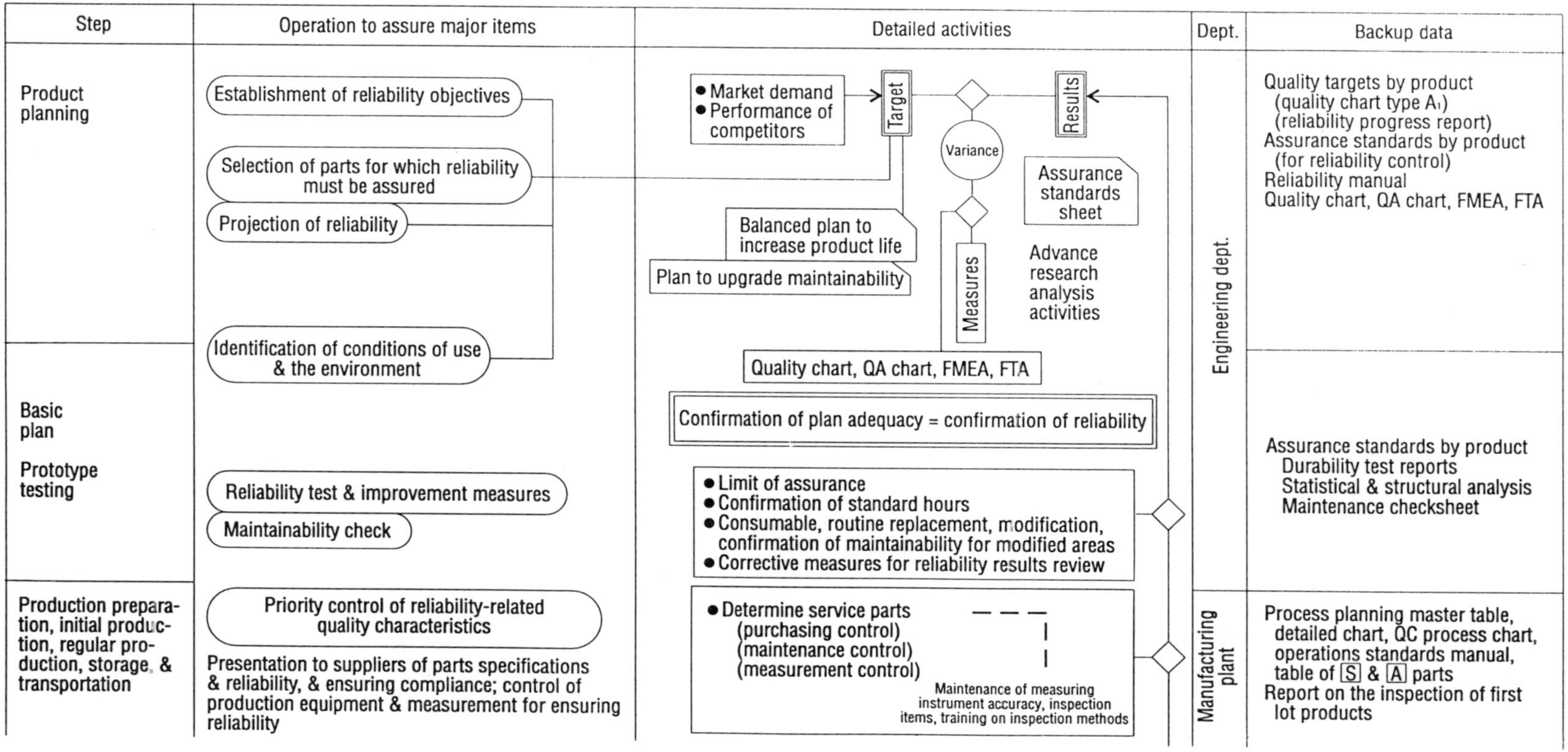
Step
Operation to assure major items
Detailed activities
Dept.
Backup data
Product planning
Establishment of reliability objectives
Selection of parts for which reliability must be assured
Projection of reliability
Identification of conditions of use & the environment
Market demand
Performance of competitors
Target
Variance
Results
Assurance standards sheet
Balanced plan to increase product life
Plan to upgrade maintainability
Measures
Advance research analysis activities
Quality chart, QA chart, FMEA, FTA
Engineering dept.
Quality targets by product
(quality chart type A₁)
(reliability progress report)
Assurance standards by product
(for reliability control)
Reliability manual
Quality chart, QA chart, FMEA, FTA
Basic plan
Prototype testing
Confirmation of plan adequacy = confirmation of reliability
Reliability test & improvement measures
Maintainability check
Limit of assurance
Confirmation of standard hours
Consumable, routine replacement, modification, confirmation of maintainability for modified areas
Corrective measures for reliability results review
Assurance standards by product
Durability test reports
Statistical & structural analysis
Maintenance checksheet
Production preparation, initial production, regular production, storage, & transportation
Priority control of reliability-related quality characteristics
Presentation to suppliers of parts specifications & reliability, & ensuring compliance; control of production equipment & measurement for ensuring reliability
Determine service parts
(purchasing control)
(maintenance control)
(measurement control)
Maintenance of measuring instrument accuracy, inspection items, training on inspection methods
Manufacturing plant
Process planning master table, detailed chart, QC process chart, operations standards manual, table of S & A parts
Report on the inspection of first lot products

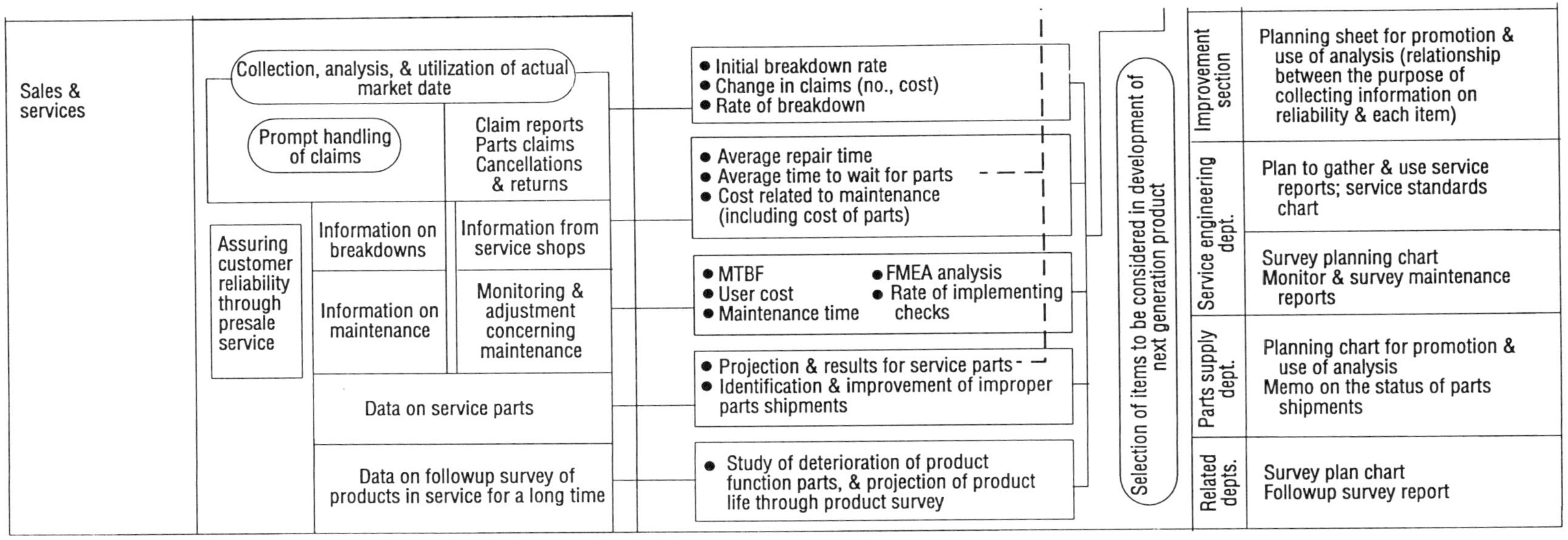

FIGURE 11.5
Current reliability control activities

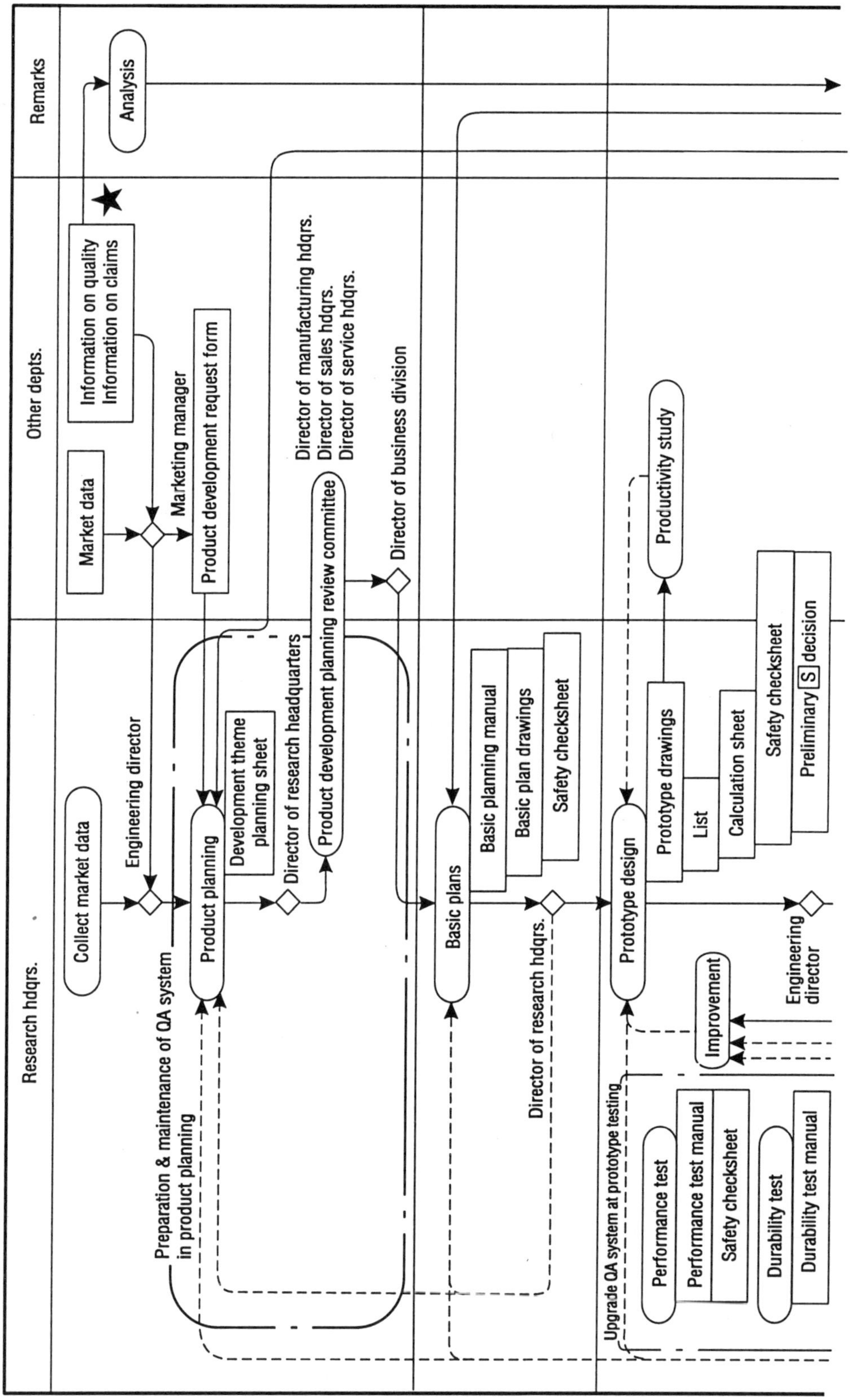
Research hdqrs.
Other depts.
Remarks
Collect market data
Engineering director
Market data
Information on quality
Information on claims
Analysis
Marketing manager
Product development request form
Preparation & maintenance of QA system in product planning
Product planning
Development theme planning sheet
Director of research headquarters
Product development planning review committee
Director of manufacturing hdqrs.
Director of sales hdqrs.
Director of service hdqrs.
Director of business division
Basic plans
Basic planning manual
Basic plan drawings
Safety checksheet
Director of research hdqrs.
Prototype design
Prototype drawings
List
Calculation sheet
Safety checksheet
Preliminary S decision
Productivity study
Engineering director
Improvement
Upgrade QA system at prototype testing
Performance test
Performance test manual
Safety checksheet
Durability test
Durability test manual

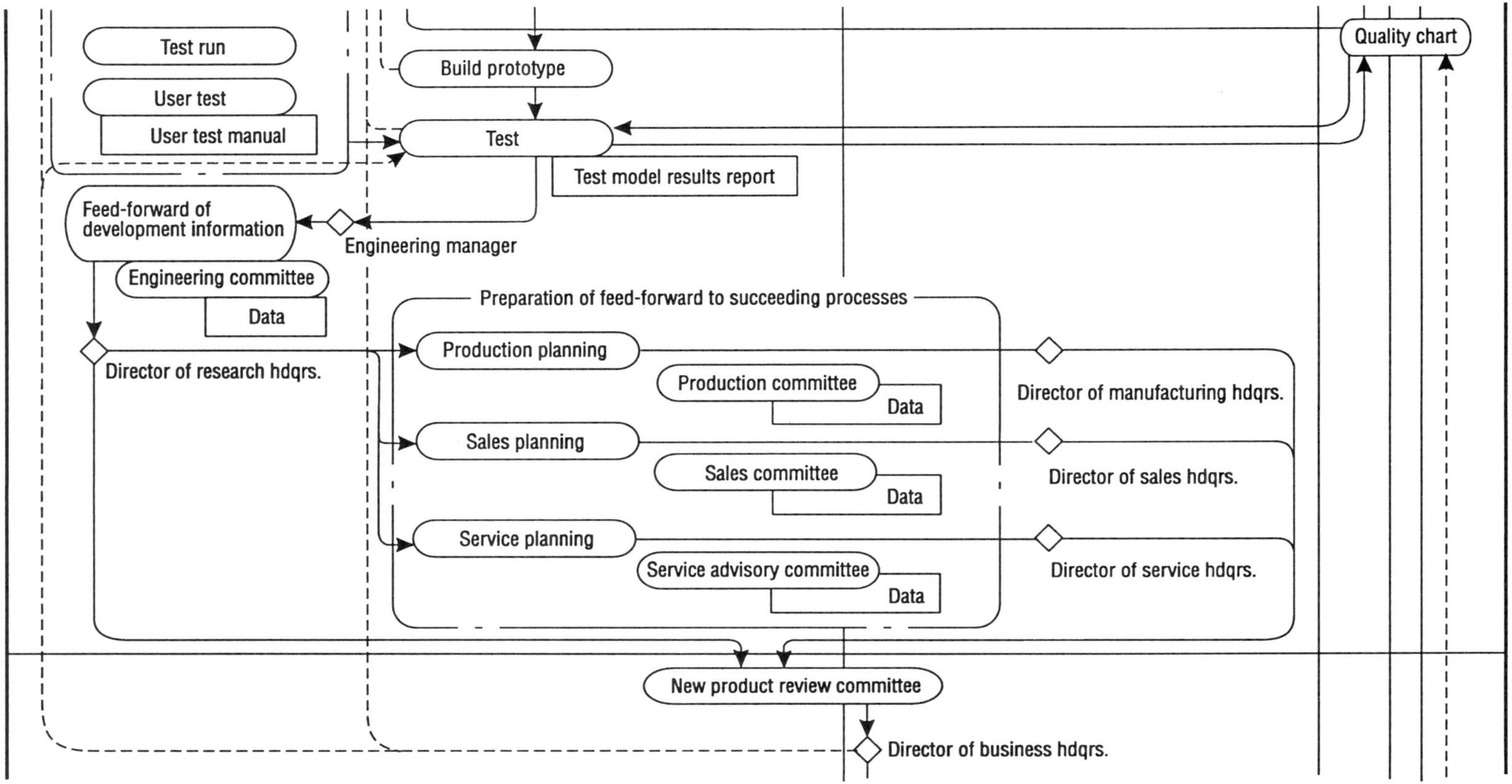

(Figure 11.6 continues)

(*continued*)

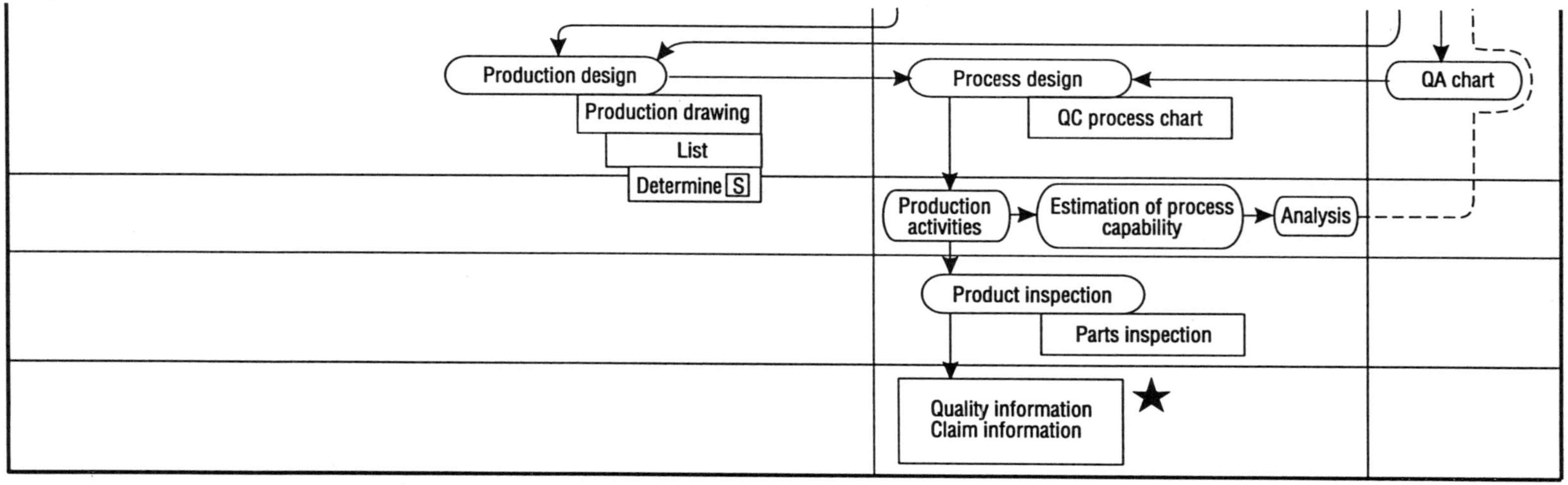

FIGURE 11.6
Quality assurance system based on research headquarters' activities

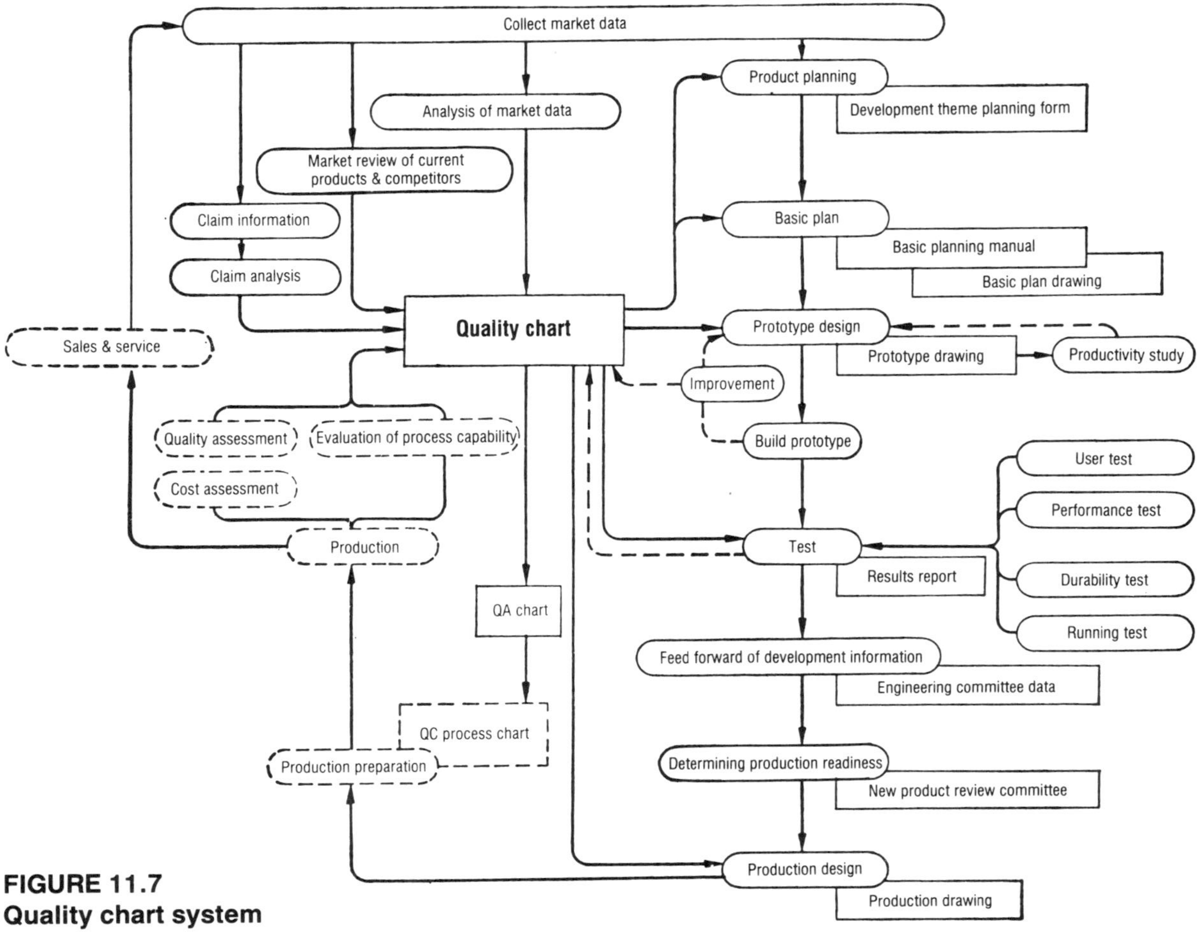

FIGURE 11.7
Quality chart system

tem explained in Figure 11.1 and with the quality chart at the center of the system in actual use.

The steps below explain how the quality chart and the QA chart are used in each step of the system shown in Figure 11.6.

1. Quality chart type A_1 (see Chapter 6, section "Using Quality Deployment in the Development Phase"), from which top management makes decisions, is attached to the development theme planning form, which is submitted to top management in the product planning phase.
2. The basic planning manual, which is submitted to the executive in charge of development in the planning phase, contains the technical methods to achieve the targets. Quality chart type A_1 defines the goals, and quality chart types A_2 and B play the major role in accomplishing those goals. These charts guide the control activities of the department and section managers.
3. The design manual, test manual, and similar documents are usually prepared in the design and prototype phases, based on quality charts types B and C.
4. The engineering advisory committee, organized by the development group, communicates quality and cost targets to departments within the company. Meetings are held to discuss the four quality charts; for the production department the QA chart is central.
5. When the engineering advisory committee meetings have been held, the following committees take responsibility for the activity: manufacturing advisory committee, QA charts types I and II; sales advisory committee, quality charts types A_1, A_2, and B; service advisory committee, quality charts types B and C.

Through activity based on the quality charts, from product planning to final design drawing release and to actual production, the quality items that were not previously communicated from the design, test, and research engineers are readily comprehended by personnel in other departments involved in the program. This has the effect of removing discrepancies between the image of a new product as envisioned by the sales department that requested it and its formation by the design engineers, and it identifies the items of market information that sales should communicate to the engineers. It is easier for everyone to understand the problems and critical items in new product development, and there is more cooperation from people involved in the program. It contributed to the solution of problem (3) in Table 11.1.

QUALITY ANALYSIS ACTIVITIES

For clarification of the relationships among the activities of quality deployment centered on the quality chart, the QA chart, and the quality characteristics, items (13) and (14) of Table 11.1 become important. The Kubota division established three targets for items (13) and (14).

1. To seek substitute characteristic values to achieve demanded quality
2. Stratification of importance ratings for factors affecting characteristics according to their importance rating, accompanied by feedback to the quality chart and QA chart
3. To make the quality chart easy to use in the design phase, while facilitating improvements in the process, and to identify the relationships among factors for individual characteristics

By following these targets, the system for promoting quality analysis was maintained. The themes for analysis gradually increased as the quality demanded by the market was identified. The analyses that were conducted to meet the quality demands and the results of these analyses were incorporated into the quality charts through the operation standards manual to achieve quality improvement.

Figure 11.8 illustrates the system of quality analysis as promoted by the Kubota division. Table 11.4 has examples of actual analyses relating to quality deployment, and Figure 11.9 shows examples of actual quality analyses.

MAINTENANCE OF THE QUALITY CHART AND QA CHART

Constant maintenance is vital for the quality chart and QA chart as the control reference for assurance activities, as shown in the quality assurance activities chart of Table 11.2. Maintenance of the two charts at the Kubota division is represented by arrows that enter the quality chart in Figure 11.7 and its relationship with each type of quality chart.

Maintenance of Quality Chart Types A_1 and A_2

Three activities are based on market information obtained from the sales, service, and export departments.

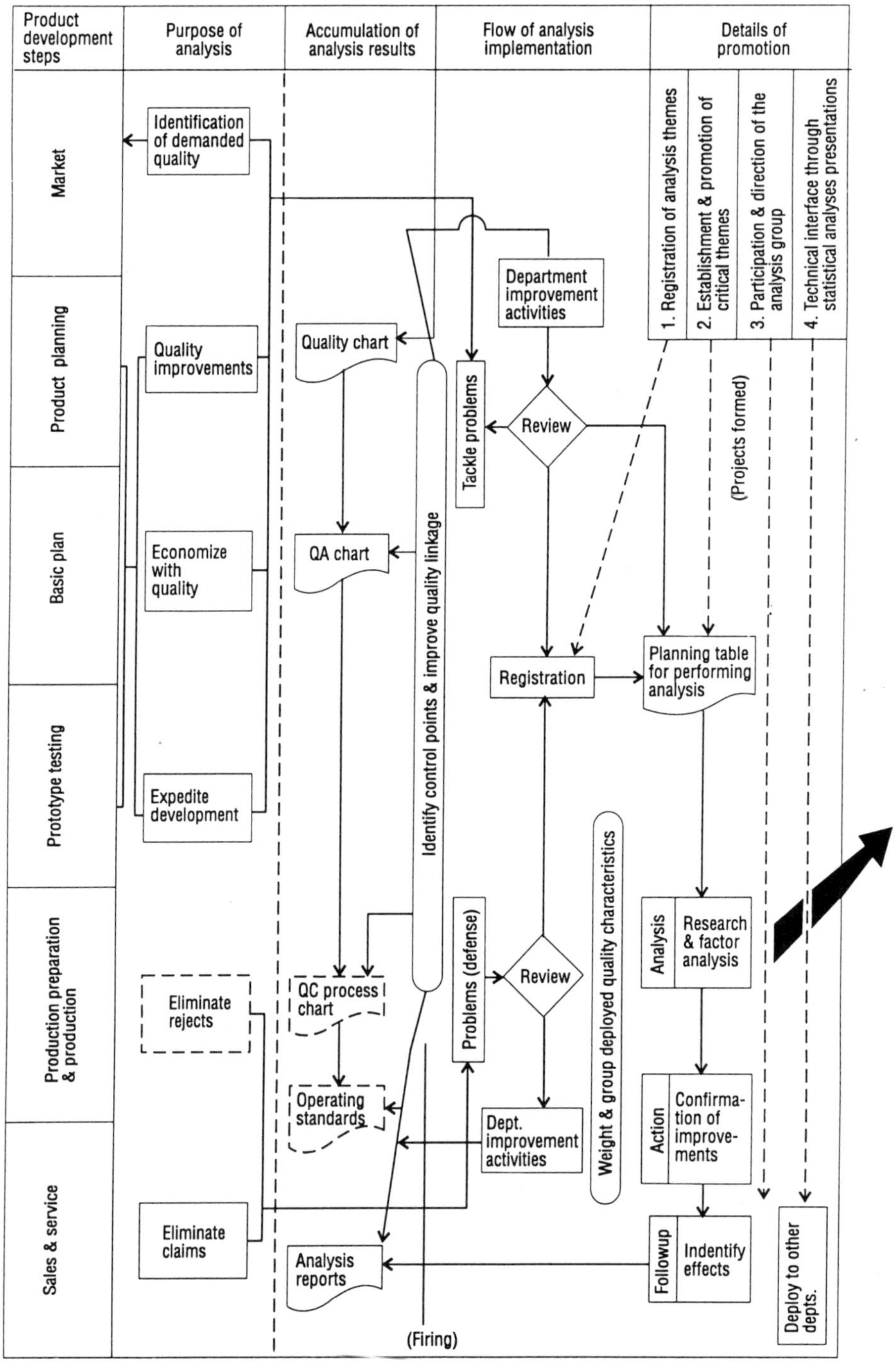

FIGURE 11.8
Quality analysis system

Computerized methods can be used regularly

Upgrading of computer systems					
	Items		Computer used I	Computer used II	Computer used III
Program packages	Statistical analysis	Programs developed in-house (design of experiment, multiple regression, other multirandom models, reliability, etc.)	○		
Program packages	Statistical analysis	BMD (descriptive statistics, regression analysis, dispersion analysis, etc.)	○		
Program packages	Statistical analysis	Quantification theories types I & II	○		
Program packages	Structural analysis		○	○	○
Program packages	Generalized engineering calculations (computer simulations, etc.)		○		
Hardware	I	Use RJE terminal at research department (connected to IBM 370/158 at corporate headquarters)	○		
Hardware	II	Computer center, Sakai subcenter, IBM 370/145 batch processing		○	
Hardware	III	IBM data center; UNIVAC data center			○
Data processing system	Data on vibration, noise, durability, stress tests				○
Data processing system	Market claim data		○		

TABLE 11.4
Example of analysis relating to quality deployment

Step	Quality deployment	Deployment details	Deployment means	Analysis details	Effects
Product development	Preparation of quality chart	To deploy & systematize demanded quality of market & identify corresponding technology	Quality-related analysis to reduce engine noise; Process analysis to eliminate processes in manufacturing of engines; Analyze process for connecting rod; Analyze processes in crank grinding; No. of QC circle activities themes; No. of improvement suggestions; Quality deployment-based existing technology	• Identify demanded quality • Determine control items for design quality • Cost reduction from new methods	In the process of achieving customer's demanded quality, problems in each step are now solved through analytic activities that are carried out by each department. The foundation of a quality assurance system for achieving target quality from initial production of a new product is now established.
	Preparation of QA chart	Determine control items for process design to achieve quality characteristics deployed in quality chart		• Balanced cost & quality • Relationship between individual process capability and product quality identified & fed back	
Production preparation	Preparation of process planning master table	Relate control items to process capability of each process, & tie into QC chart to achieve control items & control standards		• In-process determination of part tolerances • Elimination of certain processes • Cause of fluctuations identified	
Production	Preparation of QC process chart	In QC process chart, summarize control items, person responsible for control, control methods, corrective measures, etc. that are needed to assure quality in manufacturing processes		• Conformance to design quality investigated in initial production inspection • Causes of nonconformance with design quality identified • Causes of claims attributed to manufacturing identified	
	Preparation of operating standards & QC circle activities	Improve operating methods so control items in QC process chart can be executed properly		• Causes of mistakes in operation identified • QC circles can perform analysis for operation improvement	

1. Review of the degree of conformity between sales points and market trends
2. Modifications of technologies to fulfill sales points
3. Review of the advancement and improvement in Kubota's own manufacturing, engineering, and production equipment.

From basic and advanced research, and with influence from various publications, engineering revisions have been made in Kubota's department group.

Maintenance of Quality Chart Types B and C

There are five major items of information for the maintenance of quality charts types B and C.

1. Analysis of claims based on market claims information
2. Results of prototype tests from the development department and research of the publications
3. For Kubota and its competitors, a synopsis of the patents relating to deployment of quality
4. Information procured through consumer reliability studies
5. Results of plant quality assessment, results of process capabilities review, and cost of individual components

Maintenance of QA Chart Types I and II

Maintenance of the QA chart complies with the revision of quality chart type C. It is sometimes revised independently, based in items 4 and 5 above. Of course, when production drawings change and when there is a change in production equipment, a system must be in place for the related QA chart to be revised automatically.

Maintenance Control for the Quality Chart and QA Chart

Many mass-production companies make products for many different users, including automobiles, watches, cameras, stereo sets, electrical appliances, clothes, and home furnishings. The agricultural implements and small construction equipment from the Kubota division also reach the hands of many different customers (limited in this case to the agricultural and construction industries).

The uniqueness of Kubota's business from this standpoint is that, from the top division management to the bottom of the organization, there are few true users of agricultural and construction equipment. The staff members who set the business strategies, department and section managers who design the products, and the workers who build them on the production line must ship products to the market to satisfy the users, although none of these personnel is familiar with the world of the user. This situation caused the management staff to become enthusiastic about maintenance control in the QA chart and quality chart. Two of the important control items for top management are (1) how the quality chart and QA chart are used in the entire division and (2) usefulness of the quality chart and QA chart.

The second item has been assessed according to.seven criteria.

1. Changes in development by product and by various models of the product

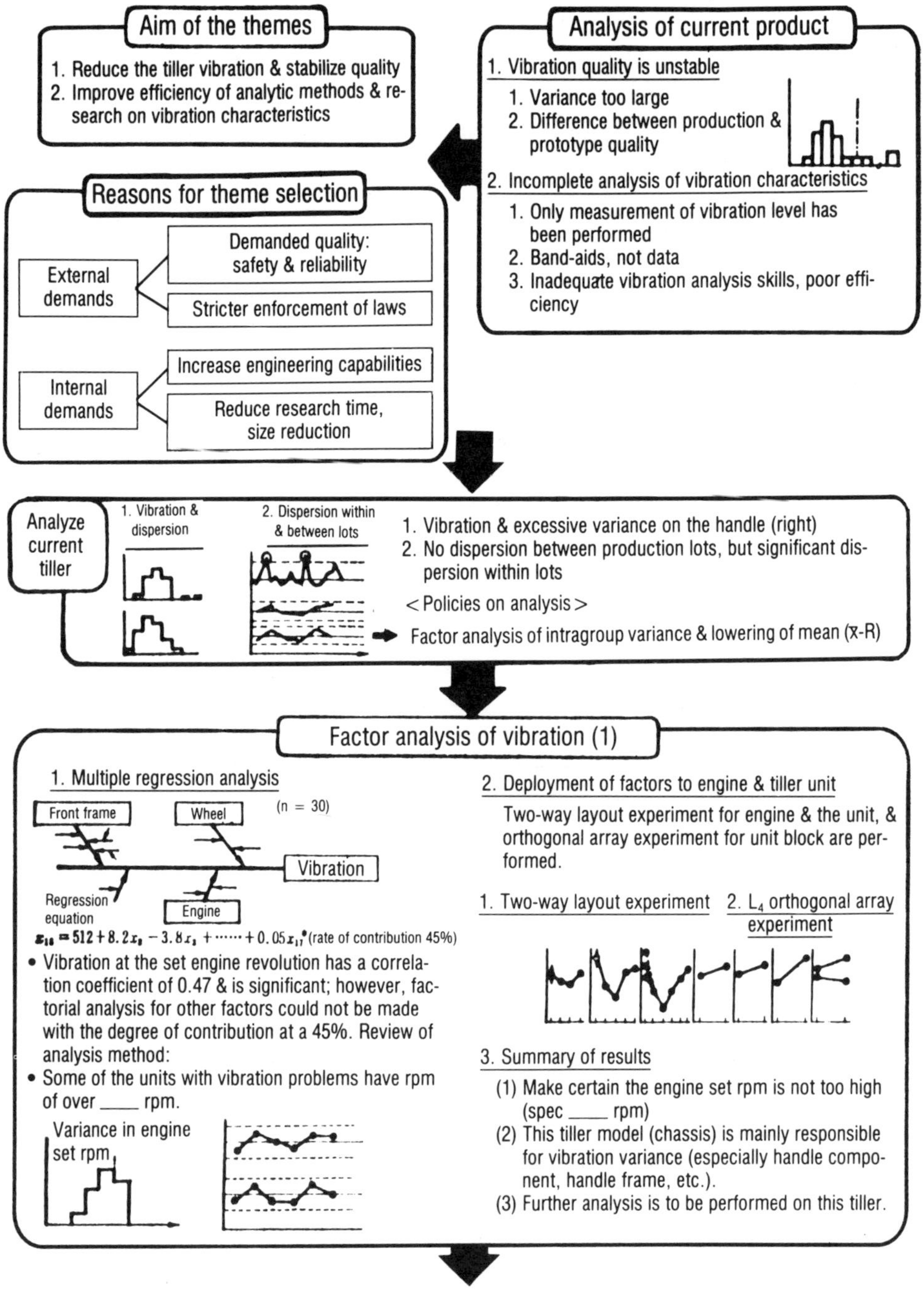

Aim of the themes
1. Reduce the tiller vibration & stabilize quality
2. Improve efficiency of analytic methods & research on vibration characteristics
Reasons for theme selection
External demands
Demanded quality: safety & reliability
Stricter enforcement of laws
Internal demands
Increase engineering capabilities
Reduce research time, size reduction
Analysis of current product
1. Vibration quality is unstable
1. Variance too large
2. Difference between production & prototype quality
2. Incomplete analysis of vibration characteristics
1. Only measurement of vibration level has been performed
2. Band-aids, not data
3. Inadequate vibration analysis skills, poor efficiency
Analyze current tiller
1. Vibration & dispersion
2. Dispersion within & between lots
1. Vibration & excessive variance on the handle (right)
2. No dispersion between production lots, but significant dispersion within lots
<Policies on analysis>
Factor analysis of intragroup variance & lowering of mean ($\bar{x}$-R)
Factor analysis of vibration (1)
1. Multiple regression analysis
Front frame
Wheel
(n = 30)
Vibration
Regression equation
Engine
$x_{18} = 512 + 8.2x_8 - 3.8x_3 + \cdots + 0.05x_{17}^2$ (rate of contribution 45%)
• Vibration at the set engine revolution has a correlation coefficient of 0.47 & is significant; however, factorial analysis for other factors could not be made with the degree of contribution at a 45%. Review of analysis method:
• Some of the units with vibration problems have rpm of over ____ rpm.
Variance in engine set rpm
2. Deployment of factors to engine & tiller unit
Two-way layout experiment for engine & the unit, & orthogonal array experiment for unit block are performed.
1. Two-way layout experiment
2. L_4 orthogonal array experiment
3. Summary of results
(1) Make certain the engine set rpm is not too high (spec ____ rpm)
(2) This tiller model (chassis) is mainly responsible for vibration variance (especially handle component, handle frame, etc.).
(3) Further analysis is to be performed on this tiller.

(*Figure 11.9 continues*)

(continued)

Factor analysis (2) — Deployment of factors to components

1. Selection of parts factors

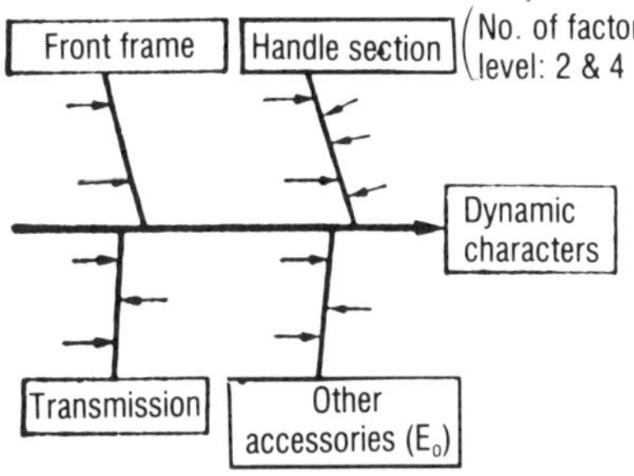

2. Orthogonal-array experiment

L_{32} Orthogonal array experiment for individual parts (level: 2–4)

(1) Results of dispersion analysis

	y_1	y_2	y_3	y_4	y_5	y_6	y_7	y_8
x_1			*				*	*
x_2		*						
x_3	*	*			*			
[illegible]								
x_8			*					
x_9								
x_{10}	*				**	**	**	**

3. Summary of results

(1) Variation vibration factors were deployed to parts.

(2) Reviewing problem characteristic "y" concerning its correlation with other characteristics revealed that handle holder is the major factor. →

(3) Study of handle holder

Study of factors (holder)

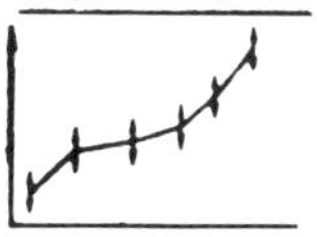

(2) Correlation between dynamic characteristics

	○Hz ± α	○Hz ± β	○Hz ± γ
Resonance F/V ○HzF/V	0.28	0.04	−0.01
○HzF/V	0.24	−0.02	−0.09
○HzF/V	0.01	−0.14	−0.43*
○Hz(○rpm)F/V	−0.45**	−0.04	−0.69**
○Hz(○rpm)F/V	−0.54**	−0.14	−0.77**

Factor analysis (3) — Deployment to part accuracy

Analytic experiment on handle holder, the major variance factor

1. Parts spec (accuracy, dimension, etc.)

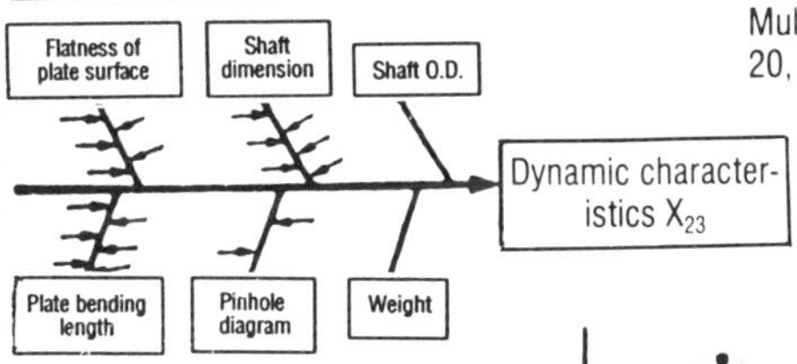

2. Multiple regression analysis

Multiple regression analysis on handle holder with n = 20, 21 factors; these regression equations were obtained:

	Contribution
$x_{23} = 325.52 - 22x_1 + 6.74x_{10} - 4.3x_{13} - 8.2x_{19}$	ratio 84.6%
$x_{23} = 285.91 - 22x_1 + 6.8x_55 + 3.7x_9 - 41x_{13} - 8.3x_{19}$	" 85.6%

3. Summary of results

(1) Factors of variance in holder vibration: x_1, x_5, x_{10}, x_{12}, & x_{19}.

(2) From single regression analysis of variables, X_5 and X_{10} can be accounted for.

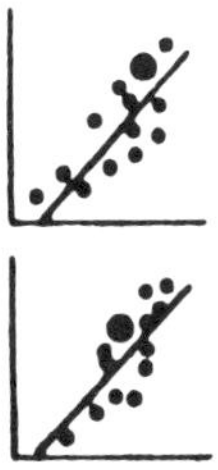

4. Review & future course of action

(1) QA chart deployment & remaining problems:

- Should adjustable propeller shaft be a factor based on the correlation of x_5 and x_{10}?
- Technical reasoning cannot be made for x_{13}.

(2) Expanding the results of analysis of factors to improvement of vibration (reduction of mean value)

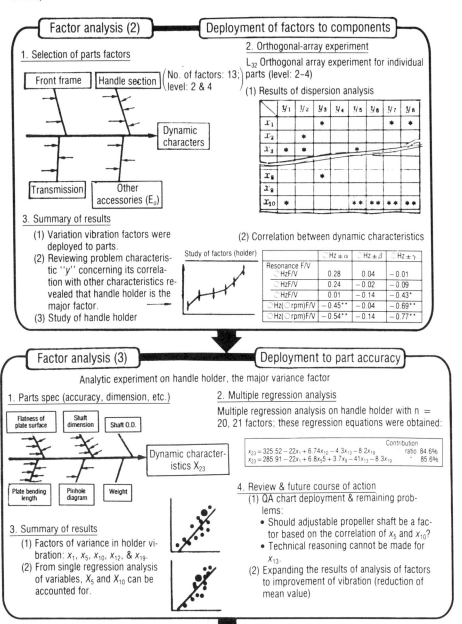

(Figure 11.9 continues)

(*continued*)

Analysis of dynamic characteristics of unit structure

1. Analysis of measurement of vibration & its characteristics

Analysis of measurement of the tiller unit is made based on results of factorial analysis.

Results & directions of improvement

(1) In high rpm zone, element of rotational primary (__-__H_2) is significant.
(2) Machine impedance changes rapidly in frequency zone.
(3) Therefore, frequency characteristics or frequency ratio must be changed.

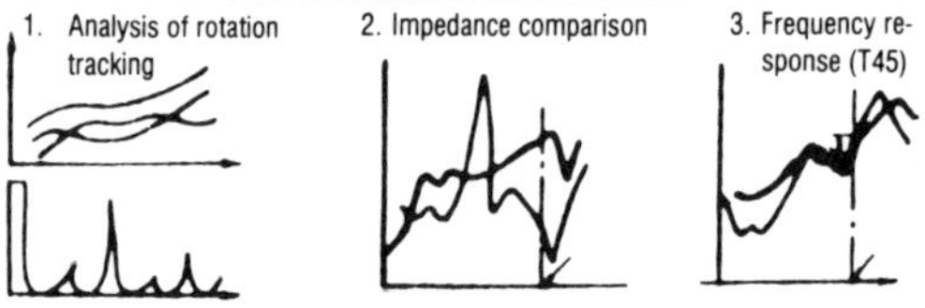

2. Mathematical analysis by finite element analysis

Conformance with measurements found in frequency response analysis, mode analysis, eigen values, & study for modeling for characteristic improvement

1. Eigen value
2. Vibration mode shadow
3. Frequency response

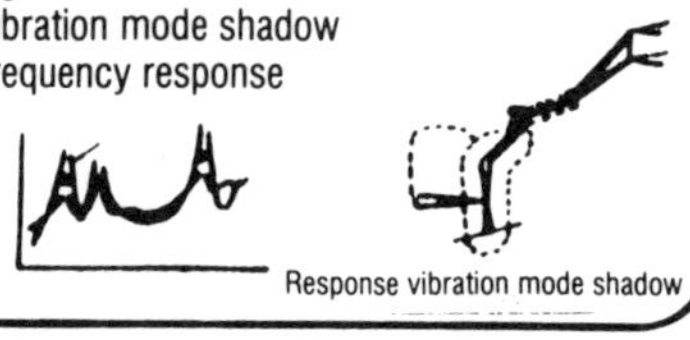

Study of improvement in dynamic characteristics (1)

Study to improve the dynamic frequency characteristic (increase the value of machine impedance in __-__ H zone)

1. Review of characteristics of rigidity & mass

(1) Big change in F/V value near __H_2 rigidity
(2) As to mass, its value changes significantly with F/V value, but not so in the affected frequency zone.

Rigidity improvement is effective here.

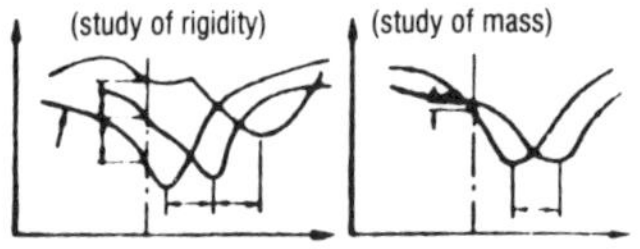

2. Mode analysis: In an effort to improve rigidity, maximum distortion energy of vibration & vibration phase of each area were measured.

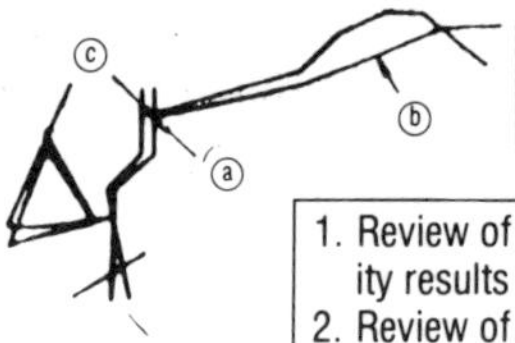

Distortion energy
Max. point: points (a) & (b)
Change position: gap (c)

1. Review of improvement of rigidity results at (a) & (b)
2. Review of dampening effect on gap (c)
3. Results (plan for improvement)

Study of improvement in dynamic characteristics (2)

1. Experiment for improvements

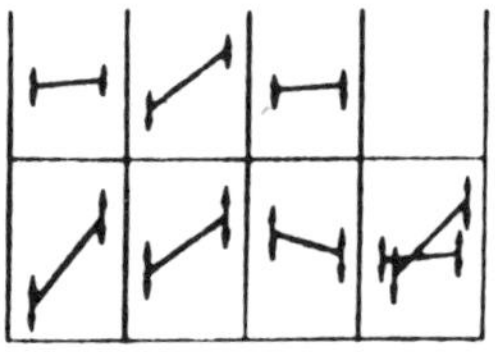

2. Results of characteristics improvement

Improvement of dynamic characteristics from experiment results brought about an increase of __-__ db (actual measurement) in machine impedance value.

3. Calculation of vibration: Vibration was calculated with finite element method for above improvement measure & a major reduction was predicted, as shown at right.

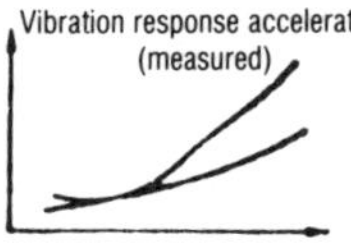

(*Figure 11.9 continues*)

(continued)

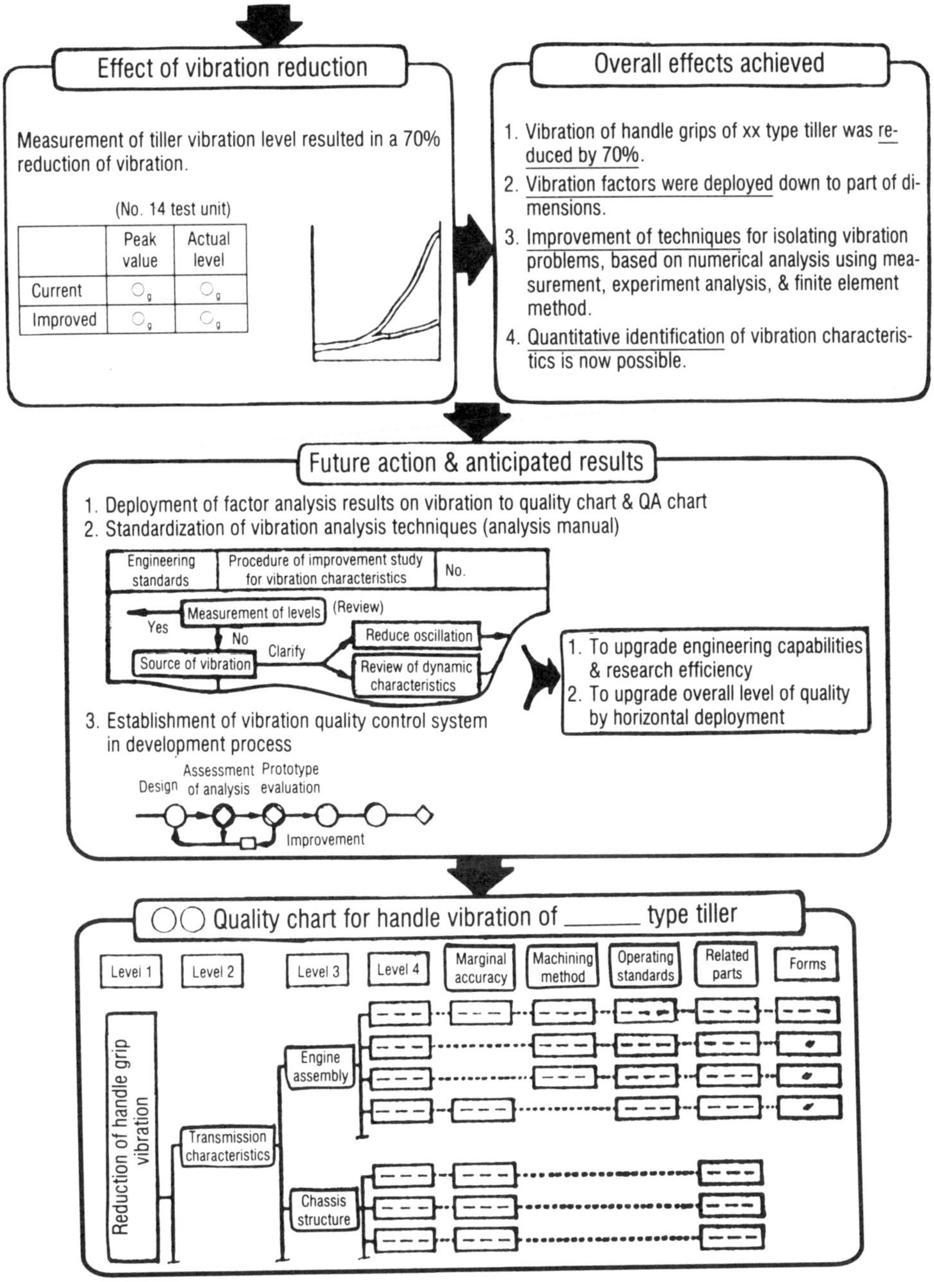

FIGURE 11.9
Examples of quality analysis

2. Changes in the level of satisfaction in the market
3. Changes in customer claims
4. Changes in frequency of defects at the plant
5. Changes in the service parts inventory and in the number of immediate deliveries
6. Changes in the number of workers committed to each product and each model
7. Changes in the cost and expenses of prototype testing

CONCERNS IN QUALITY DEPLOYMENT

Three types of major barriers obstruct the effort to make the activities of quality deployment part of the daily routine.

1. Doubt concerning the effectiveness of the activities because of the time and energy required to deploy the established technologies
2. Negative feelings that regard quality deployment as effective as a horizontal deployment of existing technologies but not effective in research and development, especially for the creation of new products
3. Doubt as to whether a true "communication of quality" can be achieved.

Based on the experience of successful horizontal deployment as a daily routine for various products in the Kubota division, I offer comments concerning these doubts.

It Is a Waste of Time and Effort to Deploy Established Technologies

This doubt is strong among experienced groups and well-informed personnel, especially when individuals have responsibility for the overall plan for products. Gradually to implement quality deployed within such an organization, it is important to clarify at the outset how the prepared quality chart is used to begin deployment in the easier areas of applications.

The several types of quality charts in the Kubota division were not set in place gradually, beginning with type A_1, but were completed over a period of time by individual application to specific needs of the engineering departments responsible for the respective products.

When the purpose of the quality chart is clear, it should be deployed for the easiest use with a given fixed format, without stress on those who apply it. For example, a tree-shaped deployment for the entire system or a two-dimensional matrix is appropriate if they are easier to view.

The quality chart may have limitations of paper size and of actual use. Certainly the deployment content used by the department and section managers for their control purposes is different from that incorporated into horizontal deployment of higher-level technologies for a relatively inexperienced staff in charge of practical operations.

When the quality chart has been completed, it is important to investigate how it is used and how its users regard it. The information obtained will serve as the basis for improvement in the manner it is deployed.

Quality Deployment Is Not Useful for the Creation of New Products

In quality deployment, the quality functions are categorized according to several quality levels to correspond to each level in the quality chart. When particular quality levels cannot be achieved by the existing technologies, they are still required to support the quality level of future products. The tendency is to deploy quality to a level that can be achieved by a single technology or by the technologies available. This occurs because quality deployment stops at the point where quality has been deployed to a level that is extremely difficult to attain. A quality chart created from this type of deployment does not lead to anything new because products of such a quality chart are merely combinations of the available technologies.

This situation is the basis of criticism that the quality chart does not suffice for research and development, particularly for the creation of future products. It is appropriate to identify unexpressed or latent needs and, regardless of the level of current technologies, to deploy demanded quality to the level where it belongs. When the current technologies cannot support it, the result will be a standstill situation or a quality chart not completely filled. The research theme is to connect the level at which deployment stopped to the technologies needed to make it come about, in order to direct what must be done in research and development of new products. This method is a pursuit of research themes in a systematic manner with organic connections (in contrast with the conventional theoretical and empirical methods). It would be easier, in response to societal changes and to competitive products, to set up long-term objectives for product development as the guideline for what must be done.

What Tasks Are to Be Completed for True "Communication of Quality"?

The quality chart and QA chart have some deficiencies, including the three listed below.

1. One factor often affects several quality characteristics, and the relationship is difficult to understand.
2. The rate of contribution to each item mentioned is not readily available.
3. It is rare for one tolerance to affect the final product characteristics. In many cases, cumulative tolerances create an overall tolerance stackup on the final product characteristics. The quality chart and QA chart cannot easily express this effect.

To summarize, many of the quality characteristics in the quality chart are related to one another, and the characteristics of one part or one functional area frequently have an offsetting effect on the quality of several items at a higher level. This topic requires review. With agricultural implements it is a complex matter because crops vary widely with changes in the natural environment. A method to solve this difficulty is the relation chart in Table 11.5, which has been subjected to experiment. For agricultural implements it is important to determine which of the combined characteristics S_n are affected by the environment and conditions of use represented by u_1, u_2, . . . in Table 11.5 and how they affect the final quality characteristics Q_n.

SALES AND SERVICE DEPARTMENTS AND QUALITY FUNCTION DEPLOYMENT

At the Kubota division, quality assurance activities for product development were formerly considered the responsibility of the research department. To identify demanded quality in development, research personnel visited local dealers and farmers to obtain their opinions and demands through meetings and testing. The purpose of this experience was the recognition of the demanded quality.

After the introduction of TQM, the responsibilities of the individual departments for quality assurance became clearer from Table 11.1, "Tasks to be performed" (1) and (2), and the sales and service departments began to participate actively in quality deployment.

Selection of Development Themes

Quality chart type A_2 is used primarily in the product planning phase. By reference to the demanded quality chart, which converts

TABLE 11.5
Relation chart

(Originated by Furukawa)

Part	Position	Characteristics of position	Relation (I)								(Process capability)	Feedback					Technical standard
A	a_1	X_{1-1}	↓						↓		x_{1-1}						
	a_2	X_{1-2}			↓			↓			x_{1-2}						
	a_3	X_{1-3}	↓				↓		↓		x_{1-3}			←			
	⋮																
B	b_1	X_{2-1}	↓				↓		↓		x_{2-1}						
	b_2	X_{2-2}		↓		↓				↓	x_{2-2}						
	⋮																
C	c_1	X_{3-1}		↓							x_{3-1}						
	c_2	X_{3-2}			↓	↓	↓			↓	x_{3-2}	←					
	⋮																
	⋮	⋮									⋮						

Combination	Characteristics of combinations	Relation (II)								Assembly process capability	Feedback					Quality characteristics		Characteristic value
A • B	S_1	→						→		Z_1								
B • C	S_2		→		→					Z_2	↑					Q_{1-1}		
A • ···	S_3						→			Z_3								
A • B • C	S_4					→				Z_4						Q_{1-2}	Q_1	
							→											
B • C	S_5								→	Z_5						Q_{1-3}		
A • C	S_6			→						Z_6			↑					
	⋮									⋮						⋮		

Environment & conditions of use	Relation (III)								Information
u_1	↑								I_1
u_2				↑					I_2
u_3								↑	I_3
⋮									⋮

market needs as identified from market research into demanded quality items, the sales and service departments contribute to the selection of development themes. Sales headquarters at Kubota assumes primary responsibility for coordination of demands and requests from sales engineering and dealers regarding product development, and conducts research in response to these demands and requests.

Check of Prototype Units through Testing

Most of the demanded quality charts have demanded qualities from the sales department that are not quantified because they have not

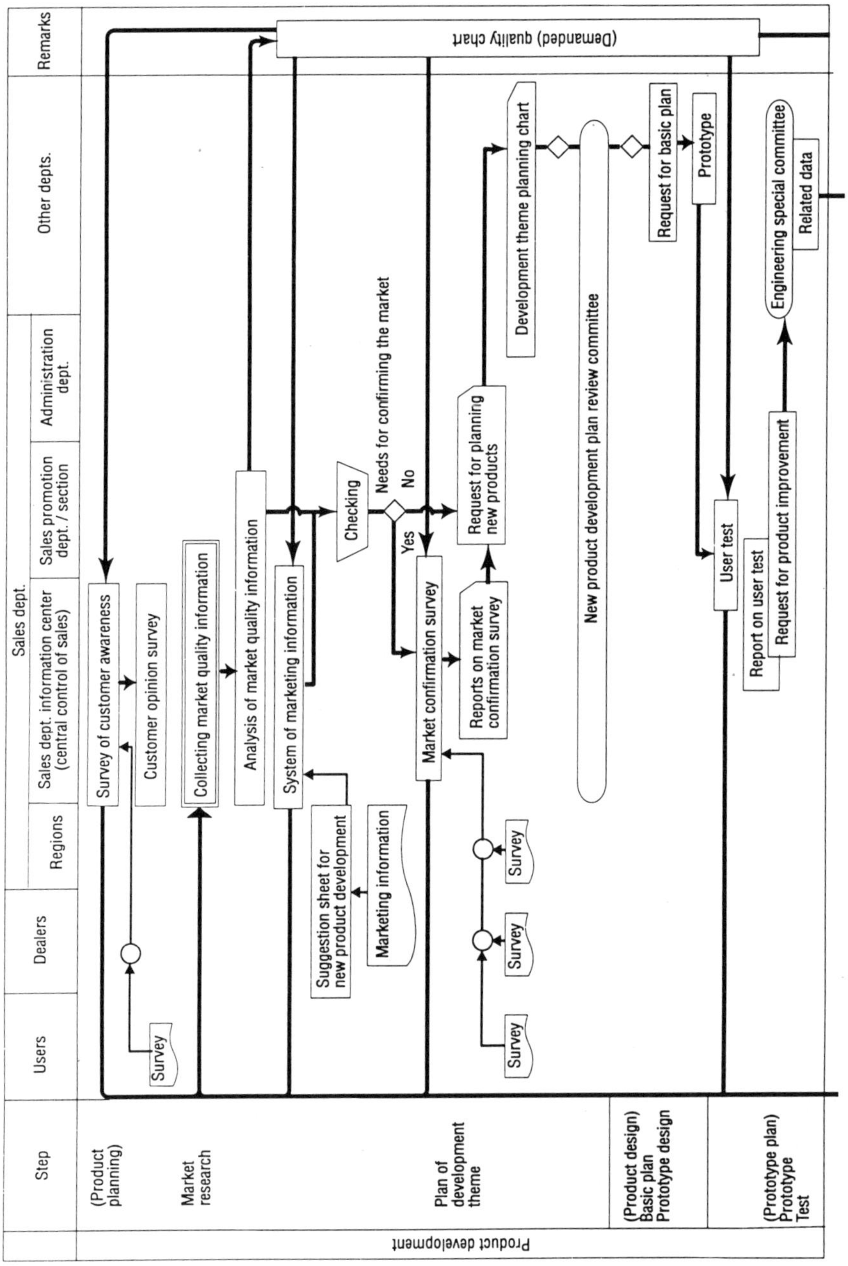
Product development
Step
(Product planning)
Market research
Plan of development theme
(Product design) Basic plan Prototype design
(Prototype plan) Prototype Test
Users
Dealers
Regions
Sales dept.
Sales dept. information center (central control of sales)
Sales promotion dept. / section
Administration dept.
Other depts.
Remarks
Survey
Survey of customer awareness
Customer opinion survey
Collecting market quality information
Analysis of market quality information
System of marketing information
Suggestion sheet for new product development
Marketing information
Checking
Needs for confirming the market
Yes
No
Survey
Survey
Survey
Market confirmation survey
Reports on market confirmation survey
Request for planning new products
Development theme planning chart
New product development plan review committee
Request for basic plan
Prototype
User test
Report on user test
Request for product improvement
Engineering special committee
Related data
(Demanded) quality chart

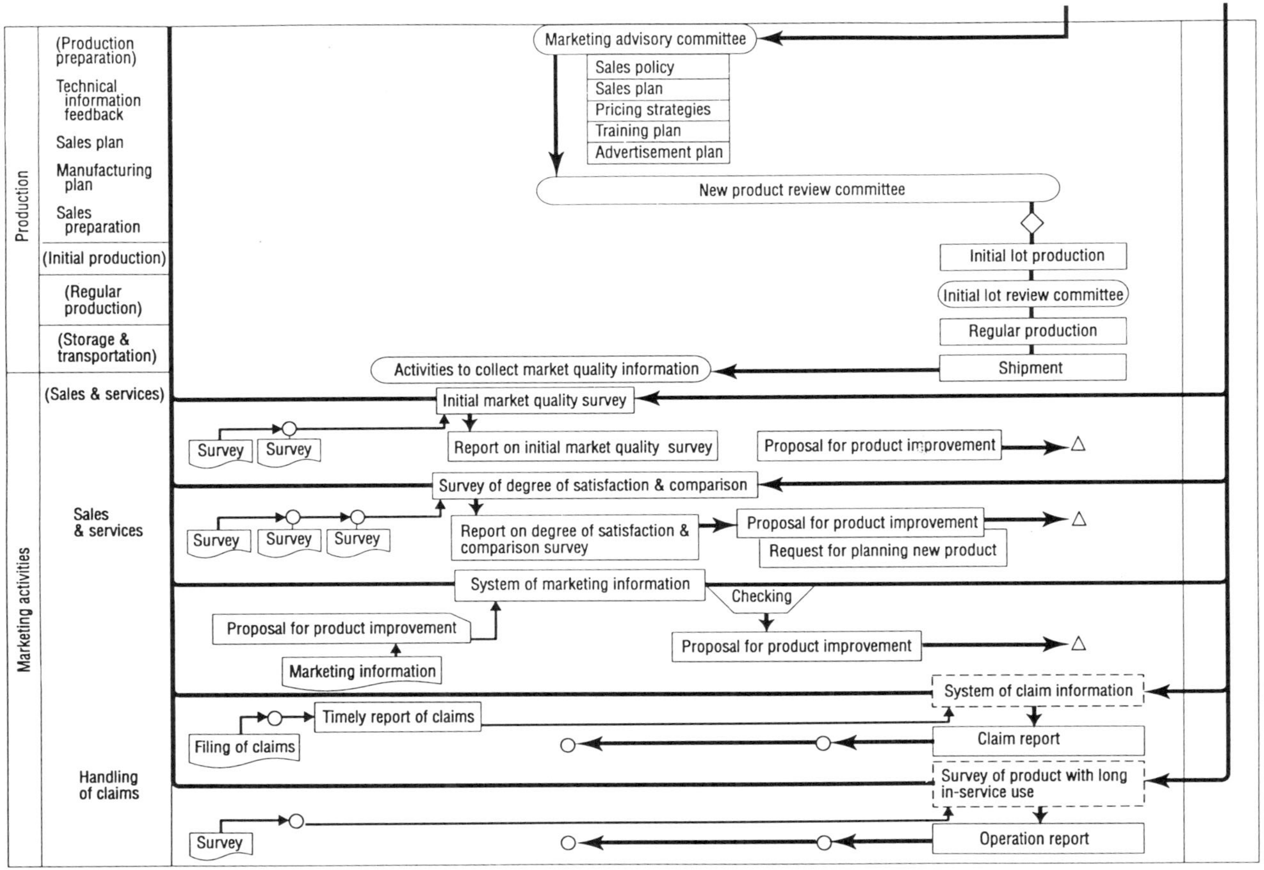

FIGURE 11.10
Flow of market quality information

been transformed into technical characteristics. With the progression of development and the deployment of the research department's quality chart into types B and C, discussion-and-coordination meetings are conducted with the sales department for clarification of the demands. Particularly in response to comparisons with competitors, which are the basis of the sales group demands, the demanded quality chart for sales has become the type B form, with revisions and accommodations to satisfy the sales department. Sales and service departments use it as a checklist for prototype units. The FMEA mentioned earlier performs the same function.

Sales Preparation

When the quality targets projected in quality chart types A_1 and A_2 have been completed, several committees are organized to proceed with production. These include the engineering advisory committee, the sales advisory committee, the service advisory committee, and others. For the sales and service group, the committees review and establish sales plans and selling prices with attention to market size and quality level in response to sales and service policy. They submit these decisions to top management. The sales points selected have a significant influence on the plans described above, and the demanded quality chart for the evaluation of Kubota's own products against the competition plays a significant role.

Activities after the Sale

After the sale, the sales and service groups conduct research to support the maintenance of the quality chart.

1. Early market quality research
2. Research on satisfaction level
3. Follow-up research on units in use for an extended period

These are the major items of research by the sales and service groups. Data obtained from 1 and 2 and from claims are valuable for the maintenance and upgrade of various quality charts, especially according to function (failure mode) on the quality chart as prepared by the research headquarters. These data support the development of next generation products and the prevention of recurring claims. Figure 11.10 outlines these activities.

CONCLUSION

The quality chart has been the centerpiece for quality function deployment in its communication of quality, and it plays an important role in the production development phase, especially in the design and in the initial production phases. When sales and service departments are included, there is room for improvement in many areas of the system. The development group is closely related to other groups, and it must conduct its activities in close coordination with other groups in the program. The quality chart serves to clarify this relationship with each group. It is most valuable in its completed form. The significance of true development activity is the process of making the product better, and this is believed to be the driving force for company growth.

The intention is to continue to upgrade and to maintain the quality chart (1) to support the analysis of critical quality items and to improve their usefulness by quantitative definitions and (2) to clarify how the quality chart relates to cost, so that better quality at lower cost can be achieved.

Chapters 6, 7, 8, and this chapter have presented actual applications of this method at the Kubota plant, with guidance by such professionals as Shigeru Mizuno. The kind guidance of Yasushi Furukawa has been most helpful for the quality control activities of quality function deployment based on the quality control chart, simultaneous multidimensional design, QA chart, QC process chart, and so on. Hearty appreciation is expressed to these people for their efforts.

PART V
Recent Approaches and Future Issues of Quality Function Deployment

12

Recent Approach of Quality Function Deployment

Yoji Akao

INTRODUCTION

The number of reports relating to quality function deployment in representative Japanese quality control magazines—*Quality Control* (JUSE), *Standardization and Quality Control* (JSA), and *Quality* (JSQC)—between 1966 and 1977 are charted in Figure A.1. Figure 12.1 shows the number of QFD cases reported each year over the period 1966–1982.

The survey also revealed the departments in which QFD was implemented between 1978 and 1986. Figure 12.2 shows that QFD was most frequently implemented in the design phase, followed by the planning, development, and manufacturing phases. As the years passed, more implementation began to occur in the planning and development phases. This observation illustrates an increasing trend toward focusing on the source of management issues.

The first four parts of this book primarily addressed quality deployment characterized by a major focus on the coordinated development of products that are successful because they fulfill user demands. In other words, the focus is on building in positive quality.

In the methodology of quality deployment, the use of prioritization (see Chapter 5) involves overexpansion of deployment. While this method may prevent excessive design changes or failures in the deployed areas, prioritization alone makes it difficult to suppress negative qualities in areas not deployed. The effective use of reliability methods can avoid negative qualities, and an effort to link these methods to quality deployment has been reported.

Emphasis on quality alone can also lead to cost increases. From this concern has arisen an attempt to pursue both quality deployment and cost deployment to facilitate some trade-off.

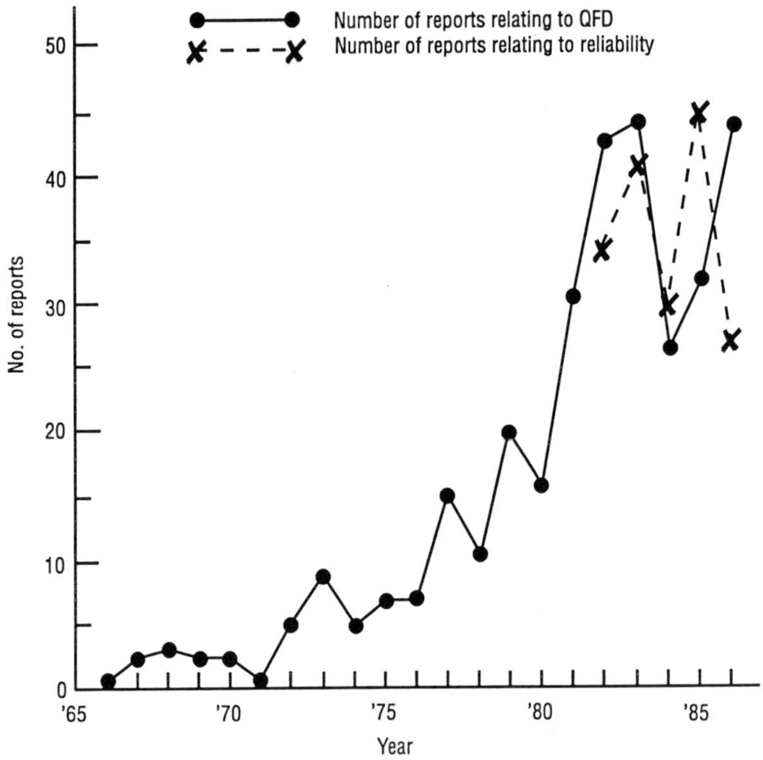

FIGURE 12.1
Number of cases of quality function deployment reported annually

Source: Yoji Akao and Ohfuji Tadashii, "Recent Trends in Quality Deployment," *Quality* 13, no. 3 (1983): 9–12.

What actually improves quality is the challenge to engineering technology, not management technology. When a departure from conventional methods fails to improve quality, it becomes a major delay factor in the development schedule. Professor Yasushi Furukawa named this impeding technology bottleneck engineering (BNE; NE in Japan).[1] The challenges of management technology are systematic extraction and efficient solution of these bottlenecks. Attempts have been made to achieve consistency in quality and in technology, and to deploy both by the coexisting flow of quality deployment and technology deployment. This chapter introduces these new approaches that have appeared and come into use since the initial publication of this book.

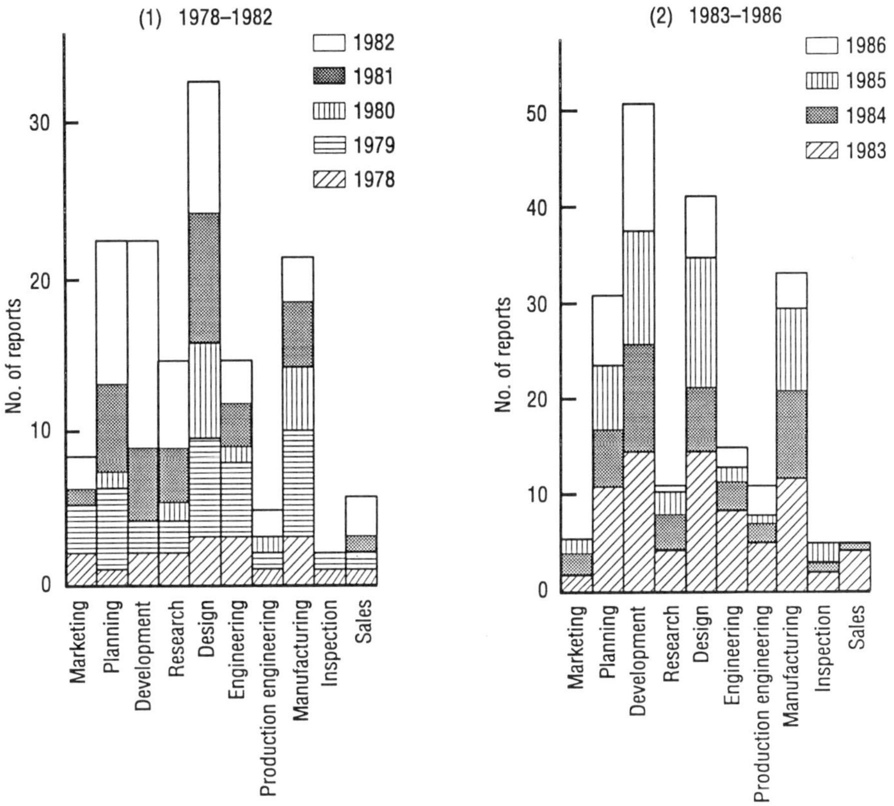

FIGURE 12.2
Implementation phase of quality deployment

Source: Yoji Akao and Ohfuji Tadashii, "Recent Trends in Quality Deployment," *Quality* 13, no. 3 (1983): 9–12.

RELIABILITY DEPLOYMENT

Quality deployment is deployment of positive qualities. It carefully transmits the demanded qualities from the users to control points in the process and in the subsystems. A quality problem of some type can still occur, regardless of the effectiveness of the corrective measures. To manage such negative events, it is advisable to link reliability control methods, developed in the United States and introduced into Japan around 1960, with subsequent broad use in Japanese quality control, to quality deployment.

The concept of failure does not exist in the study phase of the quality chart, during which user demands are converted into quality characteristics to determine design quality. It is, in a sense, a software

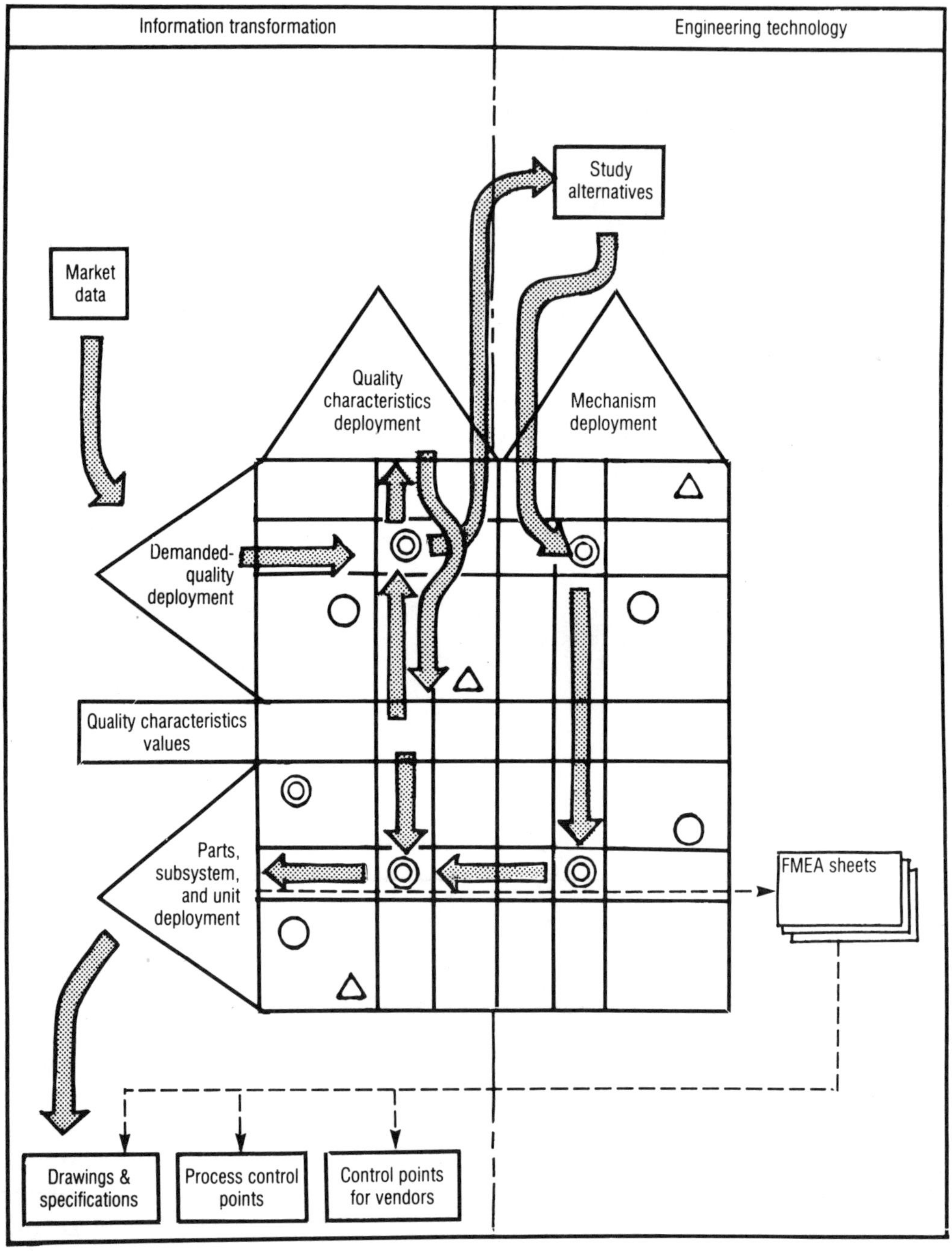

FIGURE 12.3
Positioning FMEA in the quality deployment system

Sources: Yoji Akao and Norio Kamisawa, "Quality Function Deployment and FMEA," *Quality Control* 30, no. 8 (1979): 12–18; and N. Kamisawa, I. Ishizuka, and Y. Akao, "Quality Evolution (Deployment) System and FMEA," *ICQC 1978 Tokyo Proceedings, B4:* 19–28.

phase. The concept of failure is apparent when a designer completes a part drawing, which precedes part production. Failure modes (FM) inherent in this specific item become predictable in this phase; hence failure mode and effects analysis (FMEA) should be performed at this stage.[2] Through FMEA the failure mode is predicted, the causes and the effects on the product are studied, and the causes of failure are eliminated through corrective measures prior to part production (Figure 12.3).

In the limit switch example of Figure 12.4, when the drawing has been completed and the part (in this case, a diaphragm) has been selected, the failure mode of this part becomes predictable. Since this is still the design phase, which is prior to building the part, it is an appropriate time for preparation of the FMEA sheet. Clearly, in quality deployment FMEA should be positioned in the part deployment phase.

Figure 12.5 is a quality chart for the limit switch. Figure 12.6 shows FMEA applied to a disc, a component of the diaphragm. See the upper area of the parts deployment chart. The function of the disc is to "receive absolute pressure." A possible failure mode that could impede this function is "damage to the disc." Although the disc has not been made, the chart shows many causes for failure. After clarification of

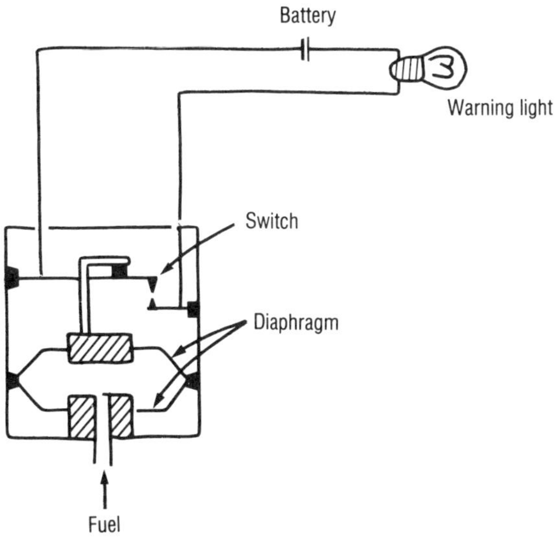

FIGURE 12.4
LP limit switch

Sources: Yoji Akao and Norio Kamisawa, "Quality Function Deployment and FMEA," *Quality Control* 30, no. 8 (1979): 12–18; and N. Kamisawa, I. Ishizuka, and Y. Akao, "Quality Evolution (Deployment) System and FMEA," *ICQC 1978 Tokyo Proceedings, B4:* 19–28.

Quality deployment: Primary	Secondary	Tertiary	Code no.	Setting accuracy	Hysteresis	Shift	Voltage	Operating current at switch contact	Normal position error	Rotated position error
			Primary (characteristics deployment)	Performance						
			Secondary	Precision			Operating power supply		Positioning error	
Transmit abnormal drop of fuel pressure	Detect fuel pressure change (1100)	Store fuel pressure (1120)	Hold fuel	1122							
			No fuel leak	1123			○				
		Receive fuel pressure (1130)	Form surface to receive pressure	1131	◎						
			No distortion from pressure	1132		○	○				
			No fuel leak	1133			○				
	Send electrical signal	Convert pressure change into movement	Displaced by pressure	1211	◎	◎	○				

Parts deployment: Primary	Secondary	Tertiary	Quaternary	PSI	PSI	PSI	· V	· A	PSI	PSI
Limit switch assembly	Base assembly	Sensor assembly	Upper diaphragm	Disc	◎	◎	◎			△	△
				Fitting	◎	◎	◎			△	△
				Pin	◎	◎	◎			△	△
			Lower diaphragm	Disc	◎	◎	◎			△	△

(Characteristics value row: PSI, PSI, PSI, · V, · A, PSI, PSI)

Key: ◎ Strong relationship ○ Average relationship △ Weak relationship

FIGURE 12.5
Quality deployment system for limit switch (Ishikawajima-Harima Heavy Industries Co., Ltd.)

Sources: Yoji Akao and Norio Kamisawa, "Quality Function Deployment and FMEA," *Quality Control* 30, no. 8 (1979): 12–18; and N. Kamisawa, I. Ishizuka, and Y. Akao, "Quality Evolution (Deployment) System and FMEA," *ICQC 1978 Tokyo Proceedings, B4:* 19–28.

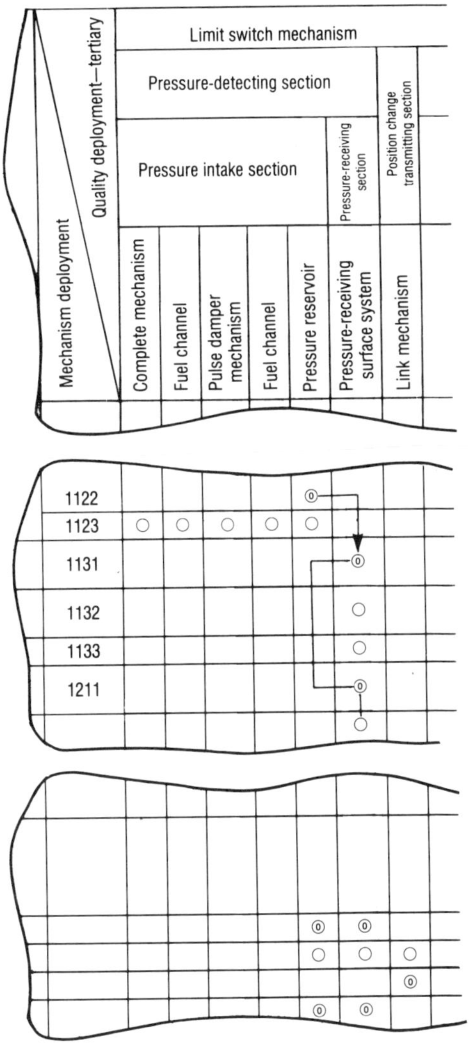

Quality deployment—tertiary	Limit switch mechanism							
	Pressure-detecting section					Pressure-receiving section	Position change transmitting section
Mechanism deployment	Pressure intake section						
	Complete mechanism	Fuel channel	Pulse damper mechanism	Fuel channel	Pressure reservoir	Pressure-receiving surface system	Link mechanism
1122						⊚	
1123	○	○	○	○	○		
1131						⊚	
1132						○	
1133						○	
1211						⊚	
						○	

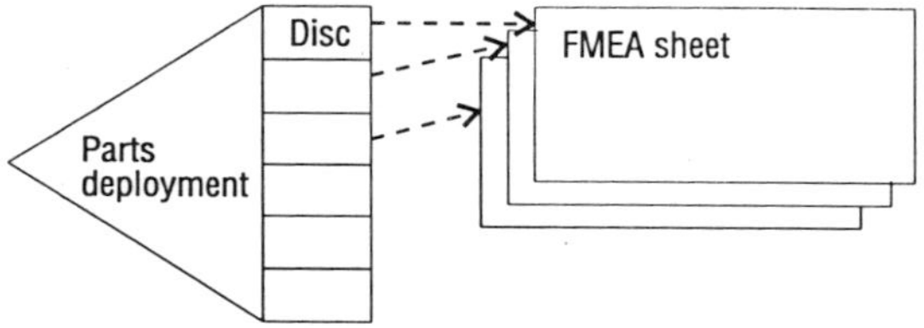

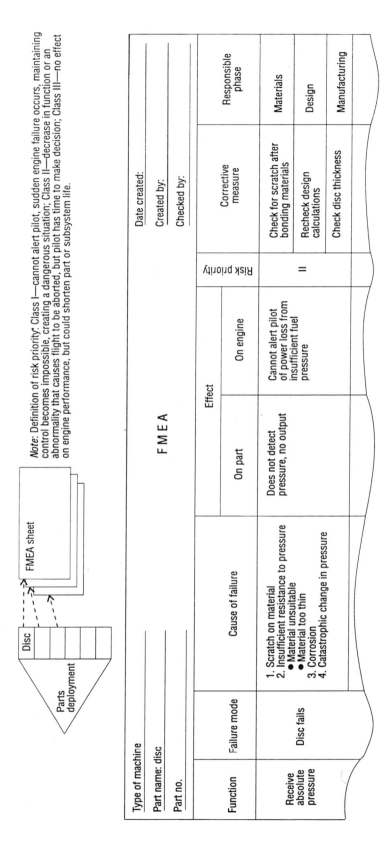

Note: Definition of risk priority: Class I—cannot alert pilot, sudden engine failure occurs, maintaining control becomes impossible, creating a dangerous situation; Class II—decrease in function or an abnormality that causes flight to be aborted, but pilot has time to make decision; Class III—no effect on engine performance, but could shorten part or subsystem life.

Type of machine ____________   **FMEA**   Date created: ____________

Part name: disc ____________   Created by: ____________

Part no. ____________   Checked by: ____________

Function	Failure mode	Cause of failure	Effect		Risk priority	Corrective measure	Responsible phase
			On part	On engine			
Receive absolute pressure	Disc fails	1. Scratch on material 2. Insufficient resistance to pressure • Material unsuitable • Material too thin 3. Corrosion 4. Catastrophic change in pressure	Does not detect pressure, no output	Cannot alert pilot of power loss from insufficient fuel pressure	II	Check for scratch after bonding materials	Materials
						Recheck design calculations	Design
						Check disc thickness	Manufacturing

FIGURE 12.6
Example of FMEA (from Ishikawajima-Harima Heavy Industries Co., Ltd.)

Sources: Yoji Akao and Norio Kamisawa, "Quality Function Deployment and FMEA," *Quality Control* 30, no. 8 (1979): 12–18; and N. Kamisawa, I. Ishizuka, Y. Akao, "Quality Evolution (Deployment) System and FMEA," *ICQC 1978 Tokyo Proceedings, B4:* 19–28.

the effect of the failure mode on the upper-level system and the degree of risk of that failure, corrective measures for preventing the predicted causes of failure are planned.

By taking prioritized corrective measures on critical parts, particularly on a potentially high-risk failure mode, it is possible to suppress negative qualities during the design phase. Figure 12.7 shows a case study of a wiper system performed at Toyota Auto Body during its model change. In this example, the first FMEA was performed in the preliminary drawing phase and the second in the prototype drawing phase.

Fault tree analysis (FTA), which is deployment of failures from the top mode in reliability, can be positioned in the upstream phase of the quality chart. In Figure 12.7, FTA is shown at (2). Figure 12.8 shows the detail.

Failure of the wiper motor, wiping failure, or some other failure causes the failure of a wiper system. Wiper motor failure is caused by abnormality, nonoperability, or some other factor. These are indicated with an "or" gate. Poor tightening of the gear shaft occurs only when insufficient clamping torque and two other causes exist at the same time. These are expressed by an "and" gate.

With a failure rate history assumed to be 100, the wiper system can be given a distribution based on reliability theory with the logic symbols of "and/or" gates.

Implementation of the improvement plan on the right will reduce the failure rate of 4 for worm relief to 2. The failure rate targets reflect these predicted results. It is reported that the initial target was achieved by thus implementing the improvements.

COST DEPLOYMENT

The typical method of cost study is value engineering (VE). Widely applied today, VE is a method of clarifying product function (workings) and systematically determining the least costly alternative that achieves the function. Although it is desirable that this method be efficiently linked to quality deployment, in reality the two are done separately.

The first attempt to link quality deployment and cost deployment was reported by the Hiroshima division of Japan Steel Works,[3] under the guidance of Professor Yasushi Furukawa (see Figure 12.9).

Planned quality and planned cost are set together, and the cost reduction plan according to item of expenditure and part (CR plan) is drafted from a study of the estimated cost and profit. The issues of quality assurance (QA) become a concern here. For this reason, the

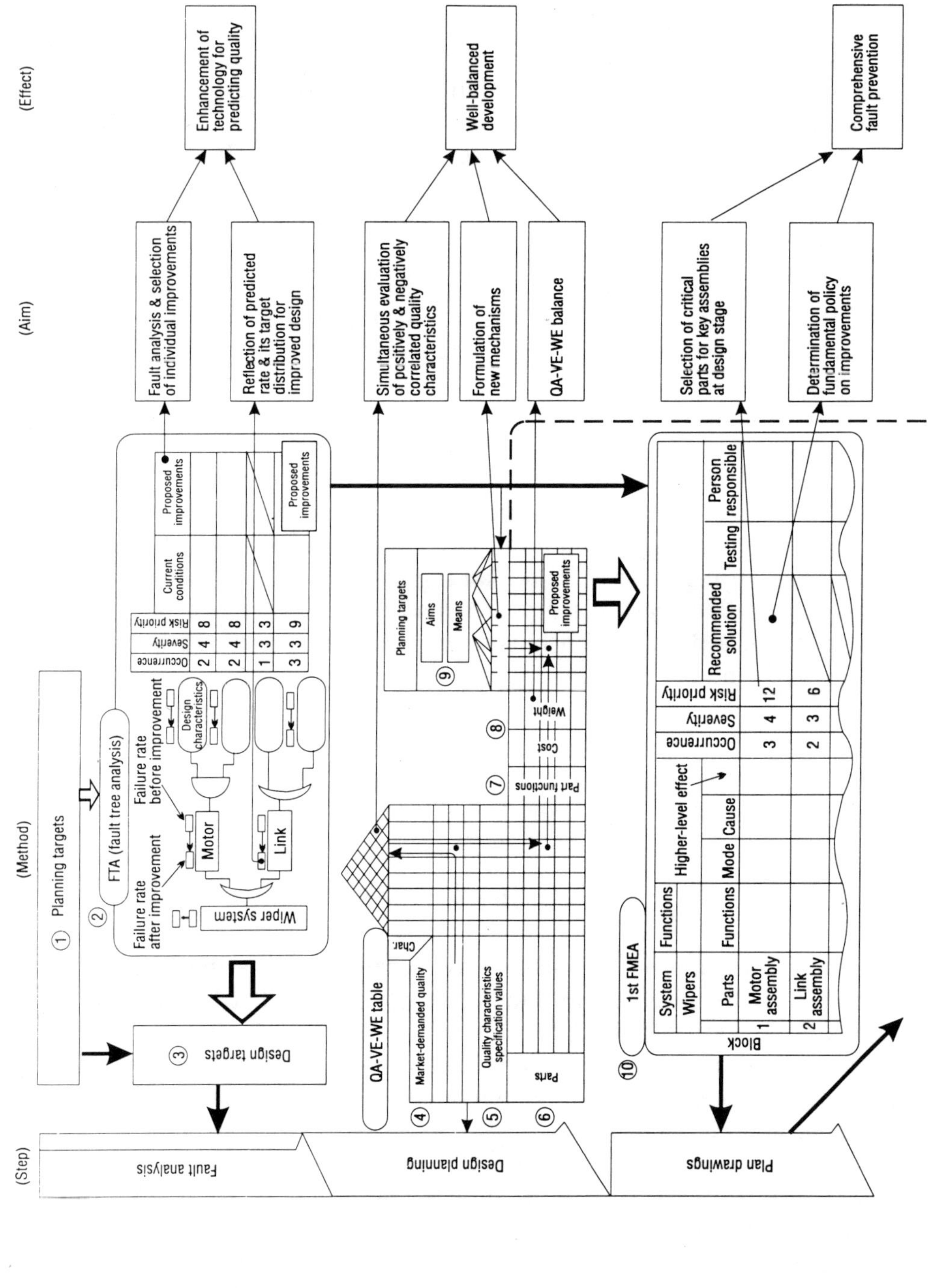
(Step)
(Method)
(Aim)
(Effect)
Fault analysis
Design planning
Plan drawings
① Planning targets
② FTA (fault tree analysis)
③ Design targets
Failure rate after improvement
Failure rate before improvement
Wiper system
Motor
Link
Design characteristics
Occurrence
Severity
Risk priority
Current conditions
Proposed improvements
QA-VE-WE table
④ Market-demanded quality
⑤ Quality characteristics specification values
⑥ Parts
Char.
⑦ Part functions
⑧ Cost
Weight
⑨ Planning targets
Aims
Means
⑩ 1st FMEA
Block
System
Wipers
Parts
Functions
Higher-level effect
Mode
Cause
Recommended solution
Testing
Person responsible
Motor assembly
Link assembly
Fault analysis & selection of individual improvements
Reflection of predicted rate & its target distribution for improved design
Simultaneous evaluation of positively & negatively correlated quality characteristics
Formulation of new mechanisms
QA-VE-WE balance
Selection of critical parts for key assemblies at design stage
Determination of fundamental policy on improvements
Enhancement of technology for predicting quality
Well-balanced development
Comprehensive fault prevention

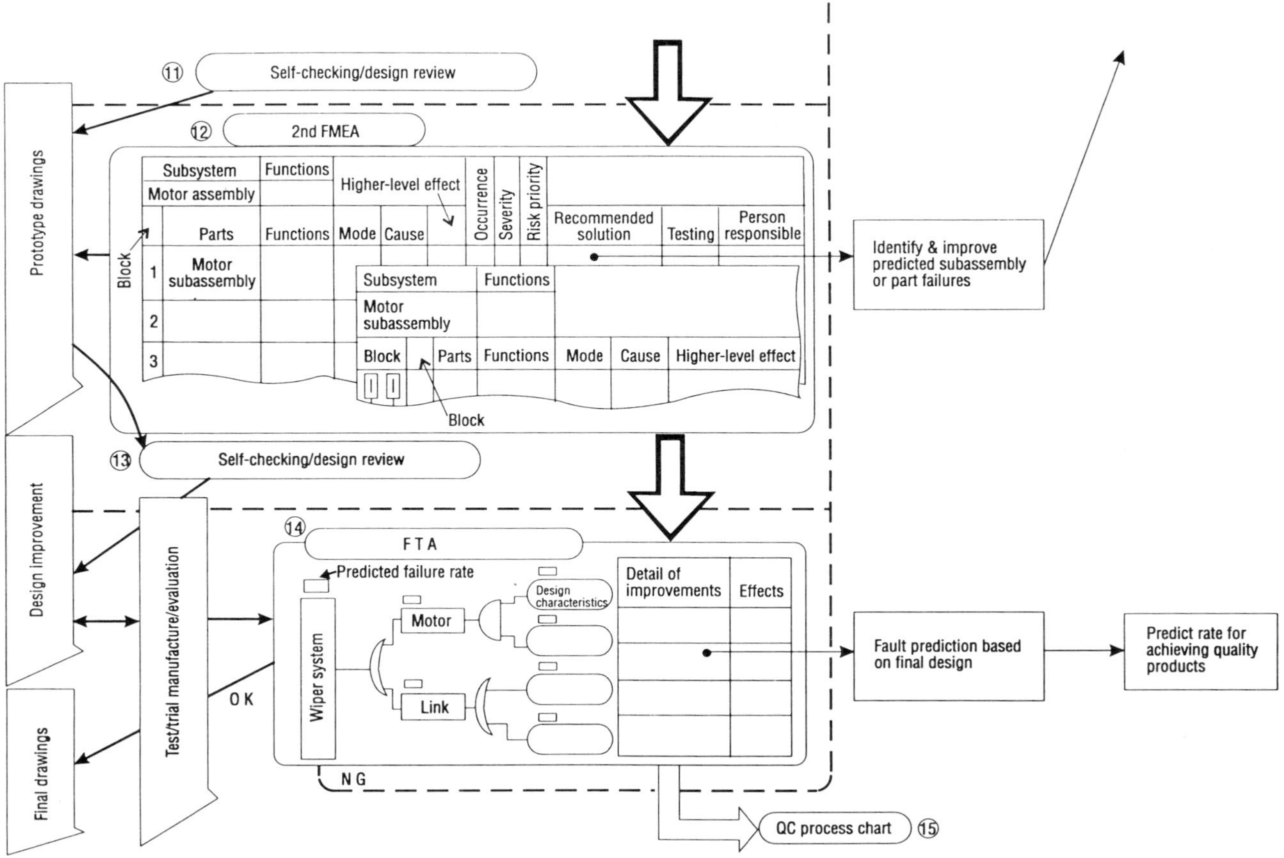

FIGURE 12.7

Quality deployment including reliability and cost (at Toyota Auto Body)

Source: Toshio Kawai, "FTA, QA-VE/WE Chart, Design Activity Using Combination Two-Tier FMEA: Wiper Design," *Quality Control* 31 (November 1980): 129–131 (spec. ed.).

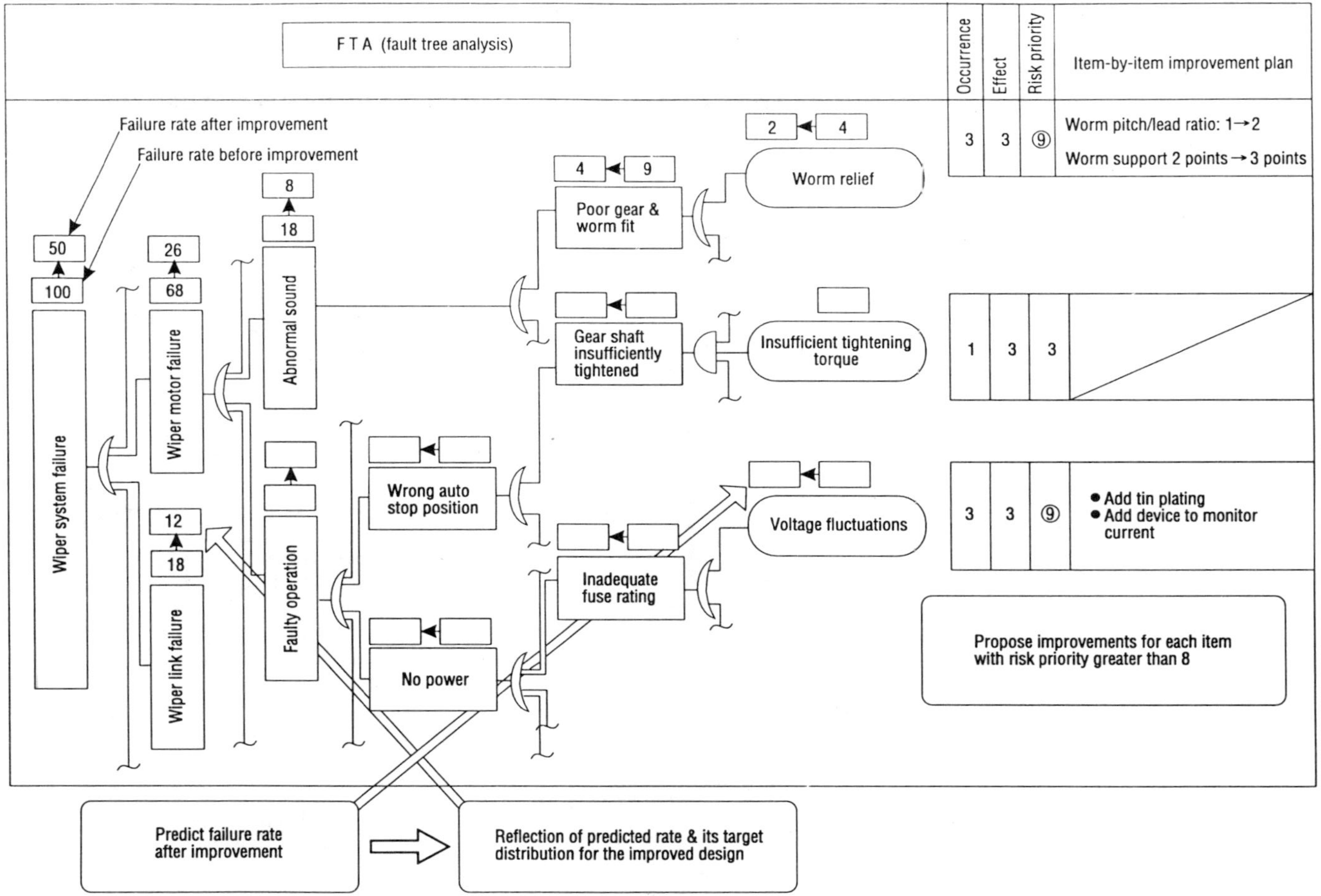

FIGURE 12.8
FTA for wiper system (example from Toyota Auto Body)

Source: Toshio Kawai, "FTA, QA-VE/WE Chart, Design Activity Using Combination Two-Tier FMEA: Wiper Design," *Quality Control* 31 (November 1980): 129–131 (spec. ed.).

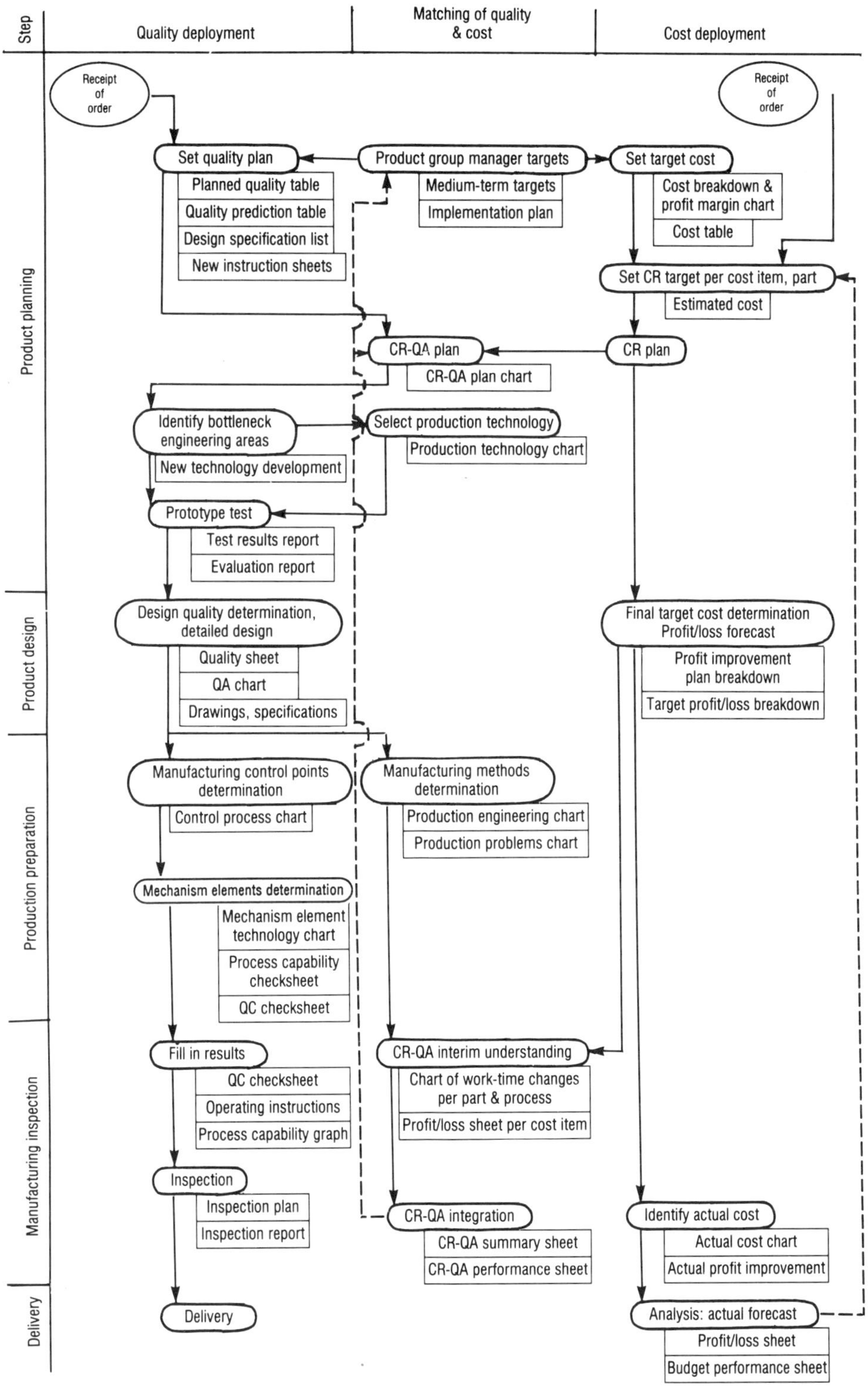

FIGURE 12.9
CR-QA system chart at Japan Steel Works (Nippon Seiko-Sho)

Source: Takehiro Yasumori, "CR-QA Activities in Product Design," *Quality Control* 30 (November 1979): 297–302 (spec. ed.).

cost reduction-quality assurance (CR-QA) plan chart is created during the upstream phase of the plan. (See Figure 12.10.)

For example, when a cost-reduction suggestion for making a part thinner was proposed, the finite element method and other methods predicted possible problems, such as damage, and offered a corrective measure in the form of prevention, which is the quality assurance position. Confirmation checks during the development process were followed by final confirmation prior to production deployment. Engineering for such corrective measures is called bottleneck engineering. These measures were listed on the production engineering chart.

In addition, Toyota Auto Body reported a method (Figure 12.11) of clarifying functions for each part listed on the parts deployment chart, by specifying current weight and cost, as well as target weight and cost to achieve them, systematically. The first step was to establish the basic means for material conversion, size reduction, integration, and so on. This became the means deployment chart, which was placed in a matrix with the parts deployment chart. The expected weight and cost values, based on the means, were listed on the right of the chart. The total of these parts became the basis for determining whether the targeted cost reduction could be achieved.

TECHNOLOGY DEPLOYMENT

Figure 12.12 shows Furukawa's first application example[4] of technology deployment at Kayaba Industry Co., Ltd. Improvement of quality requires the solution to engineering bottlenecks that affect quality. In the example, production engineering charts that listed bottleneck engineering areas were made for each quality chart in each phase, so that the quality could be formed through studies focused on the bottleneck engineering areas.

I have developed a method of identifying bottleneck engineering areas and named a chart for this purpose, the technology deployment chart. In previous usage, in the demanded-quality deployment chart the user-demanded items expressed in words and the function deployment items from value engineering were intermingled. I feel that the latter should be positioned as a bridge to technology deployment.

The demanded-quality deployment table and function deployment chart are to be connected as a matrix, with user demands converted into product functions. In addition, the function deployment chart and the mechanism deployment chart should be connected as a matrix, with the functions of the product transformed into mechanisms appropriate to the product. Include engineering standards or other engineering documents in this mechanism deployment chart.

(*Text continues on p. 330*)

Heavy machinery design section p. 1/4

Process #MK9-0126 | Machine 00 | Class 0556

Drawing #1-291181, 0-291182 | Part name 00

54.6.18

Approved:	Inspected:	Person responsible:
Matsuki	Matsuki	Tsushima

Current product (standard process #MK80560)	CR	QA			
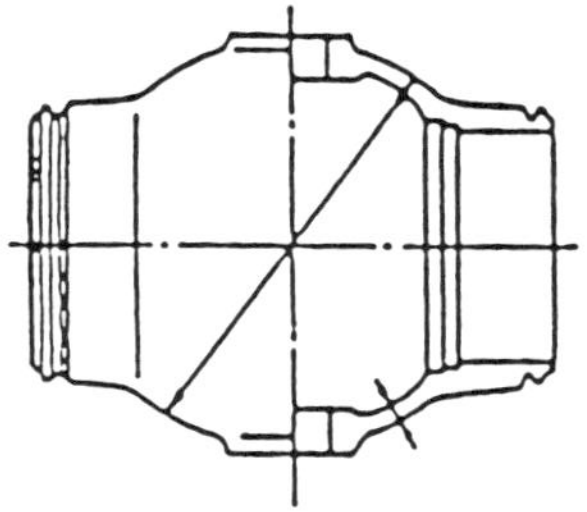 Weight 0.T 0kg	Improvement: thinner wall thickness or reduced outside diameter 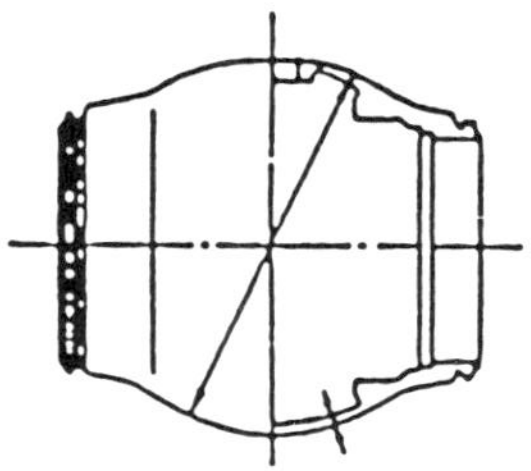 Weight 0.T 0kg	Document no.: Use 3D finite element method to calculate tensile strength (UP78-1507) Test data sheet VP78-2314	Quality characteristic: Material Thickness	Possible claim: Catastrophic force to body could cause deformation resulting in seat area leaking.	Preventive measures
Cost (thousands of yen) Piece cost (Outside supplier ______ pc.) (Internal supplier ______ pc.)	Cost (thousands of yen) Estimated piece cost ______ pieces (Outside supplier ______ pc.) (Internal supplier ______ pc.)	Expected effects ($__.__) ______ units	Estimated delivery (no. months if done the current way):		
			Actual delivery:		
	Actual cost (thousands of yen) piece cost	Actual results (thousands of yen)	Other (selected mfg. process #):		

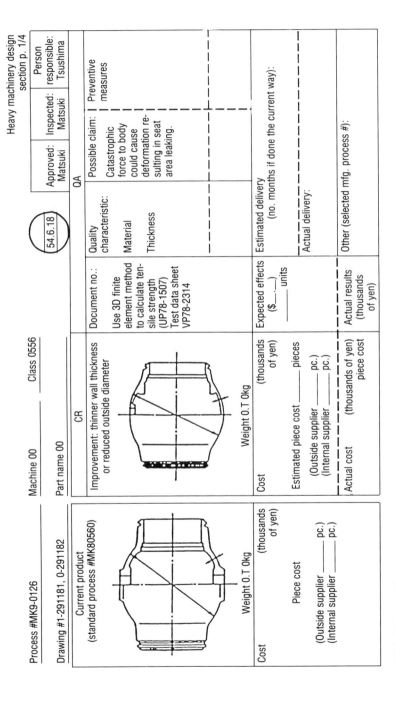

FIGURE 12.10

CR-QA planning chart (Japan Steel Works)

Sources: Takehiro Yasumori, "QR-QA Activities in Product Design," *Quality Control* 30 (November 1979): 297–302 (spec. ed.). The English translation of this figure has already been published in Y. Akao, ed., *Quality Function Deployment—Integrating Customer Requirements into Product Design* (Cambridge, MA: Productivity Press, Inc., 1990).

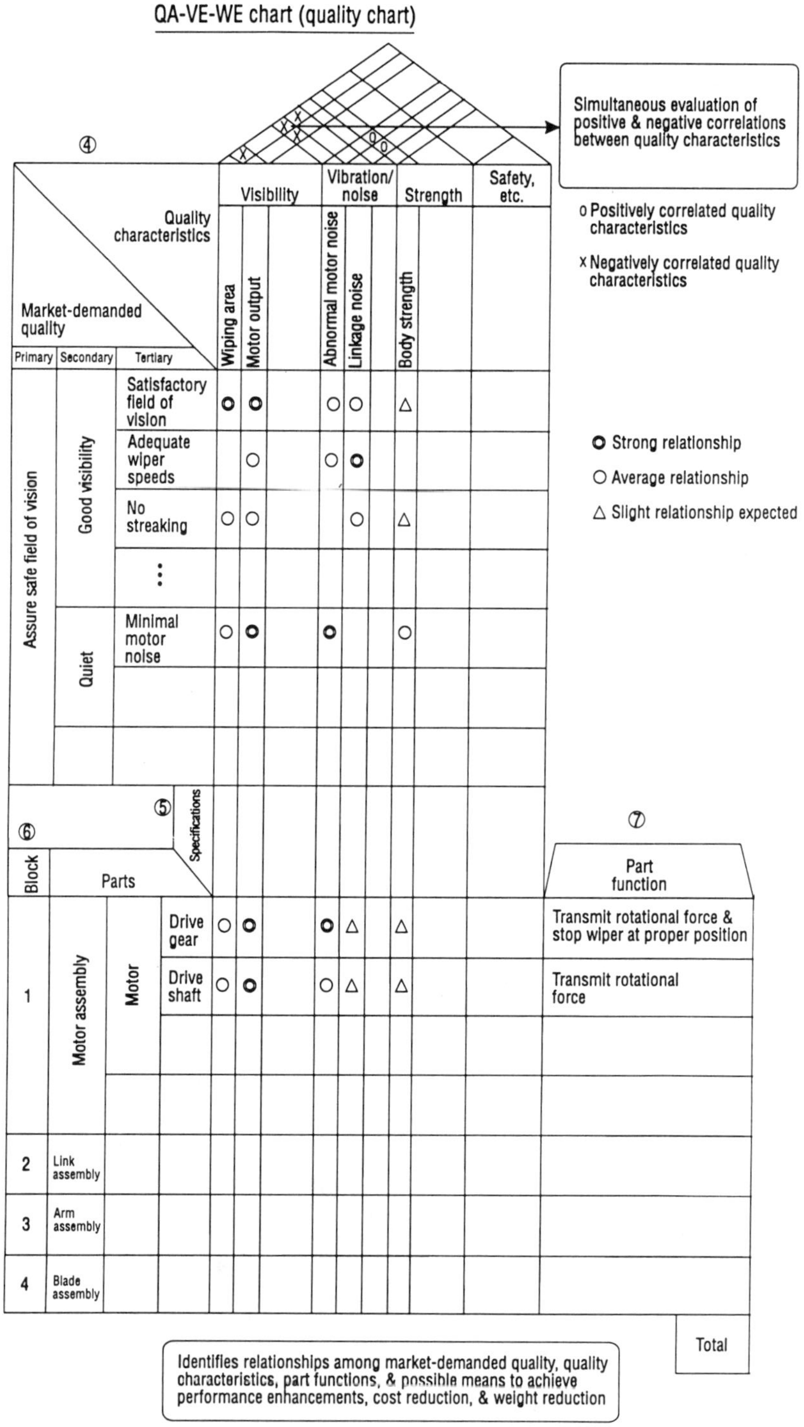

FIGURE 12.11
Quality and cost deployment chart (Toyota Auto Body)

Source: Toshio Kawai, "FTA, QA-VE/WE Chart, Design Activity Using Combination Two-Tier FMEA: Wiper Design," *Quality Control* 31 (November 1980): 129–131 (spec. ed.).

Use of the QA-VE-WE chart (quality chart) helps select new mechanisms that exhibit the improved functionality cost & weight reduction objectives for the wiper system

Plan objectives

Cost: reduction from current vehicle "A"—10%

Weight: reduction from current vehicle "A"—10%

Quality: durability of at least______cycles; failure rate index less than 50

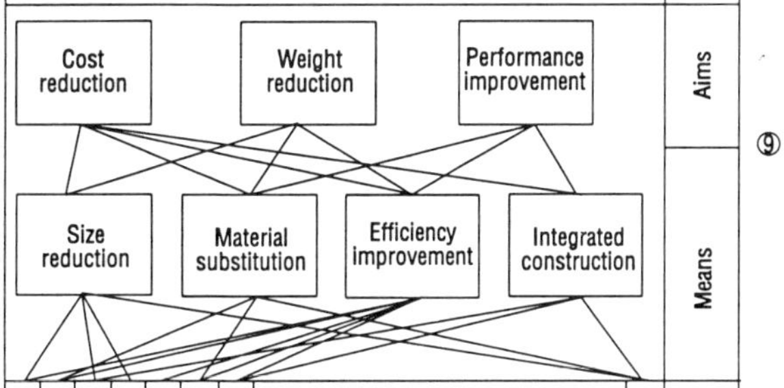

⑧

Cost Target	Cost Current	Weight Target	Weight Current	Increased worm to lead angle	Reduced bearing wear	Integrated construction for shaft & gear							Items	Prediction Cost	Prediction Weight
				O	O	O							Quality		
				O	O								Weight		
9	10	9	10	O		O							Cost		
9	12	9	12	O		O								9	9
					O	O								9	9
130	200	180	200	O	O	O	O	X	O	△		X		178	180

O Used X Not used △ Under study

Helps selection process of proposed means that balance, yet achieve performance enhancement, cost reduction, & weight reduction targets

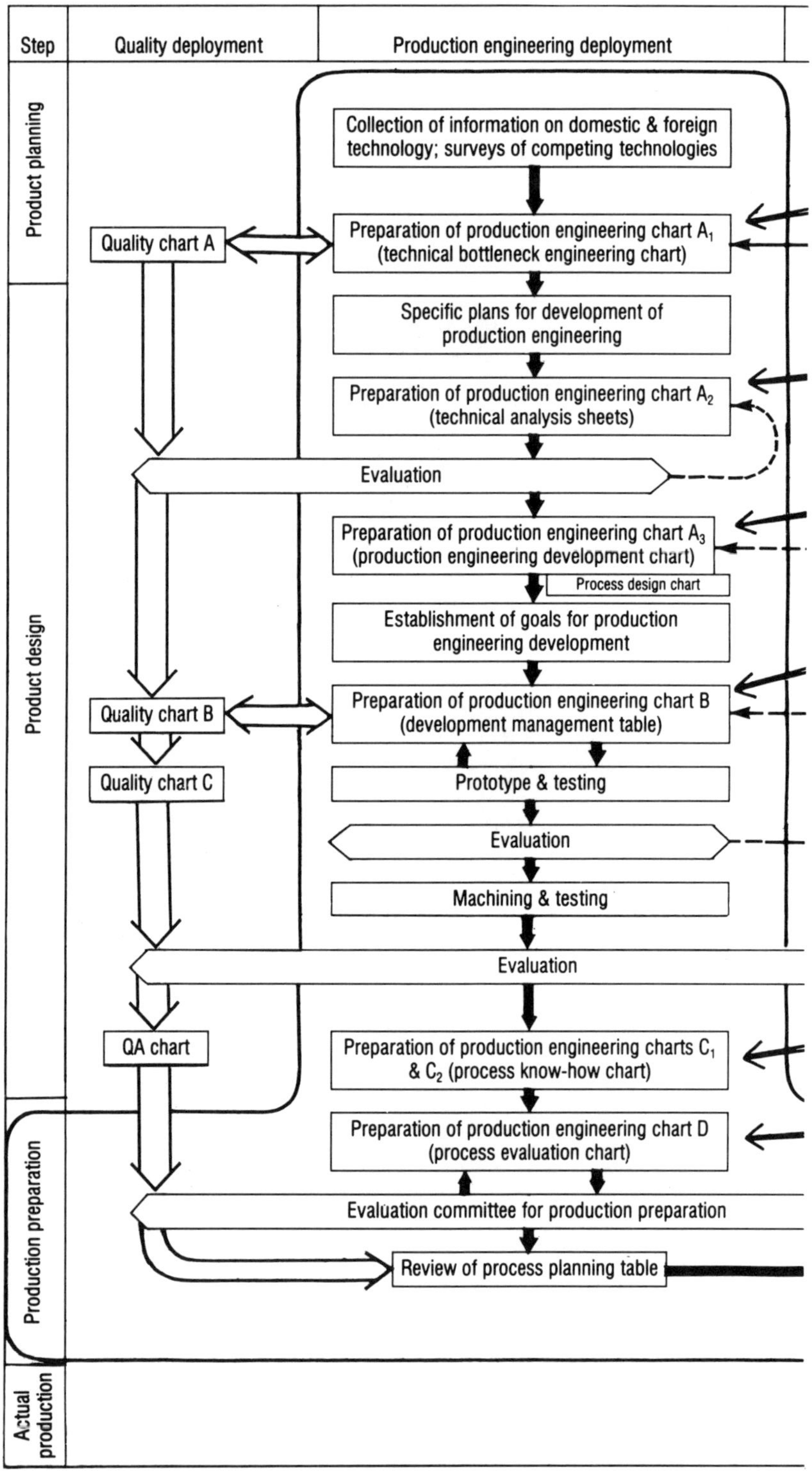

FIGURE 12.12
Production engineering chart systems diagram: quality deployment and technology deployment (Kayaba Industry Co., Ltd.)

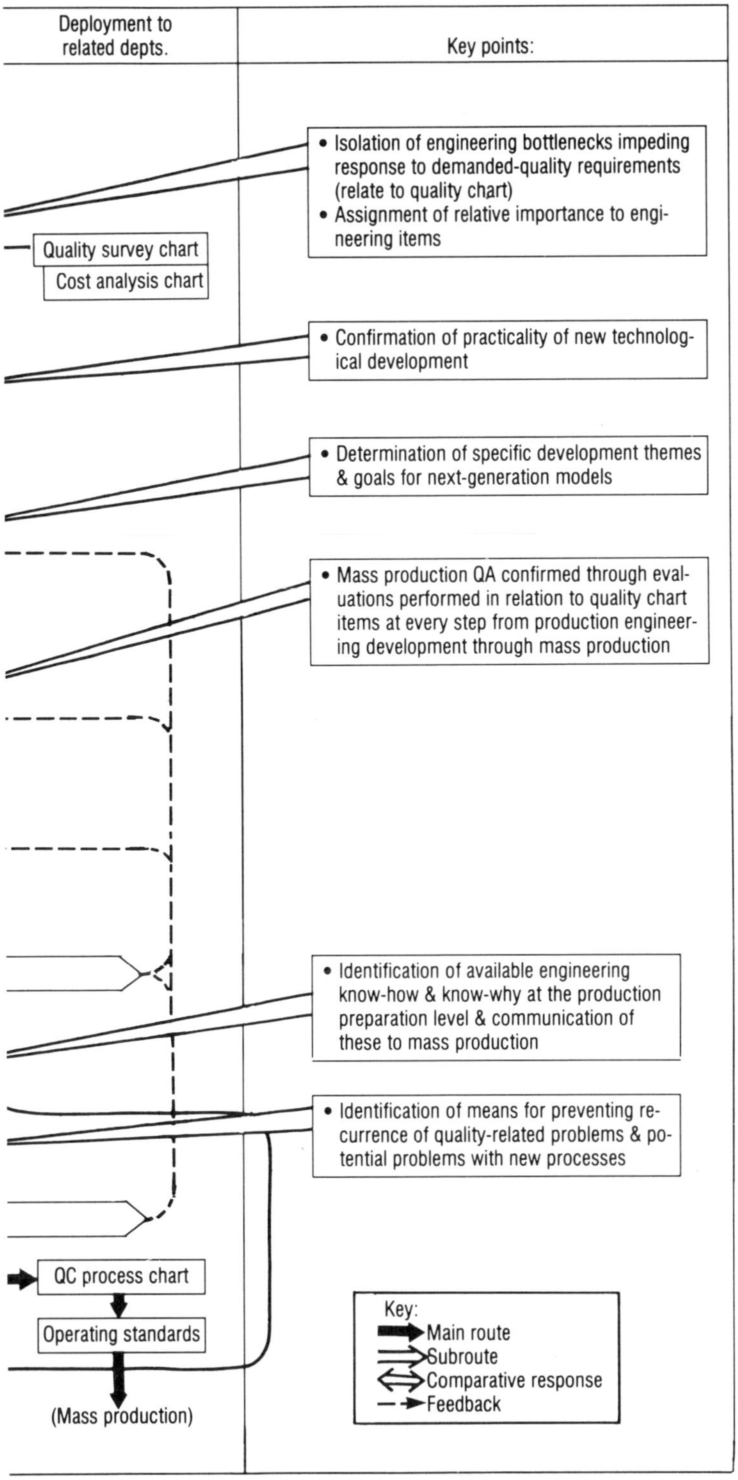
Deployment to related depts.
Key points:
• Isolation of engineering bottlenecks impeding response to demanded-quality requirements (relate to quality chart)
• Assignment of relative importance to engineering items
Quality survey chart
Cost analysis chart
• Confirmation of practicality of new technological development
• Determination of specific development themes & goals for next-generation models
• Mass production QA confirmed through evaluations performed in relation to quality chart items at every step from production engineering development through mass production
• Identification of available engineering know-how & know-why at the production preparation level & communication of these to mass production
• Identification of means for preventing recurrence of quality-related problems & potential problems with new processes
QC process chart
Operating standards
(Mass production)
Key:
Main route
Subroute
Comparative response
Feedback

Source: Ikuzo Ishitsu, "Utilization of the Production Engineering Chart in Advanced Development System," *Quality Control* 31 (November 1980): 43–45 (spec. ed.). The English translation of this figure has already been published in Y. Akao, ed., *Quality Function Deployment—Integrating Customer Requirements into Product Design* (Cambridge, MA: Productivity Press, Inc., 1990).

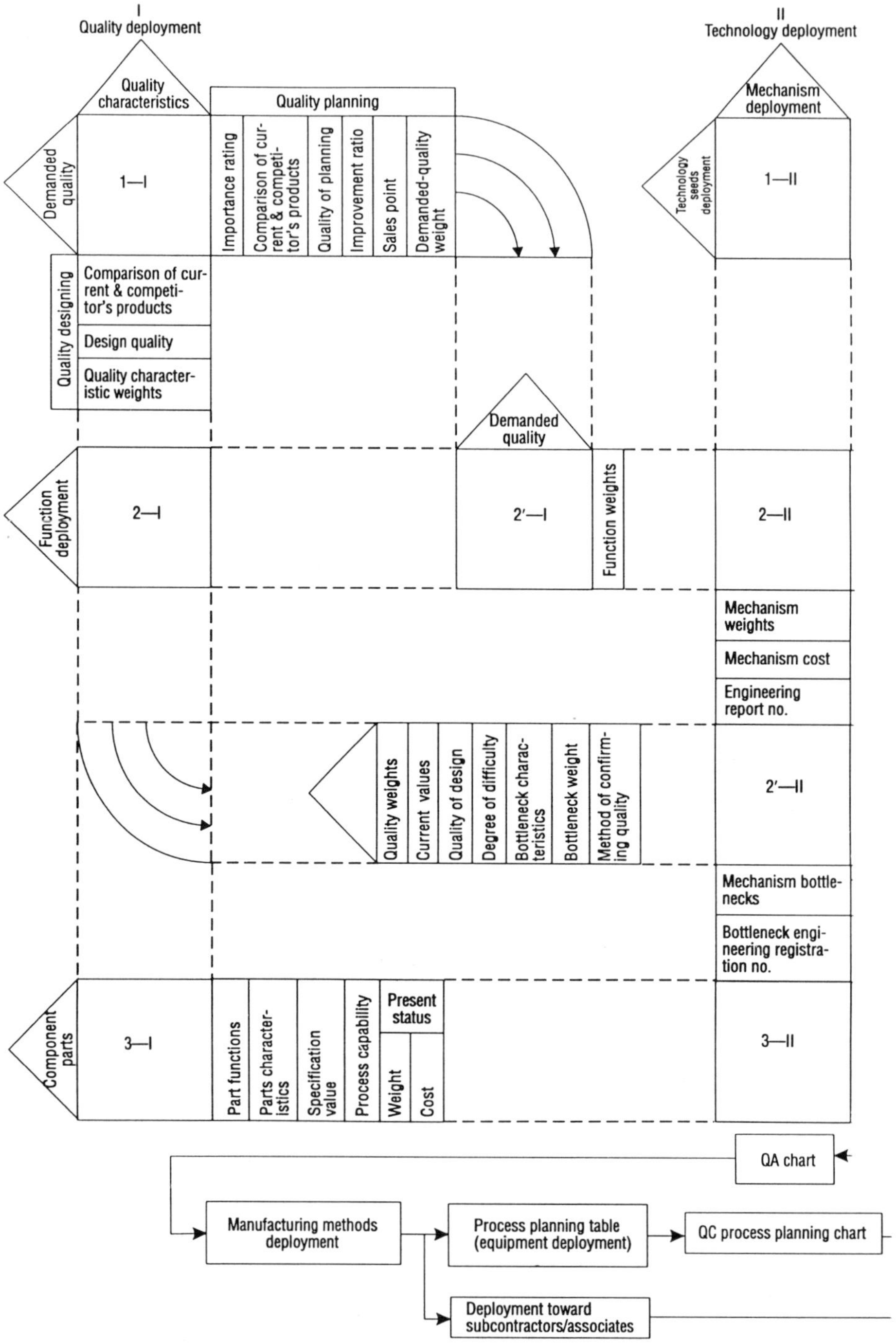

FIGURE 12.13
Quality deployment including technology, cost, and reliability

Sources: Yoji Akao, Sadatoshi Ono, Akira Harada, Hideo Tanaka, & Kazuo Iwasawa, "Quality Deployment Including Cost, Reliability, and Technology," *Quality* 13, no. 3 (1983): 61–77. The figure has been published in Y. Akao, ed., *Quality Function Deployment—Integrating Customer Requirements into Product Design* (Cambridge, MA: Productivity Press, Inc., 1990). The translation used here is original and has not been published previously.

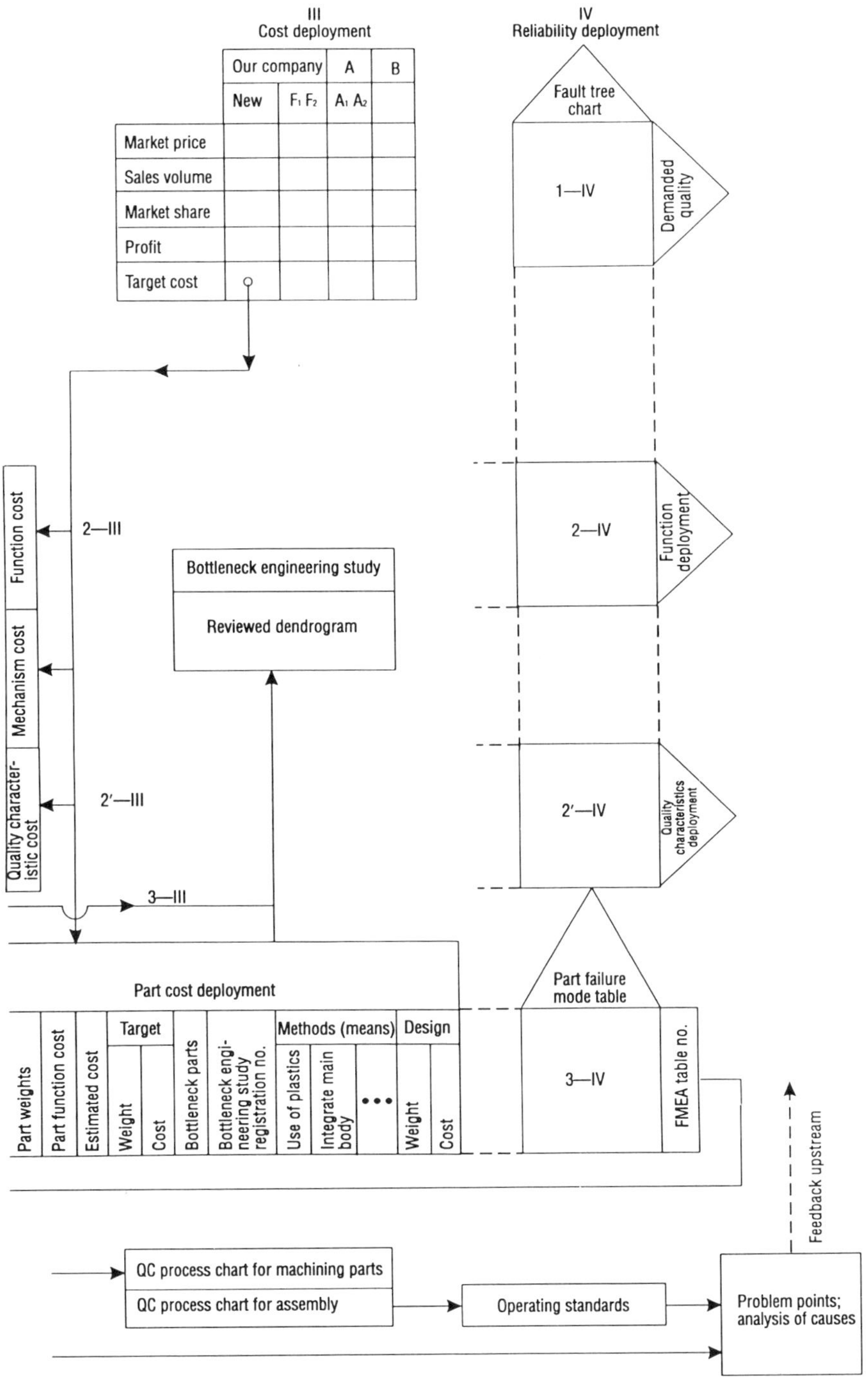

III
Cost deployment
Our company
A
B
New
F1 F2
A1 A2
Market price
Sales volume
Market share
Profit
Target cost
IV
Reliability deployment
Fault tree chart
1—IV
Demanded quality
2—IV
Function deployment
2′—IV
Quality characteristics deployment
Function cost
Mechanism cost
Quality character-istic cost
2—III
2′—III
3—III
Bottleneck engineering study
Reviewed dendrogram
Part cost deployment
Part weights
Part function cost
Estimated cost
Target
Weight
Cost
Bottleneck parts
Bottleneck engi-neering study registration no.
Methods (means)
Use of plastics
Integrate main body
Design
Weight
Cost
Part failure mode table
3—IV
FMEA table no.
Feedback upstream
QC process chart for machining parts
QC process chart for assembly
Operating standards
Problem points; analysis of causes

Based on the matrix of the demanded-quality deployment table and the quality characteristics deployment table and the mechanism deployment chart, each item that improves demanded quality should be checked against the mechanism technology reference. If the quality is not expected to improve with conventional technology, mark it as a bottleneck engineering area. Focusing on and seeking a solution to these bottleneck engineering areas will boost development efficiency.

The New Seven QC tools PDPC method[5] and the reviewed dendrogram[6] are also useful in solving bottleneck engineering problems.

AFTERWORD: USING QFD TO IMPLEMENT COMPANYWIDE QUALITY CONTROL

Almost twelve years have passed since the initial publication of this book. This revision highlights representative examples of reliability deployment, cost deployment, cost deployment, and technology deployment that have been applied by companies during this period.

My colleagues and I reported a comprehensive deployment, called "quality deployment including cost, reliability, and technology."[7] One figure (Figure 12.13)[8] from it appears in this book.

NOTES

1. Yasushi Furukawa, Hideomi Ikeshoji, and Akira Omori, "Basic Study on the Relationship of Quality Structure (Preliminary Report)," *Quality* 12, no. 2 (1982): 23–24; Yasushi Furukawa, Hideomi Ikeshoji, and Hideya Ishizuchi, "Theoretical Study on the Structure of the Quality Management System (Preliminary Report)," *Quality* 11, no. 2 (1981): 30–36; and Yasushi Furukawa and Hideya Ishizuchi, "Theoretical Study on the Structure of the Quality Management System (Secondary Report)," *Quality* 11, no. 2 (1981): 37–42.

2. Norio Kamisawa, Isao Ishizuka, and Yoji Akao, "Quality Evolution (Deployment) System and FMEA," in *ICQC–1978 Tokyo Proceedings, B4* (Tokyo: JUSE, 1978), pp. 19–28.

3. Takehiro Yasumori, "CR-QA Activities in Product Design," *Quality Control* 30 (Nov. 1979): 297–302 (spec. ed.).

4. Ikuzo Ishitsu, "Utilization of the Production Engineering Chart in the Advanced Development System," *Quality Control* 31 (Nov. 1980): 43–45 (spec. ed.).

5. QC Methods Development Group, ed., *New Seven QC Tools for Management and Staff* (Tokyo: JUSE Press, 1979) (in Japanese). Also available in English: Shigeru Mizuno, ed., *Management for Quality Im-*

provement–The 7 New QC Tools (Cambridge, Mass.: Productivity Press, Inc., 1988).

6. Akira Obata and Atsumi Himori, "The Reviewed Dendrogram System–Systematic Deployment of the Development Design Plan," *Quality Control* 31 (Nov. 1980): 37-42 (spec. ed.).

7. Yoji Akao, Sadatoshi Ono, Akina Harada, Hideo Tanaka, and Kazuo Iwasawa, "Quality Deployment including Cost, Reliability, and Technology." *Quality* 13, no. 3 (1983): 61-77.

8. Yoji Akao, ed., *Practical Application of Quality Deployment for New Product Deployment* (Tokyo: JSA, 1987) (in Japanese). Translated into English as *Quality Function Deployment–Integrating Customer Requirements into Product Design* (Cambridge, Mass.: Productivity Press, Inc., 1990).

13

Quality Function Deployment and Future Challenges

Shigeru Mizuno and Yoji Akao

QUALITY FUNCTION DEPLOYMENT IN THE UNITED STATES

It is now evident that the know-how of Japanese TQM has been extensively exported overseas, especially to the United States, as a form of software that does not cause trade repercussions. During a four-day seminar, "Companywide Quality Control and Quality Deployment," held in 1983, QFD was introduced into the United States.[1] The seminar was organized by the Cambridge Corporation (Masaaki Imai, chairman) with the American Society for Quality Control a cosponsor. The lecturers included Masao Kogure, Yoji Akao, Yasushi Furukawa, Naohiro Yagi, Shuzo Moroto, and Kaisaku Asano, with QFD lectures mostly by Akao and Furukawa. American lecturers included Dr. J. W. Leek, then chairman of the American Society for Quality Control, and Dana Cound from Gencorp Automotive. The seminar was attended by 78 people. The majority of them were quality managers of well-known American companies, with some participants from Sweden and Italy. Alberto Galgano, who currently promotes QFD in Italy, was one of the participants.

Hinshitsu tenkai was originally translated as "quality evolution," but on the advice of Mr. Imai it was called "quality deployment" for the first time at that seminar. Hence, *hinshitsu kino tenkai* is "quality function deployment." QFD being a totally new concept at that time, it did not gain adequate understanding at this seminar, but it seems that the text presented became the foundation for the spread of QFD in the United States.

During this time Masao Kogure and Yoji Akao published "Quality Function Deployment and CWQC in Japan,"[2] the first QFD literature published overseas. It received wide attention and has been cited often.

Although the status of QFD in the United States was not followed, in March 1986 GOAL/QPC and American Suppliers Institute invited Akao to deliver QFD lectures. It was then learned, to our surprise, that QFD had been rapidly catching on in the United States.[3]

GOAL/QPC, an organization established by Bob King in 1978, has organized seminars by Dr. W. Edwards Deming since 1980. GOAL/QPC members studied QFD through use of the textbook used in the 1983 Chicago seminar, and provided many QFD seminars and seminars led by Dr. Deming. Later they also began to promote Japanese-style quality control, including *hoshin* management and cross-functional management. GOAL/QPC's annual conference in 1984 had over 900 participants, and the organization continues to grow rapidly.

American Suppliers Institute (ASI), founded in June 1983, has L. P. Sullivan[4] as chairman. The center for Taguchi methods, with Dr. Genichi Taguchi as its executive director, promotes Taguchi methods throughout the United States. Yoshihiro Iwata, managing director of Central Japan Quality Control Association, serves as a special adviser to ASI and Akira Fukuhara (former production engineering manager at Toyota Auto Body), the assistant director of the association, has been promoting QFD, mostly under ASI auspices.

The second symposium on quality function deployment, cosponsored by ASQC, ASI, and GOAL/QPC, was held in June 1990. The Kaizen Institute of America (Masaaki Imai, chairman) also has been promoting QFD. Mizuno lectured at a three-day QFD seminar that was cosponsored by the University of Michigan School of Engineering and ASI. Mizuno lectured mostly on three QFD issues.

1. Recent trends of TQM in Japan
2. The system of QFD and quality assurance
3. QC in new product development.

Of the 90 people who attended the seminar, the majority were senior engineers from Ford, which is near where the seminar was held. Others included professors from the University of Michigan and chief engineers from Chrysler, Caterpillar, GM, Motorola, and other component manufacturers, a total of 23 people.

Through many examples, I showed that the application of management methods, such as QFD in new product development, prevented difficulties related to upstream phases. As a result, production time was shortened, quality was stabilized at an early stage, and potential discrepancies were completely prevented while achieving a significant reduction in development cost. The results reflect the characteristics of Japanese TQM.

During the question-and-answer period, the importance of a longer design period during development and of many design changes was argued. Indeed, "A" platform vehicles produced that year by Ford were well received in the marketplace and were selling well. It was unthinkable to have fewer design changes and a shorter development time, as seen in Japan. The sponsors emphasized that correction of misunderstandings was the aim of the seminar. It was also heard that the conventional development system often led to too many problems during the initial sale period.

In the past, I had analyzed the design change content and had become convinced that 80% of the changes could have been prevented by adequate analysis during an earlier phase and by the use of the analysis results in QFD. When I reported this, the audience began to recognize that there was a control method to reduce the development time while fully assuring quality.

This seminar was attended by many Ford executives, and on the last day it was reported that Ford declared its commitment to systematic introduction of QFD.

In the United States considerable time is spent on solving product troubles caused by design-related problems. While U.S. product design is based on the voice of the engineers, in Japan control is deployed and transmitted from the design through manufacturing phases based on the voice of customers. Efforts are also focused on inadequate technology (bottleneck engineering) to resolve technically difficult quality characteristics.

Internal Ford information concerning Japanese auto manufacturers (such as loss at the time of production startup for each model) was found to support the effects of QFD. This information is probably not available in Japan.

In the United States, where each division or department of product planning, design, manufacturing, and other areas operates independently, it was inconceivable for them to cooperate. QFD has been valued as a powerful tool for building cooperation among these departments or divisions into a system. The need for fundamental organizational changes is also emphasized if QFD is to be successful.

THE FUTURE OF QUALITY FUNCTION DEPLOYMENT

To understand QFD correctly, it is necessary to return to its roots (see Part I and Appendix). Quality deployment has become what it is today through the efforts of many companies and individuals.

Not all of the quality deployment charts were invented at its inception. Many of them existed much earlier. For example, the QC process chart was introduced by Mizuno in his *Plan of Quality Control*, published in 1954.

Fifteen years have passed since the first application of quality deployment in Japan. The first Japanese edition of *Quality Function Deployment* was published in 1978. Since then the efforts of many people have elevated QFD to the systematic method it is today. While quality control has a long history in the automotive industry, quality deployment is relatively new. Hino Motors and Toyota Auto Body Co., Ltd., of the Toyota Group were pioneers in using QFD in their industry. They spent four years intensively examining QFD in their internal QFD study group before starting implementation in 1979. Since then QFD has been used by their affiliated companies in many improved formats, with remarkable results. It can be said that QFD is now one of the established norms in assembly-type industries. Raw materials and material manufacturers that use QFD include Nippon Zeon and Nippon Carbon, which also equally experience benefits. Today, the range of application is expanding.

Using QFD simply as a method will not adequately produce the expected results, but the utilization of QFD as a part of TQM/CWQC activities will produce even greater results. Very early Mizuno stressed the mistake of regarding QFD as simply another method.

Despite the simple appearance of a quality chart, listing demanded qualities and quality elements in it requires the organizational and application skills to relate engineering data on quality to market quality data. An inventory chart of managerial resources, including technology maps (an inventory of available technology), should be in place, and a quality information system should be established and available for use. Generally, the current status is not adequate on this point. In addition, analysis is required to clarify the type and degree of relationship among quality characteristics, to aid in identifying critical items.

Analysis of the relationships between process-related process elements and quality characteristics is called *process analysis*. Analysis of the relationship between quality characteristics of a completed product and characteristics of the functional parts or quality characteristics of component parts is called *quality analysis*. In 1960 I spoke of the need for these. Process FMEA narrows down the major QA items in the QA chart. Clarifying how to use multivariate analysis, quantification method analysis, and other approaches in QFD are future issues. Dr. Donald Clausing is studying a way to connect Taguchi methods and QFD. Total systematization, including these issues, must be achieved.

In addition, efforts should be made to ensure better use of the knowledge gained from statistical analyses, such as quality analysis and process analysis. For this to occur, it is important to analyze the quality data of tests, production, and products in the marketplace as they become available, and to feed back the results to the upstream steps.

The quality demanded by customers changes rapidly, and how a product is used also changes as lifestyles and technology progress. Thus it is important to read these changes early, to prevent the occurrence of quality problems. Therefore, both an analytic approach and a design approach become necessary. Some may argue that the design approach is not QC-like because data do not substantiate it and because uncertain elements accompany the design. Instead of sitting idly by, one must be assertive and take action up front. Striving to optimize design elements through repeated efforts such as QFD is QC of the development phase applied to planning and design.

It will be reassuring to me and to others when those QC professionals who are skeptical of QFD discover that they are wrong. QFD is gaining recognition for its value, as can be seen from the fact that the recent JUSE-sponsored QFD course, which is offered four times a year in four-day sessions, was sold out upon announcement, requiring JUSE to offer two additional courses.

The design approach offers many methods. FTA is one of these, and so is the New Seven QC Tools. How to combine these effectively will be an issue for future study. QFD should be used as a system, not merely as a method. QC methods (QC activities, to be exact) in the development phase include an early warning system developed by Nippon Denso, multidimensional design developed by Kubota, and QC-PERT, as tested by Mitsubishi Heavy Industries and Kubota with remarkable results.

These methods are currently implemented on a limited basis. Setting up a system to combine these methods with QFD and its permanent operation will be a future challenge for me and my associates. QC for the development phase still has many issues to be resolved. For example, quality charts may be stratified into initial production types and full-scale production types. The results of the quality deployment may then be applied according to the schedule of the individual project, which is called QC-PERT.

It is very encouraging that QFD has attained wide use in the United States. Unfortunately, there are many misapplications of or deviations from the QFD fundamentals. The first of such misapplications is mixing characteristic values and methods with demanded quality. The demanded-quality deployment in the left column of the quality chart constitutes the voice of the customer, which must be expressed in the customer's words. Even when a customer specifies a certain characteristic value, the wants underlying the specified value (that is, why the value was specified) must be understood. If a means of implementation or measure has been specified, the demands underlying why such a means or measure was necessary must be captured. Since customers do not make the demanded-quality deployment chart, it is important that manufacturers make it as if they were the customers. This is "market-in" in the true sense.

The second misapplication involves immediately listing implementation means in the top row of the quality chart. A quality chart is a chart for setting design quality by transforming true quality that customers demand into quality characteristics. Clarifying design quality at this point and transmitting important points from the QA viewpoint to assure design quality is QFD. The aim here is QA throughout. QFD that forgets about QA is no longer QFD and should be regarded as a different approach.

It is said that quality characteristics as a concept are difficult to understand. In short, they are technical characteristics, such as dimensions and weight. Unless these characteristics are clarified, it is impossible to implement QA specifically. The quality characteristic deployment table on the top of a quality chart uses the words of technology and is the world of technology. In other words, a quality chart is a transformation chart into the world of technology from the world of customers. Mixing technical characteristics in the demanded-quality deployment table goes against this meaning.

The third misapplication involves prioritization. Listing all implementation means on the top row against demanded quality is not prioritization. Rather, the importance rating of a demanded-quality item should be determined and transformed into an importance rating of the quality characteristics, and then the specific design quality should be set for the critical quality characteristics. Only then should the means to achieve the quality characteristic be found. This procedure requires the process decision planning chart and the reviewed dendrogram.

Often demanded qualities and characteristics are unsorted and unorganized, so separating the demanded qualities into primary, secondary, and tertiary levels is another important step. It is important to understand the importance rating at each phase.

We must further enhance the quality function deployment itself while enriching the content and expanding its application. In Japan, a quality function deployment research committee was set up in JUSE in 1988. In the first year, a group study was performed for each type of business. In the second year, the study pursued a different theme. Since late 1990 the monthly magazine *Quality Control* has published the results. They include those listed below.

- How to understand demanded quality: a method of conversion from customer demands to demanded quality
- Use of the quality chart: quality charts for deploying "image"
- Application of QFD to new fields
- Transmission of quality information (from the quality chart to the QC process chart)
- Comprehensive quality deployment (technology deployment, reliability deployment, cost deployment)
- Computer-aided quality deployment systems

The third year of study is under way. Since practice has taken precedence in QFD, the formulation of the theory of QFD is another issue for future consideration. The theory group of the research committee is working on it.

QFD is an important activity in Japanese CWQC. In the United States it is recognized, as Dr. Armand V. Feigenbaum claimed, that TQC has become a practical, effective activity for the first time through QFD. In contrast, the recognition of QFD is just becoming important in Japan.

The greater necessity for further development of TQM (CWQC) in the future is to promote TQM as a cooperative system involving all people. This, of course, reflects the need for self-discipline, spoken of by the late Shigeru Mizuno.

NOTES

1. Seminar "Companywide Quality Control and Quality Deployment – In Search of Excellence in Developing Customer-Oriented Products," Chicago, October 31–November 3, 1983.
2. Masao Kogure and Yoji Akao, "Quality Function Deployment and CWQC in Japan – A Strategy for Assuring That Quality Is Built into New Products," *Quality Progress* 16 (October 1983): 25–29.
3. Robert King, "Listening to the Voice of the Customer: Using the Quality Function Deployment System," *National Productivity Review* 6 (Summer 1987): 277–281.
4. L. P. Sullivan, "Quality Function Deployment – A System to Assure That Customer Needs Drive the Product Design and Process," *Quality Progress* 19 (June 1986): 39–50.

Appendix

Development History of Quality Function Deployment

Yoji Akao

INTRODUCTION

Part V showed that an approach called quality function deployment or quality deployment has spread rapidly and produced significant results in numerous companies. This is a method to transform user demands into design quality, to deploy the functions forming quality, and to deploy methods for achieving the design quality into subsystems and component parts, and ultimately to specific elements of the manufacturing process.

This appendix addresses the development history of quality function deployment in Japan from 1966 to 1977, based on a survey of literature concerning quality function deployment published in *Quality Control* (issued by the Union of Japanese Scientists and Engineers), *Quality* (issued by the Japanese Society for Quality Control), and *Standardization and Quality Control* (issued by the Japanese Standards Association).

Figure A.1 plots each literature reference and the corresponding date. From the information in this figure, quality function deployment is basically classified into area (A), which emerged from distilling quality assurance into its control points, and area (B), which flowed from function deployment used in value engineering. The development of the quality chart (C) has emerged from these two.

QUALITY DEPLOYMENT AS A CHAIN OF QUALITY

Table of Process Assurance Items

Akao's approach to quality deployment was given a boost with the production process assurance items chart (Figure A.2), reported by

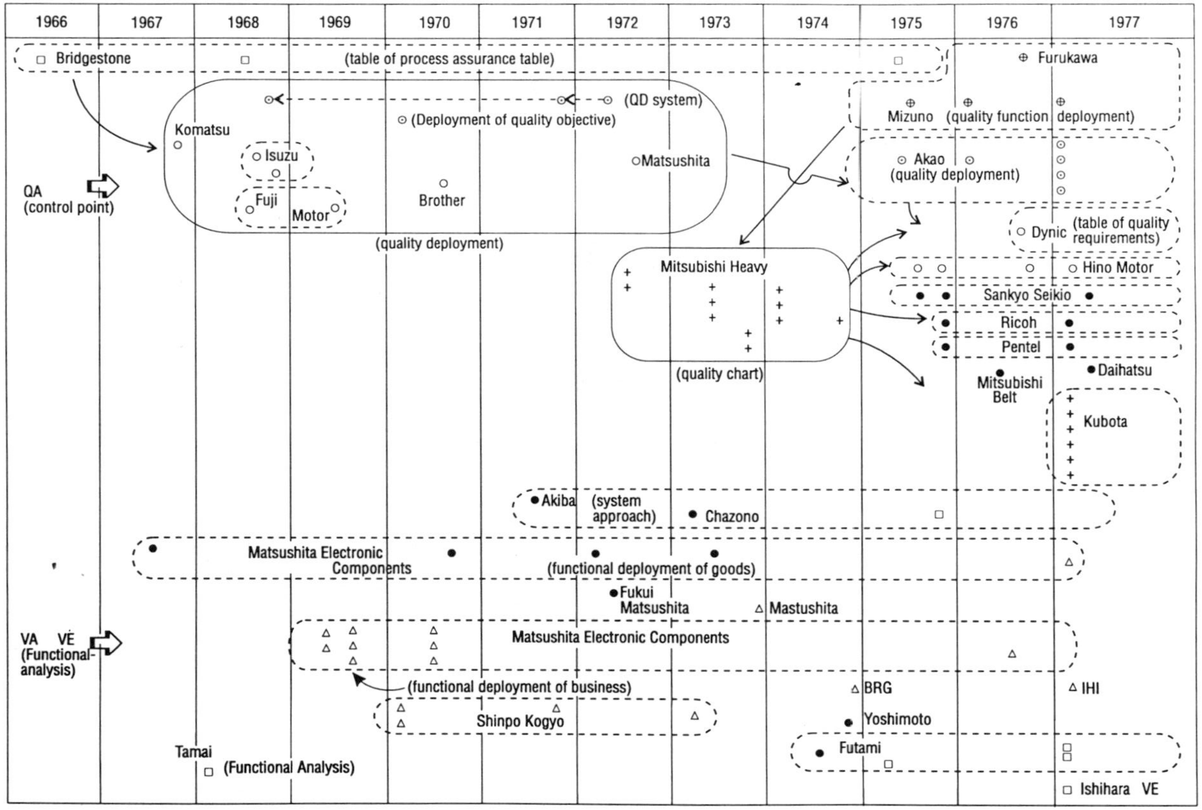

Notes: Point shows one literature; ⊙ : Akao, ○: with Akao, ⊕ : Mizuno or Furukawa, + : with Mizuno or Furukawa, ●: others, △: FD of business, □ : allied literature

FIGURE A.1
Trends in references to QFD

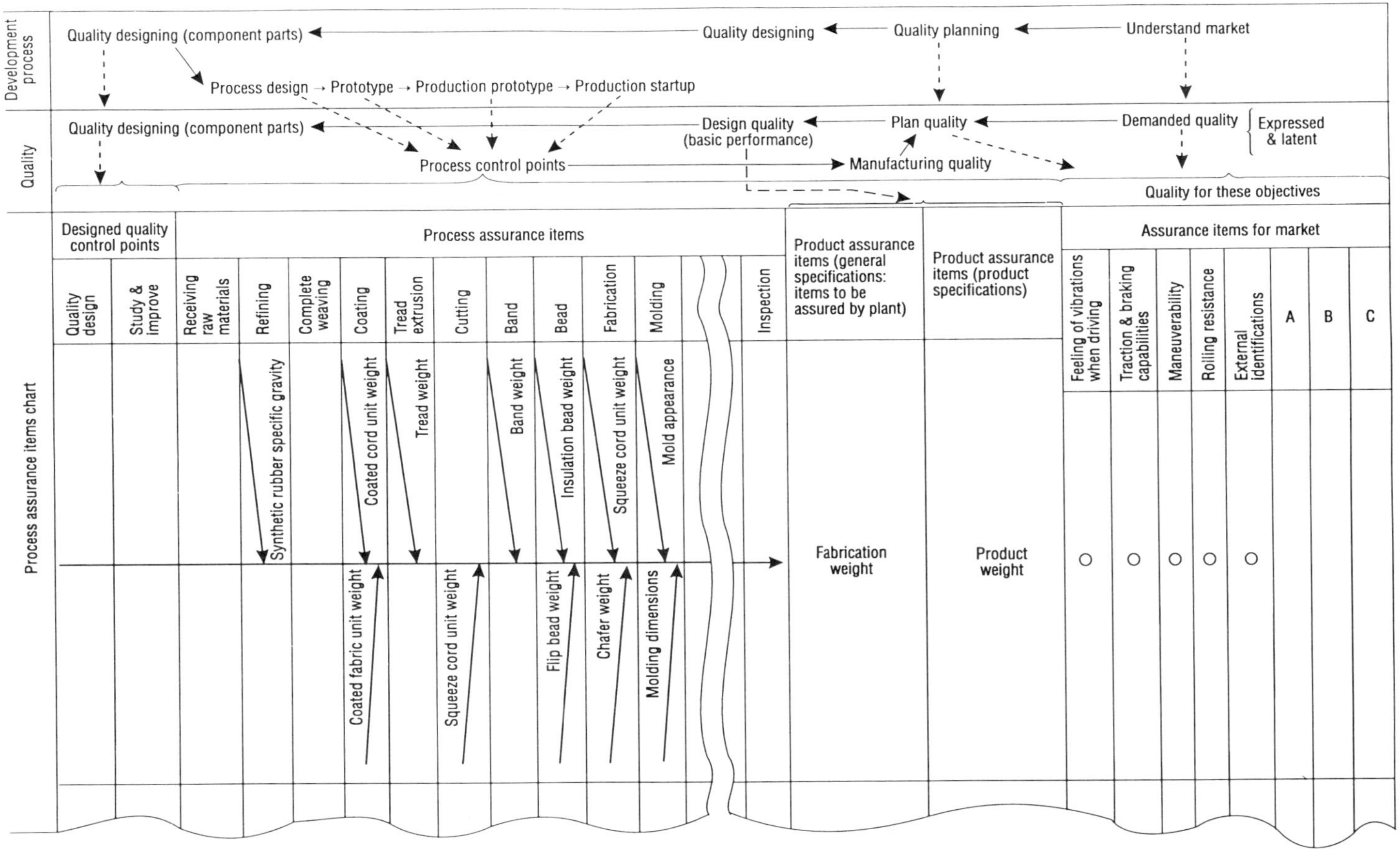

FIGURE A.2
Production process assurance items chart

Kiyotaka Oshiumi[1] of the Bridgestone Tire Kurume plant. In this chart items to be assured to the market externally, listed in the upper right column, were equated to true quality demanded by users. The chart also showed the corresponding product assurance items, that is, quality characteristics, as a matrix that was the original form of what in Chapter 2 was called a quality chart. The procedure was done for each important characteristic, and important factors in each manufacturing process were clarified by a cause-and-effect diagram in order to prepare the quality assurance system.

Formerly, production sites used what was called a control process chart or QC process chart. They were normally prepared by on-site personnel who in most cases did not consider user demands. Professor Kaoru Ishikawa stressed the importance of true quality demanded by users, but its relationship to process control points was too distant and a method for integrating it was not yet known. I was searching for such a method when the idea came to me to use Figure A.2 as a medium for tying into the QC process chart. For example, when the QC process chart was needed for a refining process, important factors for each characteristic could be extracted, such as the specific gravity of the compound rubber as a factor for the product characteristic of weight, or degree of mastication of the compound rubber as a factor for wear resistance. The control points for these important factors could then be set in the QC process chart, the traditional QA viewpoint. With the addition of control points for building in manufacturing quality, user-demanded quality could be tied into the QC process chart in a chain.

Quality Deployment System

Bridgestone used this chart to prepare a quality assurance system for mass-produced products. On the other hand, I thought that this chart should be used to form a chain of quality by studying and adding items, one by one, to the process of new product development, and I recommended that companies apply this chart for this purpose.

The top of the chart shows the development process. A column for quality design and improvement studies is added as the point of design quality in the left column. I added both. This is called *mokuhyo hinshitsu tenkai* (objective oriented quality deployment).[2]

Based on this experience, I identified seventeen steps (Table A.1) as a system of quality deployment. It shows the concept of this chain of quality in which items needing assurance from the users' standpoint are clarified and deployed into detailed areas through a companywide

TABLE A.1
New Product Development and Quality Assurance: A System of Quality Deployment

Setting planned quality and design quality
1. Setting of target product
2. Study of targeted quality
3. Comparison and analysis of competitors' products
4. Determination of sale points
5. Determination of targeted quality
6. Setting of quality goals
7. Evaluation for development decisions

Detail deployment of design quality goals
8. Deployment into each element—a table of quality characteristics
9. Study of quality in the prototype process
10. Evaluation of quality of prototype products

Deployment into process control points
11. Table of important quality items
12. Deployment into the control process chart
13. Deployment to vendors and supplier plants

Analysis of causal factors and quality assurance
14. Analysis of internal and external claims
15. Aggressive analysis of factors
16. Special control for safety, maintenance, and reliability
17. Feedback to the next product development or model upgrade

Source: Yoji Akao, "New Product Development and Quality Assurance—System of Quality Deployment," *Standardization and Quality Control* 25 (April 1972): 9–14.

approach. This is a chain of qualities (objectives), not a chain of methods. Reconnecting these elements produces a product that can be quality assured to users. Although items 1 through 7 were conceived prior to the quality chart and were not adequate, the quality function deployment given in steps 8 through 17 design quality is determined is conceptually almost as it is today.

There are references in the upper left of Figure A.1 to studies by Komatsu Ltd., Fuji Motors,[3] and Isuzu Motors, Ltd. At that time, I called this "quality objective deployment."[4] Studies by Brother Industries, Ltd., and the iron press division of Matsushita Electric Industrial Co., Ltd., also have been reported. In addition, Konika Corporation has experienced good results by introducing quality deployment at the production preparation phase for development of a new copier. It was a critical shift for Konica, a camera manufacturer, to develop a copier, but the development went well. Mitsuboshi Belting, Ltd., also has implemented QFD in a similar manner.

Relationship with Control Points

I feel that the study of control points, which began with Dr. J. M. Juran's control points[5] and became popular in many companies through the control items chart for each job title[6] developed by the Teijin Company, were the indirect cause of my attention to the Bridgestone chart. In a report presented at the 1964 Quality Control Convention (symposium on control points),[7] I emphasized that a control network could be set up with a cause-and-effect diagram, and that through this diagram the control points for a plant manager could be linked to operator inspection items. Figure A.2 is a network to control quality, and is intended for use in the deployment of target quality.

Another motive behind QFD was that historically, quality assurance rules set by companies addressed operational flow but did not specify what should be assured and did not clarify the deployment of design quality into detailed areas. I treated these as a framework of quality assurance.

Since January 1975, meetings to study quality deployment have been held by the Quality System Research Committee of the Japanese Society for Quality Control; I have served as the chairman. Based on case studies from past presentations, the procedure for a quality deployment system was later proposed.[8] The simple case studies led to creation of a computer system based on these findings.[9]

This *hinshitsu tenkai* is now called "quality deployment." (Although the first edition of this book used the English translation "quality evolution," the term was changed after the first U.S. seminar in 1983, on the advice of Masaaki Imai.) The system incorporates the quality chart (to be discussed) and other methods.

QUALITY DEPLOYMENT BASED ON THE QUALITY CHART

Quality Chart at Mitsubishi Heavy Industries, Ltd.

The Kobe shipyard of Mitsubishi Heavy Industries, Ltd., presented a quality chart[10] in May 1972 and issued a series of reports through 1974. The quality chart was defined as a way to systematize true quality centering on functions and as a standard for implementing quality control activities.[11]

Although the method of function deployment used in value engineering was the basis for systematizing functions (true quality), the quality chart originated in quality assurance. I think the significance of the quality chart is the transformation of quality through the use of a matrix (two-dimensional chart). In cost control or production quantity control, a constant gauge, such as money or time, can be used for measurement, but quality presents a difficulty because the dimension or physical makeup is subject to change. It becomes necessary to use a relationships matrix for transformation of true quality into quality characteristics. Substitute quality characteristics of a final product are similarly transformed into subsystem or part characteristics. Transformation also becomes a process. Although Figure A.2 includes this transformation, steps 1 through 7 (Figure A.1) were not adequate to assure quality to the market or to create the corresponding chart of product assurance items. The quality chart solved this problem.

Since the quality chart originated from many changes in TQM implementation, each division developed a different format but achieved the same results. In the deployment of design quality, issues that were previously considered part of engineering technology have been brought forward as issues of management technology. The result is an increased implementation of quality control in the design phase.

Professors Shigeru Mizuno and Yasushi Furukawa led the implementation of TQM focused on the quality chart. Chapter 1 describes Mizuno's philosophy. Much earlier he had advocated quality engineering,[12] later realized in the form of the quality chart. Furukawa has developed a QC organization theory in collaboration with other researchers,[13] and he is studying basic system theories of quality function deployment.

Quality Charts of Various Companies

The quality chart of Mitsubishi Heavy Industries was rapidly incorporated by other companies, and many reports exist. A description of the major methods follows.

Mr. T. Tanizawa proposed deployment of quality as a chain of quality (objectives). The method, described in Chapter 9, deployed methods that could achieve this quality and selected the minimum-cost method that could meet the demanded quality.

The demanded-quality deployment table proposed by Dynic used only the tree of demanded-quality deployment from the quality chart. It was incorporated into matrices with Dynic's other charts, including charts on competitors, for setting the sales points or planned quality (see Chapter 4).

Kubota, Ltd., has proposed other approaches and is developing proposals under the guidance of Mizuno and Furukawa. The design work was normally separated for products in a product line. It imposed separate design man-hours and diversified parts, and it reduced productivity. A concept of simultaneous multidimensional design was proposed to mitigate this. The concept was to design a product parallel to the design of other products in the same product line. This approach has produced noteworthy results, including the reduction of design man-hours and better part utilization (see Chapter 6).

An additional proposal was a QA chart to serve as a bridge between design and manufacturing. It deploys and embodies targeted quality from product development into the production phase. It also clarifies, in the design phase, the effects of unfulfilled tolerances (design quality) of the part quality characteristics (design quality) on the end product, and conveys these effects to the manufacturing division (see Chapter 7). Kubota also presented a method of priority control in which critical-to-safety parts [S] and critical-to-function parts [A] are extracted from quality charts and regulations (see Chapter 8).

In addition to the above activity, Hino Motors, Ltd., began companywide implementation of quality deployment activities in 1975 and reported several application examples. Process deployment by Takao Tanizawa was one of them. Sankyo Seiki Manufacturing Co., Ltd., in response to customer demands, studied the design of a micromotor by means of three matrices with three axes: function, part, and function of component. The Ricoh development division made a Q-T (quality tree) chart that showed the relationship of demanded-quality deployment and characteristic values, and the production engineering division made Q-P (quality process) chart that deployed these characteristics into the process to stabilize quality. Pentel used multiple regression analysis to improve quality function deployment for the "writing feel" characteristics of their pens.

VALUE ENGINEERING AND FUNCTION ANALYSIS

L. D. Miles's *How to Cut Cost with Value Analysis*[14] has been updated by Professor Masakazu Tamai's *Function Analysis*.[15] This book describes the method now called function analysis. The earliest case mentioned in *Quality Control* magazine was by Katsuyoshi Ishihara of the parts division of Matsushita Electric Industrial Co., Ltd. (currently Matsushita Electronic Components). It is a series of reports as shown in Figure A.1. They can roughly be categorized into function deployment of the product and function deployment of business operations.

Function Analysis of the Product

Function analysis, as a part of value engineering, originally began as function deployment of the product. The chart presented by Kazutaka Murakami[16] corresponds to a functional family tree of product functions (functions of the product, or true objective), a materials tree, and a manufacturing element tree through the use of a matrix. This is almost the same as a quality chart. It is significant that this chart was introduced at the same time the quality chart was proposed. The parts division at Matsushita not only used a control process chart (a QC process chart) for a long time but also developed a control process chart for the quality characteristic factors, to which a corresponding chart with product quality characteristics was added.[17] They were basically equivalent to the quality chain system. Unfortunately, they did not lead to a quality deployment system for a larger system-level product that would begin with user-demanded quality. The likely reason is that the system provided sufficient quality assurance because of the nature of the product, an electronic part in which performance was readily expressed by quality characteristics.

Yuji Nakae's ". . . Method of Setting Control Points . . . "[18] is also worthy of mention because it uses function analysis. At the parts division of Matsushita Electric Industrial, control points are divided into check items and control items. Check items require the checking of factors that greatly affect the process results. Control items are the process result characteristics that require checking the process (operation) for proper completion as specified by the standard. These definitions are almost identical to mine,[19] but an effective method to distinguish them was not available. Nakae introduced a method to separate control items from process results by searching out the functions and setting check items based on process causes through industrial engineering operations analysis. This search for functions can be called reverse function deployment, by which the functions of a process (why the process exists) are sought by searching for upper-level functions. Then control items are selected accordingly. Chapter 10 of this volume explains it.

The detailed literature of function analysis for the product itself came from Shigeru Yamashita's "An Example of Functional Quest in Quality Design."[20] It introduced the concept of function evaluation, function family trees, and function definitions, including application examples on the structural components of a receiver.

It has often been said that quality deployment from the design standpoint started in automotive engines. In the construction industry it began around 1968.[21]

Ryoji Futami compiled the method of the systematic diagram[22] from an analysis method by using a tree similar to the function deployment chart and the method of a matrix diagram[23] that integrated two-dimensional charts like the quality chart.

Function Analysis of Business Operations

Based on the method of product analysis described, business operation functions can be similarly analyzed. *Quality Control* magazine has published numerous reports on this type of analysis since 1969, many of them by Katsuhoshi Ishihara of the parts division of Matsushita Electrical Industrial Co., Ltd. For example, the quality function family tree[24] analyzes the first-level function "assure quality" and the second-level "give direction to quality control activities," "make a quality plan," and "greater levels of detail." This process clarifies the content of quality control operations and highlights omissions in the operation. It is performed from the standpoint of efficiency improvement in the TQM department, in conformity with the corporatewide *hoshin* of efficiency improvements in other divisions. Many examples of function analysis on other operations have been reported.

The quality function deployment (in the narrow sense) means business operation function deployment for quality assurance.

The quality assurance activities table used by Toyota Motors designates the person responsible for assurance, operations critical to assurance, and assurance items for each phase of making standards, design, prototype, and production.[25] A column for "operations critical to assurance" can be included, but deployment of quality-related functions should be done prior to creating this table.

Shimpo Industries has reported examples of function deployment for clarifying quality control and other operations.[26] The details of these reports, with the TQM implementation process, are included in their publications.[27] Today companies make broad use of function analysis of business operations, and applications to assembly process design and standardization are available. Ishihara compiled a VE text for the job site detailing value engineering.[28]

Systems Approach

The introduction of the system approach was first reported in *Quality Control* magazine in 1969 by Katsuyoshi Ishihara and Masayuki Hojo of Matsushita Electric Industrial.[29] Although the concept of the functional family tree uses the system design method, organizing operations into a system of targets and means by viewing each as a function deploying these operations as a system is called "function research." Function research uses the systems design theory step in the quality control system structure, which includes the transformation function of quality and the check function (search function) as its elements. In 1971, a completed general theory of system approach by Masao Akiba, who supported the implementation at the company, was reported.[30] He introduced a form similar to the quality chart by creating matrices of the departments involved in quality, quantity, delivery date, and cost requirements of users.

As shown above, what is called quality function deployment today was developed from quality assurance and value engineering. This volume describes the quality function deployment of the product itself, that is, quality deployment, mainly from the QA aspect but includes value engineering, with emphasis on current applications from many companies.

One advancement of this systems research includes a 1973 report by Toshiaki Chazono.[31] It involved a claims processing system that used a quality matrix developed in cooperation with the JUSE Quality System Committee, chaired by Professor Shigeru Mizuno from August 1971 through March 1973. The system, based on systems theory, employed a quality matrix that included function, component, use condition, and processes. Although it was equivalent to the quality chart, it featured a system depicting both interfunctional and intercomponent relationships. Each plan and implementation of the product or process became the subject of a system under the claims processing matrix, and was formed into another matrix with function, element, and movement at the system phase. This inclusiveness ensured that possible causes of claims would be included within this defined frame. Six decision tables were available for combinations of six phases. The report discussed an example of tracking down the cause of the claim by using the decision tables.

Later the system approach was applied to quality control at a housing material plant by Masao Akiba and others.[32] The housing material section of MITI also tried this deployment.

NOTES

1. Kiyotaka Oshiumi, "Perfecting Quality Assurance System in Plants," *Quality Control* 17 (Spring 1966): 62–67 (supp.).

2. Yoji Akao, "Concerning Quality: Using Characteristics of Quality Control as Background," *Quality Control* 29 (May 1969): 37–41.

3. Tomita Yushichi, Yoshishige Ishikawa, Yasuji Kondo, and Ki-

yoshi Watanuki (Fuji Motors)," A Case Study in Quality Assurance Activities," in *International Conference on Quality Control 1969* (Tokyo: JUSE, 1969), pp. 243–246.

4. Akao, "Concerning Quality."

5. J. M. Juran, *Quality Control Handbook*, 2nd ed. (New York: McGraw-Hill, 1962).

6. Haruichi Nagasawa, "Quality Control of Our Company," *Quality Control* 13 (July 1962): 42–48.

7. Yoji Akao, "Concerning Check Points, Control Points, and Evaluation Points," *Quality Control* 15 (Spring 1964): 42–48 (supp.).

8. Yoji Akao and Ryoji Yamada, "Quality Deployment System and Its Case Study – Computer Research Committee Report (1)," *Quality* 7, no. 3 (1977): 30–37.

9. Hisakazu Shindo, Yoji Akao, and Takashi Shirachi, "Quality Deployment Computer System QECS-1 – Computer System Reporting Committee (2)," *Quality* 8, no. 1 (1978): 33–39.

10. Koichi Nishimura, "Ship Design and Quality Chart," *Quality Control* 23 (May 1972): 71–74 (spec. ed.).

11. Akira Takayanagi, "Quality Control in Production-to-Order at Our Company (1): Quality Control Activities for Made-to-Order Products – Re: Concept of a Quality Chart," *Quality Control* 23 (May 1972): 63–67 (spec. ed.).

12. Shigeru Mizuno, "Quality Engineering," *Engineers* (July 1965): 2–7.

13. Yasushi Furukawa, Norikazu Mizuno, Yoji Kubota, and Hiroshi Iimori, *Theoretical Analysis of Quality Control Organization, Ninth Reporting Session of Research Presentation* (Tokyo: Japanese Society for Quality Control, 1976), pp. 20–23.

14. L. D. Miles, *Techniques of Value Analysis and Engineering* (McGraw-Hill, 1961).

15. Masakazu Tamai, *Function Analysis* (Tokyo: Sangyo Noritsu Junior College Publishing, 1967).

16. Kazutaka Murakami, "Implementation of Cost Down (VE) Activities Emphasizing Quality in Manufacturing," *Quality Control* 23 (May 1972): 82–86 (spec. ed.).

17. Kenji Hashimoto, "Quality Control in the Electronics Part Assembly Process," *Quality Control* 23 (May 1972): 61–64 (spec. ed.).

18. Yuji Nakae, "Research and Practice of the Method of Setting Control Points in the Manufacturing Process," *Quality Control* (Nov. 1973): 11–15 (spec. ed.).

19. Akao, "Concerning Check Points, Control Points, and Evaluation Points."

20. Shigeru Yamashita, "An Example of Functional Quest in Quality Design," *Quality Control* 18 (Nov. 1967): 85–89 (spec. ed.).

21. Shigeru Mizuno, "Deployment of Quality Function," *Quality* 6, no. 2 (1976): 3–8.

22. Ryoji Futami, "Deployment and Analysis of Quality Characteristics Using the Function Analysis Method," *Quality Control* 26 (May 1975): 208–212 (spec. ed.); Hiroshi Tsuchiya and Ryoji Futami, "Technology Supporting Business in a Low Growth Era – Weekly Report and Practice of Value Engineering," *Plant Control* 21 (1975): 6–63; and Ryoji Futami, "Tree Diagram – A Method of Systematically Searching for the Best Means for Achieving Goals," in *Collection of Research Presentations by the QC Method Development Committee* (Tokyo: JUSE), sect. I, pp. 1–73.

23. Ryoji Futami, "Matrix Diagram – A Method of Clarifying Problems Using the Multi-dimensional Approach," in *Collection of Research Presentations by the QC Method Development Committee* (Tokyo: JUSE), sect. V, pp. 1–30.

24. Katsuyoshi Ishihara and Masayuki Hojo, "Functional Study for Improving Implementation Method by the Quality Control Division," *Quality Control* 20 (Nov. 1969): 84–89 (spec. ed.).

25. Shigeru Mizuno, "General Theory of the QC Process Chart," *Quality Control* 26 (April 1975): 4–9.

26. Masashi Kashiwabara, "Implementation of Quality Assurance Activities at Shimpo Industries (1) – Outline of QA Implementation before and after Receiving the Deming Prize," *Quality Control* 21 (Nov. 1970): 107–111 (spec. ed.).

27. Shimpo Industries, ed., *Corporate-wide Quality Management – Activities and Results* (Tokyo: JUSE Press, 1970).

28. Katsuyoshi Ishihara, *On Site VE Textbook* (Tokyo: JUSE Press, 1977).

29. Ishihara and Hojo, "Functional Study for Improving Implementation Method by the Quality Control Division."

30. Masao Akiba, "System Approach to Quality and Roles of Staff," *Quality Control* 22 (June 1971): 49–53.

31. Toshiaki Chazono, "An Attempt for a Claim Processing System Using a Quality Matrix," *Engineers* (May 1973): 32–37.

32. Housing Industry Section of MITI, ed., *Quality Control of Housing Materials* (Tokyo: JSA, 1975).

Epilogue

Interview with Shigeru Mizuno

Norikazu Mizuno

Dr. Shigeru Mizuno, one of the editors of this book, died May 21, 1989, without seeing the revised edition published.

While in his sickbed, he was eagerly looking forward to the foreign publication of this book. It was his ardent wish that Japanese CWQC/TQC be introduced abroad through this book.

Deeply concerned about the epilogue for this revised edition, for which he had made a commitment, he spoke passionately about his thoughts and experience as his son, Norikazu Mizuno, interviewed him at his bedside.

The following epilogue is their dialogue. It has been edited by Norikazu Mizuno with utmost care to preserve and communicate the contents to our readers.

–The Editors

USING QFD TO IMPLEMENT COMPANYWIDE QUALITY CONTROL

Norikazu Mizuno (NM): You have long been involved with CWQC and QFD as well as PLP, PERT-QC, and advanced quality assurance, which are new product developments, so to speak, in management technology for CWQC. First, would you tell us about the need for QFD in order to clarify the position of QFD in CWQC?

Shigeru Mizuno (SM): While CWQC is called companywide QC or comprehensive QC, it cannot be called companywide QC if each division or department of the entire company is working only on improvements of its own operation. Similarly, the term "comprehensive quality" is not appropriate when each target of quality, cost, and quantity of a company is worked on individually. I regard as CWQC the activities that are carried out on a companywide, comprehensive basis for the purpose of quality assurance.

In Japan, CWQC is called TQC. Dr. A. V. Feigenbaum, who invented the term TQC, emphasized the importance of the quality system in TQC by saying, "The quality system is the network of administrative and technical procedures required to produce and deliver a product of specified quality standards." [The definition is also given in Chapter 1, section "Quality Deployment and Quality Function Deployment."]

Now, the issue is how this quality system specifically should be built. This is where QFD seems very effective.

NM: Do you remember the time when we visited General Electric about 15 years ago? As we talked about TQC, the QC engineers at GE had a perplexed look. When we asked how they had been using the TQC of Dr. Feigenbaum, who was a former vice president of GE, they replied that only the technical aspects of TQC were then being used, as I recall. Do you think the QFD way of thinking, which required horizontal links, was needed for a company where departmental role assignment was very distinctively divided?

SM: I think so. As you just mentioned, in America, role assignment is very clear. This is a wonderful thing that we don't have in Japan, but it could lead to too much decentralization. Furthermore, the engineering and QC departments were also dividedly assigned, thus leaving the role of determining quality characteristics to the engineers. This caused various quality problems, and solving them required time. I think Dr. Feigenbaum warned about this in his TQC book. Unfortunately, this warning was heeded more . . . by Japan than by America. At that time, Japan did not have the engineering capability of today, and both those in the engineering technology field and those in the QC field yielded to the word "total" in TQC as if the matter was their own. They took the word "total" as a subject to be reflected on their traditional QC, and thereby created various thoughts and methods for it.

In 1966 I . . . advocated the need for a system of engineering quality under the name of quality engineering, which I had begun to study about ten years earlier. The method of QFD was born as an extension. . . . It can be said that QFD came into existence for the total systematization of QC toward TQC.

NM: It was at the Kobe shipyard of Mitsubishi Heavy Industries where the quality chart, the main method in QFD, was first used. I think I have an understanding of the content, since I . . . was involved with the quality control theme. The background or history of it was introduced in this book by Mr. [Akira] Takayanagi. What is your thought on why the quality chart was born at Mitsubishi Heavy Industries, its background, essentially?

SM: The method of function deployment in QFD lies in the method of value engineering, not QC. Matsushita Electric Industrial used it in their operations deployment. Shimpo Industries also used the concept with successful results.

The staff at Mitsubishi Heavy Industries heard about it and created a tool called the quality chart. There were two points that became the background for this chart. One of them was this: In the process of raising the added value of a ship built at the shipyard in Kobe, where the price of land was very high, they decided to call such a ship with high added value "a sophisticated ship." This became their quality *hoshin*.

Meanwhile, Professor Yasushi Furukawa, who had guided the quality control at the shipyard ten years prior, had been studying quality systems from the standpoint of systems engineering. This became another point.

Based on these two, that is, deployment of quality *hoshin* and systematization of the quality system, the quality chart was born and incorporated into a system with a QA chart and QC process chart. Furthermore, Professor Yoji Akao, who had started the study of quality target deployment earlier, presented his quality deployment system about the same time. Thus QFD came into existence and developed from these two flows.

NM: It seems that there is another significant point in addition to these: the issue of technology. In the past, technology was divided into engineering technology and control technology. Under this thinking, QC fell under control technology, and some distance stood between it and the engineering technology. After the birth of QFD, however, QC actively began dealing with issues of engineering technology as well.

SM: It is impossible to draw a clear line between engineering technology and control technology. It is more troublesome if engineering technology has not been molded into the kind of technology that can be transmitted to people. Sometimes people become evasive by saying "This is an engineering issue." The QC staff, too, often backs away from the engineering technology by saying "QC falls under control technology." If this occurs, I would like to challenge them with "What is the purpose of quality control?" It is fortunate that Japanese QC has had cooperation without such divisiveness and thus has contributed to improvement of technology. QFD offers the concept of bottleneck engineering, where the gap between the quality target and the current achievement level can be filled through analysis. I think this kind of approach is necessary.

ANALYSIS AND DEPLOYMENT

NM: Next, I would like to discuss the relationship between the thinking represented in statistical quality control and the deployment way of thinking in QFD.

We see approaches to improvement as the analytical approach vs. the design approach, that is, analysis vs. deployment. This is discussed in a book called *Ideal System Design* by Gerald Nadler.

According to Nadler, conceiving the ideal system and trying to fuse it with the current state of affairs produces a higher level of improvement ideas than making improvements through the analytic approach. In other words, the design approach is superior. Although this thinking may not be appropriate in all cases, with this in mind, how do you think we should comprehend analysis and deployment?

SM: I think it is narrow thinking to separate analysis from QFD simply because it is a design approach. Rather, QFD should be put to better use for analysis, I think. QFD should be used to find deficiencies in the existing technology, and the deficiencies should be filled through analysis. As deployment occurs by using the quality chart, QA chart, QC process chart, and operating standards, not only is the link organized through such forms and sheets, but . . . the connection is established through analysis. This is an important point here. I think this way of thinking is important.

Some companies that incorporated QFD are thinking that they completed QFD simply by making a quality chart. It is still incomplete. We must reach a level of doing analysis more efficiently as we begin QFD.

NM: Analysis, as often stated, relates to the saying "dividing is understanding." This means subdividing the cause, the cause of the cause, and so on. On the contrary, deployment, as represented by QFD, while it also means dividing, uses dividing to look at the whole, I believe.

As a small child, I remember disassembling an alarm clock out of curiosity about why it rang at a set time. The purpose was not disassembly, but . . . a means for finding out "why." I think deployment is something like this.

SM: There is a way of thinking called *bunbetsuchi* [differentiating knowledge] in Buddhism. This means . . . that dividing is understanding. *Bunbetsuchi* is considered . . . a superficial thinking level in Buddhism, though, and people who reach spiritual enlightenment have achieved *mu-bunbetsuchi* [nondifferentiating knowledge], that is, looking through to the true essence from an instantaneous look at the whole rather than looking at a whole through a collection of fragments. In other words, looking at something from a total view, as in TQC.

The concepts of analysis and deployment are used in the scientific method for this purpose. I recommend that we look at it this way. In any case, I hope that QFD will be placed into greater use for analysis, not simply as a scientific deployment method.

GREETINGS TO QUALITY CONTROL PROMOTERS

NM: On the occasion of publication of the English version of QFD by the Asian Productivity Organization, please share your message with these readers.

SM: There is a statement that has remained in my mind. It was given earlier by my predecessor, the late Eizaburo Nishibori, who was the leader of the first winter party of the Japanese Antarctic observation team. He said, "Making standards or rules, introducing CWQC. . . . These all look at QC statically, but QC must be taken more dynamically."

It is my hope that QFD be used as a living method and way of thinking by companies, as with the traditional method developed earlier. For example, in America, traditionally each division or department of product planning, design, manufacturing, sales, and so forth performed independent operations, and a cooperative system among them was rarely given thought. QFD has been recognized as a powerful method for creating a system of cooperation among these divisions.

At the same time, the need for fundamental changes in the traditional system should be emphasized. This should also help QFD to succeed.

NM: As internationalization and opening of borders progress, it is necessary to promote international cooperation and collaboration. Under such a situation, what will be the role of quality control promoters?

SM: This is not an issue limited to the promoters. I think it is important for the top management of companies and industry leaders to have awareness of the quality of their own products.

We can produce products without doing CWQC. But through CWQC, we can output a product of higher quality level that demonstrates the pride of the company.

I wonder if we could make a product that demonstrates the pride of the country or company and widely contributes to the culture, like the Japanese *ukiyoe* once influenced the paintings of the French Impressionists. I wonder if it is possible for us to enhance the quality of a product to that level.

NM: To reach that level, I think we need "total" in the truest sense. By this, I mean becoming total in terms not only of the people working inside a company but also of the users, an awareness of people, even to the level of technology and culture. Do you think we can do this through CWQC/TQC?

SM: It has been only 40 years since Japanese QC thinking was introduced. Dr. W. Edwards Deming, the father of QC, stressed the need for broad-range systematic efforts based on emphasizing quality [quality responsibility] to satisfy the market. This was his position as a market research expert. Later, Dr. J. M. Juran, through his experience as a consultant, taught us that QC was useful in breaking through the status quo of management.

In Japan, many QC approaches and methods, including QC circles, which is in practice quality of work life, were developed through cooperation by people in both corporate and noncorporate sectors. In other words, CWQC has developed through TQC.

We should consider this as just a beginning, rather than being completed. I expect that under the changing environment in the future, QC will continue to progress as an integrator and coordinator for diverse technology and for the awareness of all people who are touched by it.

SELECTED WORKS BY SHIGERU MIZUNO

"Planning Quality Control," *Quality Control* 5, no. 10 (1954): 19–23.

"General Theory of the QC Process Chart," *Quality Control* 26, no. 4 (1975): 4–9.

"Deployment of Quality Function," *Quality* 6, no. 2 (1976): 3–8.

"Quality Deployment – New Trend of Quality Control," *Engineers* no. 346 (1977): 1–5.

"Concerning Quality Deployment," *Quality Control* 33, no. 5 (1982): 418–421.

"Deployment of Quality and Deployment of Quality Function," *Quality* 13, no. 3 (1983): 3–8.

Check List for Quality Operations. Tokyo: Association of Taxation and Accounting, 1984.

About the Editors and the Contributors

EDITORS

Shigeru Mizuno was born in 1910. After graduating from the School of Electrochemistry of the Tokyo Institute of Technology in 1934, he was successively professor at the Tokyo Institute of Technology, director of the Resource Chemistry Center at the Tokyo Institute of Technology, and professor at Science University of Tokyo. He was professor emeritus, Ph.D. engineering, at Tokyo Institute of Technology for many years, including at the publication of the first edition of this book. Professor Mizuno received the Deming Prize for Individuals in 1952, a Purple Ribbon Medal in 1974, and the Third Order of Merit with the Cordon of the Rising Sun in 1982. He died May 21, 1989. Major books by Professor Mizuno include *Quality Control Textbook for Beginners* (Tokyo: JUSE Press, 1960), developed by the QC Research Group, with Mizuno as Chief of the editorial board; *Product Liability Prevention Plan* (Tokyo: JUSE Press, 1975), which he edited and to which he contributed; and *Company-Wide Total Quality Control* (Tokyo: Asian Productivity Organization, 1988).

Yoji Akao was born in 1928. After graduating from the Department of Ceramics of the Tokyo Institute of Technology, he worked for Koa Glass Co., Ltd., then held the positions of research associate at Tokyo Institute of Technology, assistant professor at Yamanashi University, and professor at Yamanashi University. In 1981, he became a professor at Tamagawa University and, in 1990, dean of the Faculty of Engineering. He received the Deming Prize for Individuals in 1978. Professor Akao's fields of study are quality control and statistical engineering. He has been a member of the Deming Prize committee since 1964 and has served as vice chairman of the editing committee of *Journal of Statistical Quality Control* (1985-87, 1989-91) and chairman since 1993, president of the Japanese Society for Quality Control (1990-91), and chairman of the Japan Section of the American Society for Quality Control since 1990. Among the major books by Professor Akao include *Introduction to Quality Deployment* (Tokyo: JUSE Press, 1990), which he edited; *Quality Function Deployment–Integrating Customer Requirements into Product Design* (Cambridge, Mass.: Productivity Press, Inc., 1990), which he edited; and *Hoshin Kanri–Policy Management for Successful TQM* (Cambridge, Mass.: Productivity Press, Inc., 1991), which he edited.

CONTRIBUTORS

Katsuyoshi Ishihara
Quality Engineering Research Institute

Toshio Iwahashi
Kubota, Ltd.

Norio Kamisawa
Ishikawajima-Harima Heavy Industries Co., Ltd.

Sampei Kobayashi
Dynic Co., Ltd.

Norikazu Mizuno
Management Consultant

Yoichi Negoro
Kubota, Ltd.

Akira Takayanagi
Mitsubishi Heavy Industries

Yasuhiro Tanaka
Kubota, Ltd.

Takao Tanisawa
Hino Motors, Ltd.

Mitsuo Tsurusawa
Kubota, Ltd.

Note: Places of employment are as of May 1978.

Index